SIGNALLING ATLAS

CW00742292

AND SIGNAL BOX DI.

GREAT BRITAIN AND IRELAND

SECOND EDITION

NETWORK RAIL: LONDON UNDERGROUND AND OTHER UK SYSTEMS: NORTHERN IRELAND RAILWAYS: IARNROD EIREANN: HERITAGE RAILWAYS: ALL OTHER PRESERVED AND DISUSED BOXES IN THE UK AND IRELAND.

by Peter Kay & Derek Coe

and published by the

Signalling Record Society

Maps and Photographs by David Allen
Ireland sections in association with Ken Manto

CONTENTS

Highams Park (2001) – Superseded by WARM (West Anglia Route Modernisation) and with the Chingford branch now within Liverpool Street's IECC remit, the LNER Type 11a box was redundant from 2002. Its future should be guaranteed as it is a Grade II listed building. The extra height and overhang are the result of being built in a confined space.

PREFACE AND ACKNOWLEDGEMENTS

This Second Edition of a work first written and published by Peter Kay in 1997 has been produced by Derek Coe on behalf of the Signalling Record Society in liaison with its original author. It is believed that the information given maintains the high degree of accuracy set by the First Edition, but it must be realised that absolute certainty on box opening dates and frame dates will never be achievable in all cases, and that (as those with research experience will recognise) some dates will subsequently turn out to be erroneous, albeit only by a year or two in most cases. Again, there will inevitably be a few cases where changes of a kind not reported in Notices (e.g. shortening of a frame by a few levers) have occurred recently since correspondents' last experience of the location. It must also be borne in mind that changes on Network Rail and elsewhere are ongoing and that a situation which was accurate on 1 January 2004 (the cut-off date for this edition) might well have changed, sometimes even before the publication date.

Further corrections are of course welcomed. Please send corrections and new data to Derek Coe, 14 Endsleigh Court, Colchester, Essex CO3 3QN. These will be incorporated in the next Edition. A list of corrections to this Edition will be provided at the year end on the Signalling Record Society's website – www.s-r-s.org.uk .

A considerable number of people have contributed to this Second Edition. Special thanks must go to David Allen who has produced the maps and provided the photographs and without whom this work would be of a much lesser quality. Particular thanks are also due to Tim Bourne, John Creed, John McCrickard and Julian Oxley who have always been on hand to advise and support; and to Matthew Saunders and James Hall who have undertaken a large amount of leg work in checking and obtaining details. The following have all contributed material: Mike Addison, Forbes Alexander, Nick Allsop, Brian Andrews, Ken Appleby, Malcolm Atherton, Michael Back, Roger Bell, Peter Binnersley, Andy Bowal, John Boyes, Barry Bridges, Ian Browning, Ray Caston, Mike Christensen, Chris Cock, David Collins, A.V. Colson, Tony Cornell, Stephen Courten, Larry Crosier, John Dixon, Edward Dorricott, Oliver Doyle, Graham Earl, Martin Elms, John Francis, Tony Graham, Chris Harley, John Hinson, Trevor Hodgson, David Howard, Charles Hudson MBE, Reg Instone, Paul Kampen, Richard Lemon, Simon Lowe, Dr Angus McDougall, Alan Mackie, Ken Manto, John Midcalf, Tony Miller, Robert Mills, Roger Newman, Michael Nicholson, V.B. Orchard, Chris Osment, John Phillips, Phillip Pritchard, George Pryer, Richard Pulleyn, Alan Roberts, Gordon Roberts, Ian Smith, Derek Soames, Keith Steele, John Talbot, K. Thomas, Garth Tilt, Andrew Toosey, Mike Turner, Paul Vidler, Chris Woolstenholmes, and Billy Wyndrum. Thanks to all these and to the one or two who contributed but didn't put their name on the paperwork! The authors are very grateful to the many folk representing heritage railways and other administrations who responded to requests for information.

Readers are reminded that operational signal boxes, including many on the heritage railways, are not in normal circumstances publicly accessible, also that certain preserved and disused boxes are situated on private land where visitors are unwelcome (although, fortunately, the majority are close to public roads).

An annual list of most signalling alterations, including all box openings and closures, is published by the Signalling Record Society. For details of membership send a stamped, self-addressed envelope to Barry Bridges, 38 Founceley Avenue, Dane End, Ware, Herts SG12 0NQ.

Derek Coe & Peter Kay, Colchester May 2004

REVIEW

As we enter the new century and move further into 'Act Five' of the story of mechanical signalling, it may be appropriate to consider the 'signalling inheritance' of the British railways, to give a historical context to the boxes and equipment that can be seen in use today.

What we would regard as 'traditional' mechanical signalling (in essence a feature of the relatively-stable railway scene of the 1890s-1950s period) first became evident in the 1860s with the invention of the interlocked lever frame and consequent appearance of interlocked signal boxes in fair numbers, and the confirmation of the (lower quadrant) semaphore signal as the standard form of British railway signal. The great majority of the 1860s boxes were however to prove very short-lived, as they were mostly to be found at the busiest locations where the layouts were greatly expanded soon afterwards with consequent need for replacement boxes. The oldest box in use on the Network Rail system today is probably Goole Bridge (1869) but, as that was only a bridge control cabin until 1933, the honours may perhaps more properly go to the NE's Norton East and Norton South both opened in March 1870. In the event, 1860s lever frames also proved short-lived, owing to mechanical wear problems, and none survived into recent years.

In the 1870s and 1880s, however, the interlocking of the whole British railway network was proceeded with apace, accompanied by the spread of 'Block' working (first used on certain lines in the 1840s and 1850s, but long resisted by many railway managers until the 1870s). In contrast to the rapid disappearance of 1860s boxes, boxes of the 1870s and 1880s, being in many cases on secondary routes which saw little infrastructural change subsequently, have survived in large numbers to the present day. Another development which is still readily apparent in the 21st century scene was the fact that the practical aspects of the design of lever frames were perfected in the early 1870s, with the appearance of three 'classic' frame designs that were to prove thoroughly reliable in heavy use, the Stevens Tappet, the McKenzie & Holland 1873 Patent (Hook Cam & Soldier), and the Saxby & Farmer 1874 Patent 'Rocker'. In consequence, frames dating from c1874 onwards have also remained in service in large numbers up to the present day.

Most signalling equipment in these earlier years was supplied by the various firms of signalling contractors, who also built many of the signal box structures themselves, to their own standard designs. As the years went by, however, more of the larger railway companies started doing some or all of their signalling work in-house, most notably the LNW, L&Y, Midland, and GW; and many of those other companies which continued to buy all signalling equipment from the contractors began to specify the adoption of their own standard designs for equipment irrespective of which contractor was supplying. This included having the signal box structures built to their own company designs. (Signal box structures were sometimes erected by building contractors as a separate job to the signalling contract, in any case.)

Owing to their impecunious nature and relatively infrequent trains many of the Scottish, Welsh, and (most particularly) Irish railway companies remained laggard in introducing interlocking, and were the prime 'culprits' at the time of the Regulation of Railways Act 1889 which made interlocking and 'Block' working compulsory on passenger lines. Very large numbers of boxes had to be built on these companies' lines in the 1890-1894 period, in consequence, and also on the most rustic branches of some of the English companies which had postponed the completion of their interlocking programmes until forced to.

After the completion of the interlocking of the system there was still much new signalling work to be done, as the 1890s and 1900s were the heyday of quadruplings and other major expansions on the main routes, with consequent provision of many new (and now much larger) signal boxes in place of earlier boxes. In the 1900s some came to think that the power frame (a primarily American invention, widely used in that country from the 1890s) would in due course supplant the mechanical lever frame, at least for major locations, but, whilst the main line companies here did install a fair number of power frames in total in the 1900s-1950s period, this never really happened in the UK (except on the London Underground lines, where power frames had 'taken over' by the interwar years and remain in use today). This can perhaps be put down firstly to the particularly perfect and entrenched state which mechanical signalling had attained in this country by the 1900s, and secondly to the way in which this country subsequently led the world in making the next technological break out of the age of the power frame and into the age of relay locking and the 'panel' in the 1930s. Today, only a handful of power frames remain in use on the Network Rail system.

The establishment of the LNER, LMS, GW, and SR companies in the 1923 'grouping' came shortly after the combining of most of the firms of mechanical signalling contractors (whose workload was declining, as the expansion of the British railway infrastructure came to an end) into the Westinghouse Brake & Signal Company combine. The LMS and GW were, indeed, to do almost all their signalling work in-house, but the LNER and SR continued to buy lever frames and much other equipment from the contractors. After 1923, however, the signalling contractors were not involved in the design or erection of signal box structures. Another development at this time was the establishment of the Irish Republic, which took the Irish companies out of the supervision of the British Railway Inspectorate and enabled the development of some different practices subsequently.

The late 1920s saw the introduction of the upper quadrant semaphore by the British main line companies, and much work was done on signal renewal in this new form in the 1930s and 1940s. Lower quadrants were still to be seen in large numbers in the 1950s, but were thin on the ground by the late 1960s, although a handful managed to survive on the BR system into the 1990s. In saying this, one excepts the GW and BR(WR), which would not accept the upper quadrant, so that lower quadrants still remain widespread on ex-BR(WR) lines to the present day; and the Irish railways, which again stayed faithful to the lower quadrant (apart from a few upper quadrants installed in Northern Ireland), and also remain so today.

Contemporary with the introduction of upper quadrant semaphores came the first large-scale main line colour light resignallings, with long stretches of automatic signals and abolition of many smaller signal boxes. The spread of the 'panel' signal box and multiple-aspect colour-light signalling (MAS) was naturally retarded by the war and economic circumstances, and it was only the money made available by the BR 1954 'Modernisation Plan' that saw things really take off on this front in the late 1950s and early 1960s. The new boxes of these years still controlled relatively small areas (by later standards) for the most part, and it was only in the late 1960s that boxes controlling 100 route miles-plus were seen (thanks to the development of more economic technologies for links to remote interlockings).

The number of signal boxes in use had already been declining from the c1900s peak of 12,000-13,000*, with rationalisation schemes in the interwar years to concentrate working on one box at lesser stations where there had previously been two or more, the impecunious and economy-seeking LNER being at the forefront of this. It was only with the Modernisation Plan and the 1960s Beeching route closures that the decline in the number of boxes became dramatic, with a reduction to around 4,000 by 1970. (Even so, the earlier Modernisation Plan schemes often retained some older mechanical boxes and complex 'historic' track layouts – a situation reflected in the fact that the West Coast Main Line is still home to so many of the largest remaining mechanical frames! – and it was only from the mid 1960s that 'resignalling' came to mean total layout rationalisation, and elimination of all existing boxes, in most cases).

The remainder of this 'Review' will be focused on the Network Rail system; for an outline of developments on the London Underground and the Irish railways since the 1920s, see the introduction to the relevant Directory sections.

So far as signal boxes themselves were concerned, many new boxes (particularly the larger ones) had been built to 'modern architecture' rather than the 'traditional' designs from the 1930s on, although standard timber or brick designs (now flat-roofed) were adopted by the various BR Regions for small mechanical boxes, which continued to be built in fair numbers until around 1972. Some of these were specifically designed for easy dismantling and re-use elsewhere, something which had always been done from time to time when timber boxes still in good structural condition were rendered obsolete on their existing site. The larger 'Power Boxes' of the 1960s were becoming substantial buildings and soon became too grand to be known by the humble name of 'signal box', the term 'Signalling Centre' becoming favoured in the 1970s and 1980s, and now 'Signalling Control Centre' and 'Integrated Electronic Control Centre' from the 1990s. A new term 'Area Signalling Centre' has also gained favour in the former BR(SR) area.

As the number of mechanical boxes being abolished increased in the 1960s, a large quantity of serviceable equipment from these boxes became available for re-use in new mechanical work and for maintenance and renewals, and this (together with the fact that new mechanical work was greatly in decline anyway) enabled the various BR Regions to cease manufacturing lever frames and most other mechanical items at different dates in the 1960s/'70s. (The use of serviceable lever frames from abolished boxes, and the construction of 'new' frames from reconditioned parts from old frames, had in fact been practiced on a fair scale since later pre-grouping days, and was particularly done by the LNER from the 1920s on).

The last new mechanical signal boxes on BR were opened in 1981, and the last installation of a replacement mechanical frame in a BR box was at Carnoustie in 1984. By the 1970s the 'panel' had become normal for small resignalling schemes as well as large, either installed in an existing box in lieu of the mechanical frame, or in a new structure.

The mid-1980s saw the arrival of a 'new generation' of signalling technology, firstly with the introduction of computer-based 'Solid State Interlocking' (SSI) instead of relay locking, and Visual Display Units (VDUs) instead of 'panels'; and secondly with the commissioning of Radio Electronic Token Block (RETB) on certain lightly-trafficked routes which had hitherto evaded modernisation. SSI is now fast becoming normal for all larger new schemes; VDUs have become normal (instead of a panel) for major resignallings, but 'panel and SSI' has been the favoured option for medium-sized schemes. The latest generation of new 'Computer Based Interlockings' (CBIs) have made a limited appearance on Network Rail, for example at Manchester South. Another notable feature of the last few years has been the introduction of 'Portakabins' for many new 'boxes', so that the new signal box as a 'building' is now fast becoming a thing of the past. In some ways this is a reversion to the practices of the 1860s, as there is no doubt that the timber signal boxes of that decade were regarded as 'temporary' structures on a quickly-changing system, and it was only in the 1870s and later that the idea of signal boxes as 'permanent' buildings grew up. An encouraging sign is the designation of some historic boxes as Listed structures, protecting them for the future, and the renovation by Network Rail of such boxes either in their original state, for example Wylam, Hexham and Haltwhistle, or rebuilds in the original style, for example Thorpe Culvert.

The Network Rail signalling scene of the 21st Century is a very dichotomous one. The train which is at one moment protected by a VDU operator using computer technology of the most advanced kind will, a few minutes later, find itself (with no less safety) in the territory of some 130-year-old signal box whose levers were, in their youth, wielded by men born in the 1810s or 1820s and brought up in a pre-industrial society. Mechanical signalling has been largely eliminated from many areas, it is true, but the hope (or fear, depending on one's viewpoint) that it would be all gone from the British railway system before the beginning of the present century has proved rather wide of the mark. Much of the energy of the signalling industry over the last decade or so has been devoted, not to replacing Victorian mechanical equipment, but to eliminating the fast-decaying 1950s and 1960s BR Modernisation Plan hardware, which has proved far less robust. In consequence, the number of mechanical boxes abolished per annum has been much reduced compared with the 1970s and 1980s. The approximate number of Block Post signal boxes remaining in use on the major systems as at 1.1.2004 was Network Rail 750; London Underground 17; NIR 6; Iarnrod Eireann 60; but there are additionally a good number of other boxes still retained as gate boxes or in other non-Block Post roles.

Much of the remaining mechanical signalling is 'patchy', particularly in such areas as South Wales, Lancashire, and Yorkshire, which were still vast empires of mechanical signalling in the 1960s. In other cases, mechanical signalling co-exists with electrification and MAS. A true feel for the pre-1960s world of semaphore signalling and old signal boxes can, therefore, only be found on parts of a few lines which have escaped the hand of large-scale modernisation, of which one might particularly mention:

Liskeard to Penzance	(ex GW)	Kidderminster- Worcester-Malvern	(ex GW)
(Dorking) to Arundel	(ex LBSC)	Shrewsbury-(Hereford)-Abergavenny	(ex LNW/GW Jnt)
(Lewes) to Hastings	(ex LBSC)	(Norwich) to Yarmouth/Lowestoft	(ex GE)
(Strood) to (Paddock Wood)	(ex SE)	(Ely) to Wymondham	(ex GE)
(Nottingham) to Skegness	(ex GN)	(Crewe) to Shrewsbury	(ex LNW)
(Spalding) to Gainsborough	(ex GN)	(Chester) to Holyhead	(ex LNW)
Gilberdyke to (Hull)	(ex NE)	Blackpool North to (Preston)	(ex L&Y)
Harrogate to (York)	(ex NE)	Carnforth-Barrow-Workington	(ex Furness and LNW)
Bedlington to Ashington	(ex NE)	Annan to (Kilmarnock)	(ex GSW)
(Newcastle) to (Carlisle)	(ex NE)	(Ayr) to Stranraer	(ex GSW)
(Bletchley) to Bedford	(ex LNW)	Falkirk-Larbert-Stirling-(Perth)	(ex NB & Cal)
(Syston) to (Peterborough)	(ex Midland)	Carnoustie to (Aberdeen)	(ex NB & Cal)
Hellifield to (Carlisle)	(ex Midland)	(Aberdeen) to (Nairn)	(ex GNS & Highland)
(Stoke-on-Trent) to Egginton Jn	(ex NS)	(Perth) to (Aviemore)	(ex Highland)

although even on these lines there is in many places a great patchiness owing to layout rationalisation and the abolition of many boxes. Of individual locations, there are the famous Shrewsbury (with the 180-lever Severn Bridge Junction now being the largest remaining mechanical frame) and Stockport (all wires and MAS, but still one of the best visual reminders of the days when giant signal boxes were everywhere); also Barnetby, Stirling, Lincoln, and Worcester. Seaside termini seem particularly favoured in the retention of sizeable stations with semaphore signalling; Blackpool North (albeit a poor shadow of the pre-1960s Blackpool) perhaps has the greatest feel of intactness, but a mention must also go to Bognor Regis, Littlehampton, Skegness, Scarborough and Holyhead.

Absolute Block working (although now all but extinct on the busier main lines as a result of the 1960s-1980s re-signallings) remains in use on a large mileage of secondary double-track routes, often with block sections of considerable length by pre-1960 standards (but the fall off of freight traffic has enabled this). Some older block instruments remain in use in addition to the BR standard blocks. In certain cases 'Track Circuit Block' rather than Absolute Block is in operation between two mechanical boxes; those boxes which 'fringe' to large power boxes also generally work 'TCB' to them.

More interest attaches, perhaps, to the current situation with methods of single-line working, where almost every technology from the most primitive to the most advanced now seems to find a place somewhere on the system! With the rationalisation of many rural and other branches to a simple passenger shuttle operation with no freight and no signalling or crossing loops, that old free-of-cost friend from the 1850s the wooden (or otherwise) One Train Staff (OTS) has if anything made a comeback of late, although many short single-track passenger branches off power box areas are now worked by One Train Working Without Staff (OTW) with track circuiting to ensure that only one train is allowed at a time. (Many goods-only branches are also now worked without a staff, under the control of a particular signal box or other person). Train Staff & Ticket (TS&T) working, once the mainstay of much of the system, is now only found on the Network Rail system on a few non-passenger lines (although several heritage railways use it). Of the 'classic' British electric token systems which dominated the scene in the 1890s-1960s period **, the Electric Train Staff (ETS) is now some years extinct on Network Rail (although still the standard system in Ireland); Tyer's Tablet is reduced to a handful of sections (plus three on NIR) all with the No.6 instrument; and their younger cousin the Key Token, although still regardable as 'current' technology, is itself now reduced to a few dozen sections only. Thus there are few places indeed where one can observe that honoured ritual from the British single-track country branch of yesteryear, the signalman collecting and delivering the token from and to the drivers of two trains 'crossing' each other.

Definitely still current technology for new installations is the Key Token's offshoot the No Signalman Key Token (NSKT), used on sections where a signal box exists at one end but with a driver-operated instrument at the other end. Although this system (or equivalent) has long been available, it has become more popular of late as it enables the abolition of signal boxes at branch termini without any great loss of operating flexibility. This system is particularly suited to lines where freight trains run as well as a passenger shuttle, or where more than one freight train may be about at the same time. (There is one section of what is effectively the equivalent to 'No Signalman ETS' (Navan to Tara Mines) in Ireland, although this is not really recognised as a distinct system from ordinary ETS operation).

In the 1980s the BR(WR) went one step further and introduced the 'No Signalman (Key) Token Remotely Controlled' (NSTR) concept, using similar instruments, under which successive sections have driver-worked instruments, with unattended crossing loops. This is now used on the Central Wales line (6 sections), the Pembroke Dock branch (2 sections),

Porth to Treherbert (2 sections), and Crediton to Barnstaple (2 sections). A similar system has been installed between Nunthorpe and Whitby (3 sections) in North East England.

Of later single-line systems, the Tokenless Block (TB), developed by BR(WR) and BR(ScR) in the 1960s to speed up services on single-line routes by eliminating the transfer of tokens, remains in use on several of the lines for which it was intended, notably Salisbury-Exeter, Perth-Inverness (part) and Aberdeen-Inverness (part). Single Line TCB has been introduced on many sections, not only between boxes with panels, but also between mechanical boxes using acceptance/direction levers, with many differences in detail in the methods (many of these installations have been somewhat ad hoc, and no overall hand has been evident). Radio Electronic Token Block (RETB), introduced on four parts of the network in the 1980s (East Suffolk line, Cambrian lines, West Highland line, and Inverness-Wick/Thurso/Kyle of Lochalsh), seems destined not to be replicated further, as the remaining sections of so-far-unmodernised single line route on Network Rail are either too short and scattered to justify the installation of this system (which is essentially suited to lengthy routes with limited traffic) or are deemed to need something causing less delay to trains. The question of what to do for such remaining unmodernised single line routes remains 'on the table' for the present.

That completes our review of the current 'Network Rail' scene, but no observer of the current British railway signalling scene can fail to be struck by the achievements of the British Heritage Railways on the signalling front, which go far beyond what has been done on the preserved railways of any other country. There are now some 100 functional signal boxes on our heritage railways (miniature gauge excluded), only a minority of which are former BR boxes left in situ and re-opened, the rest either being second-hand structures brought in from elsewhere and re-erected, or new structures (albeit with second-hand frames). In contrast to this relatively lavish provision of signalling hardware, methods of working (which, so far, is single-line in almost every case, the Great Central Railway being the major exception) on our heritage railways have tended to remain 'low tech', with many lines restricted to 'One Engine in Steam' Staff working or Train Staff & Ticket; although a growing number have now proceeded to Key Token, Tablet or ETS working, and several have Radio Block.

Finally one must mention the extraordinary number of other 'preserved' (or otherwise-extant) boxes to be seen in the UK and Ireland, whether as fully-equipped (but non-functional) museum-pieces in the hands of signalling enthusiasts, as messrooms or offices on the Network Rail system, in commercial or domestic uses in places where the rails have long gone, or simply as derelict wrecks in some farmer's field where one can hardly now believe a railway ever existed at all. If the official process of trying to preserve a selection of historically-significant signal box structures via the 'listing' process has not been an entirely happy one, there is no doubt as to the success of the British enthusiasm for keeping redundant signal boxes alive in other ways! – and the time is not far off when the number of 'preserved' (in some way) boxes actually exceeds the number of active boxes on the Network Rail system.

* This figure is an estimate of the number of Block Post signal boxes, in respect of those lines which became part of the BR system in 1948.

** For a full history of the development and use of these systems, see 'The History and Development of Railway Signalling in the British Isles – Volume 2: The Telegraph and the Absolute Block/Single Line Operation' by David Stirling published in 2002 by the National Railway Museum (ISBN 1 872826 13 X)

Berwick (2001) – The Saxby & Farmer Type 5 box of 1879 was typical of a style of signal box that was common throughout the ex-LBSC area. Despite the absence now of the locking room windows, the original design of this BTF structure with its overhanging and hipped roof and the curved framing of the upper lights is very recognisable.

INTRODUCTION TO THE SIGNAL BOX DIRECTORY LISTINGS

SECTIONS 1, 2, 3, 4 & 5

A few further introductory notes appear at the start of each section in respect of matters particular to that section only. The listings in Sections 1-5 are in the same format with nine columns viz.
- Box Name
- Quail Map Reference
- Box Type
- Box Date
- Frame/Equipment Design
- Frame/Equipment Date
- Number of Levers
- Locking
- Footnotes references

They include all signal boxes (etc.) in active signalling use (or stand-by for emergency use), or out-of-use but not yet 'abolished', as at 1st January 2004.

The definition of a 'signal box' for purposes of inclusion in the Directory goes beyond what would normally be understood by the term, and is –
- All 'Block Posts' (including those where there is no separate box structure).
- All structures containing inside them a lever frame, panel, or switches, and controlling in some way the movement of trains. (Thus all ground frames in huts are included, but not open ground frames: and crossing keepers' huts usually only if the frame (etc.) is located inside the hut).
- Former staffed signal boxes now reduced to 'Interlocking Machine Room' or 'Relay Room' status (i.e. housing mechanical or relay interlocking equipment for a Power Box located elsewhere) providing that the structure still retains its operating floor and thereby is recognisable as a former box.

In some Power Box areas there are a large number of 'Emergency Panels', usually located in relay rooms, some of which are actually used regularly in practice in order to keep the equipment in working order. These are not included in the Directory in most cases. Exceptionally, we have listed in footnotes all those in the Edinburgh, Glasgow and Paisley box areas. Also, those Emergency Panels located in former staffed signal boxes are included in the main listing, and all the Emergency Control locations on the East Coast Main Line are in fact included here under that reason.

It is impossible to fit every location into strict definitions of whether it is or is not in 'active' signalling use, and a few other boxes/locations have been included in the listings because it seemed appropriate to do so in all the circumstances in their case. Where the function or status of a box is of a peculiar kind, it is clarified in the footnotes.

Column 1: BOX NAME

The name as given in the relevant appendix and other official railway documentation, and the name as given 'in the flesh' on the box nameboard, are the same in most cases, but not in all. In those cases where the box nameboard simply retains suffixes (e.g. 'No 2', 'East' etc.) which have officially been dropped because there is now only one box left at that location, the current official name without the suffix is normally given here. In other cases it has been necessary to exercise judgement as to the most appropriate name for use here. Some boxes have a tradition of uncertainty as to their precise official name. Names may be abbreviated for space reasons, either in the listings here, or on the box nameboard itself. Where the name of a box has been changed in recent years, or in any way that might cause confusion, this is mentioned in the footnotes (but many other boxes have changed their exact name at some stage in their life without this being mentioned here).

In recent decades many boxes have been given acronymic suffixes as part of their official name, viz.:-

ASC	Area Signalling Centre	
CC	Control Cabin	(in yards, etc.)
CR	Control Room	(in yards, etc.)
GF	Ground Frame	(often 'wrongly' applied to elevated former Block Post signal boxes which have been reduced to non-Block Post status)
IECC	Integrated Electronic Control Centre	
LCF	Level Crossing Frame	(mainly former Block Post signal boxes reduced to gate box status)
SC	Signalling Centre	

SCC   Signalling Control Centre

Words given in square brackets after the box name are merely an indication of the location to assist the reader, not part of the box name proper.

Boxes are Block Posts unless stated to the contrary. If not a Block Post, one or more of the following indications of status appears after the name:-

(B)   Bridge Control Box (released by another box; some bridge boxes are however Block Posts, in which case a footnote notes the bridge function)

(E)   Box unmanned but can be used in Emergency conditions i.e. defect with normal remote operation

(EBC) Emergency Barrier Control (Iarnrod Eireann term)

(ECP) Emergency Control Panel (Iarnrod Eireann term)

(ELC) Emergency Local Control Panel (East Coast Main Line boxes – These are still subsidiary to the parent power box when in use)

(G)   Gate Box only

(IMR) Interlocking Machine Room (LUL term) – former staffed SB now reduced to unstaffed interlocking controlled from another box.

(NBP) Not a Block Post (and not a Bridge Box or Gate Box either). Generally either a box controlling yard lines, or lines not worked on the block system; or a box controlling points in the main running lines which is released from another (Block Post) signal box. Most are regularly staffed but a few are worked by train crew or other travelling staff.

(RR)   Relay Room only – former staffed SB (or could have been staffed) now reduced to unstaffed relay interlocking controlled from another box (or other active signalling equipment, if so noted in footnotes).

(SER) Signalling Equipment Room (LUL) – former staffed SB now reduced to an unstaffed equipment room.

The following are also used:-

(NNM) Not Normally Manned (usable, with signalling still in situ, but not required for existing daily/weekly traffic patterns).

(OOU) Out of Use (Although no hard and fast line can be drawn between this and 'NNM', this term is used when boxes have not been used for many years, or are situated on lines which are themselves out of use, or are derelict, or are in reality unusable).

These two terms represent our own analysis of the situation and are not 'official' terms, boxes in these categories normally appear in the Appendix without any indication of their not being in use, even in extreme cases where they become wholly derelict.

The letter 'L' to the right of the box name indicates that it is a Listed Building. Only those boxes specifically listed in their own right are so indicated; there are other boxes which are probably deemed to be listed as part of a station listing.

Column 2: QUAIL MAP REFERENCE gives the volume and page reference to the Quail Railway Track Diagrams volumes.

The editions used here are:

1   Scotland 2001 (Fourth Edition)
2   England : East 1998
3   Great Western 2000 (Third Edition)
4   London Midland Region 1990
5   England South & London Underground 2002 (Second Edition)
6   Ireland 1995

(New editions may appear with different page arrangements).

Only one reference is given: some boxes may actually appear two or more times in the volume, on different maps. When the reference is in italics, this indicates that the box is not actually shown as such on the Quail map, either because it has been opened since the Quail map date, is still in situ but no longer in use, or because of an omission. No reference is given to the Signalling Maps in this book, owing to pressure of space in the Directory tabulations; as the maps here are of a few pages length only, it was felt that the Quail references would be more valuable to users, and that boxes will in most cases be readily locatable on the Maps here.

Column 3: BOX TYPE i.e. the design of the signal box structure.

Most pre-1970s signal boxes were built to a standard design and these are categorised in The Signal Box: A Pictorial History and Guide to Designs (Signalling Study Group, OPC, 1986) which most readers with an interest in this aspect will no doubt have in their possession. It should be noted that the above book does not include Ireland; illustrations of the principal Irish signal box designs can be found in the 1997 Edition of this Directory. For the benefit of those not familiar with signal box design it should be noted that many boxes of the pre-grouping period were not built to railway company designs but to the standard designs of the various firms of signalling contractors, so that identical boxes could be seen on the lines of many different railway companies. The box designs of the following firms can still be seen today:-

Dutton & Co.
Evans O'Donnell   abbr.   EOD
Gloucester Wagon Co.   abbr.   GWCo
McKenzie & Holland   abbr.   McK&H
Railway Signal Co.   abbr.   RSCo
Saxby & Farmer   abbr.   S&F
Stevens & Sons
E.S.Yardley & Co.

The name of the railway company for which the box was built appears in square brackets e.g. RSCo [L&Y].

*   indicates that a box is possessed of some non-standard features, whilst basically to the stated design.

+   indicates that significant alterations have been made to the box structure subsequently.

2h   indicates that the box, or the greater part of it, was previously in use at another location (mentioned in the footnotes where known).

**   indicates that there is no separate box structure, normally because the frame/panel/Block Post is within the main station buildings or some other building as noted in the footnotes.

N/S   indicates that the box is 'non standard' i.e. not to any of the main standard types recognised in The Signal Box.

CT   indicates a tall Control Tower structure in yards.

PB   indicates a large Power Box. Certain Power Box designs of the early BR period have 'type numbers' allocated as relatively large number were build to the same design, but most Power Boxes are of one-off designs so that only the responsible region, plus the term 'PB' appear, e.g. BR(LMR) PB.

PR   indicates a Panel Room i.e. a small operating room within a larger Relay Room type building.

In recent years, organisation flux, and the small number of new boxes now being opened, have effectively put an end to any concept of standardised signal box buildings. 1990s boxes are generally simply shown as 'PB' or 'Portakabin' only, without any attempt to specify which part of the fragmented railway was responsible for them, as design and commissioning are more often than not now carried out under different auspices. Portakabins now appear to be almost universally used for the smaller new boxes. The use of the term 'Portakabin' is not to be taken as a reference to any particular manufacturer, and there are naturally differences between the models of different manufacturers.

Column 4: BOX DATE

The date given is the opening date. Dates of building of the box structure would have been the same in most cases, but in recent years, particularly in the case of larger power boxes, the structures have often been completed 2-4 years prior to commissioning. Many box opening dates are known to the day, and for many others the year date quoted is either definite or all but definite. For some boxes, however, opening dates are only obtainable from dubious sources or as post- or pre-dates.

c   indicates dates which are only rough (all these should be within five years of the actual date).

u   indicates unconfirmed dates which may not be correct at all.

E   (suffixed) indicates a box that has been extended subsequently (see footnotes for date of extension, if known).

-      (suffixed) indicates a box which in its present form was opened at the date stated but incorporates parts of an earlier structure (usually because of fire or other accident seriously damaging the box in its previous form) – see footnote for details.

Dates in brackets indicate a previously-existing structure which became a signal box on the date stated (having had no signalling use prior to that).

Column 5: FRAME/EQUIPMENT DESIGN

The design names (and abbreviations used therefore) for mechanical frames are those given in A Guide to Mechanical Locking Frames (Signalling Study Group, 1989). As with signal box designs, many lever frame designs were the product of the various firms of signalling contractors, whilst others were designed and manufactured by the railway companies themselves. The abbreviations used of the contractors' names are the same as in Col. 3 (vide above). Some frame designs were manufactured by several other companies in addition   to the firms which designed and originally manufactured them; this is indicated in round brackets e.g. RSCo Tappet (EOD) indicates a frame made by Evans O'Donnell to the Railway Signal Company Tappet design. Exceptionally, Stevens frames have the manufacturer noted in <u>every</u> case, as the majority of them were made by other firms; those known to have been made by Stevens themselves are shown as Stevens (Stevens). Lever pitch is not shown except (a) where it varies from the standard pitch for that frame design or (b) where frames of that design were regularly made at more than one pitch.

2h	indicates that the frame had been used previously in another box in the same state (or almost so), before use in the present box.
recon.	indicates a frame made up in a railway company's own signal works from reconditioned parts recovered from old frames, combined in most cases with some newly-manufactured parts. (There is of course no hard and fast boundary between a '2h' frame and a 'recon.' frame. Leyton frames are noted here as '2h' but York frames as 'recon.').
gf	Ground Frame
pf	Power Frame (design is also given)
OCS Panel	'One Control Switch' Panel (Certain panels of the 1980s period are commonly referred to as 'OCS' but are not in fact the same as the 'true' OCS panels of the 1950s/1960s, being effectively 'multiple function switch' panels. No official term has ever been evolved for these panels and they are noted as 'OCS' (in inverted commas) in the listing here).
NX Panel	'Entrance-Exit' Panel
IFS Panel	Individual Function Switch Panel
IFS	Individual Function Switches not grouped into a panel.

(Many mechanical boxes have had a few switches added to work extra signals etc.; the more significant cases of this sort are shown but it is not claimed that every case is noted).

Column 6: FRAME/EQUIPMENT DATE

This gives the date at which the frame/panel/etc. was brought into use in the box in question (which is not necessarily the date of manufacture, although it is in most cases); 'c' and 'u' dates are quoted as necessary as in Col. 4.

Column 7: NUMBER OF LEVERS (mechanical boxes only).

The suffix 'R' is added when the frame has been 'reduced' from a formerly larger size. Many frames have been <u>extended</u> in length since they were originally installed but this is not normally indicated, only the <u>present</u> number of levers being given.

Spares and spaces are included. For 'reduced' frames, the size given is that which is visible upstairs; in some cases the whole of the original frame supports may remain downstairs. In certain cases, it may be a moot point as to how much of a frame may be said to 'remain' and different informants may have put different interpretations on this.

Column 8: LOCKING (not included in Section Two (LUL))

The majority of mechanical frames now have tappet locking. Many of the older frames now in use had other forms of locking originally, but have since been wholly relocked with tappet locking. Eight types of non-tappet mechanical locking (as listed below) do however remain in use. The abbreviations used are:

For frames:	B&S	Bar and Stud	(LNWR Tumbler frames)
	C&T	Cam and Tappet	(McKenzie & Holland)
	DT	Double Twist	(GWR)
	Dx	Duplex Tappet	(Saxby & Farmer)
	HCS	Hook Cam & Soldier	(McKenzie & Holland 1873 Patent)
	Rk	Rocker	(Saxby & Farmer)
	Stud	Stud	(GWR)
	T	Tappet	
	T Bar	T Bar	(McKenzie & Holland 1886 patent)
	Tum	Tumbler	(Midland)
	R.T	Relocked as Tappet from original non-tappet locking. (Note – many frames which did originally have tappet locking have also been relocked subsequently with a <u>different</u> form of tappet locking, but this is not generally noted).	
For panels:	E	Electrical Locking (Relay) (a few mechanical frames also have electrical locking)	
	SSI	Solid State Interlocking.	
	CBI	Computer Based Interlocking.	

DIRECTORY SECTION ONE : NETWORK RAIL BOXES

In addition to the majority of boxes which are both owned and staffed by Network Rail, this section also includes -
- Boxes owned by Network Rail but staffed by Train Operating Companies or other organisations (mostly boxes in yards, carriage sidings, etc.). These are not distinguished.
- Boxes not owned by Network Rail (these are noted <u>NNR</u> to the right of the name) but which were originally owned by the pre-nationalisation railway companies or BR and have since passed to Associated British Ports, or to privatised owners of former BR rolling stock workshops, or to parties to whom lines have been sold; also Eurotunnel installations and a few boxes remaining on non-Network Rail lines which are essentially part of the main national railway system rather than separate systems.

Owing to the flux and confusion of recent years, it is not always clear now, even to those involved, who certain boxes are presently 'owned' by in the property sense, and it is regretted that some mis-allocating may have occurred here in this respect. Boxes are shown here as Network Rail-owned unless it is definitely known to the contrary.

A number of large power stations and similar locations have 'control rooms' and signals (usually 'creep signals') for movements in hopper/loading areas. These are <u>not</u> included here (although it is recognised that it could be argued that they might be) except in cases where they also participate in some form of block working with a Network Rail box.

Ashford IECC (1997) – This 1993 creation of a highly utilitarian nature is at least within sight of the railway lines. Responsible for many miles of the South Eastern network and the recently completed section of the Channel Tunnel Rail Link, Ashford's signallers use VDUs to set routes and monitor the progress of trains.

Uffington & Barnack (2001) – A block post on the ex Midland route between Peterborough and Leicester and a fringe box to Peterborough PB, this Midland Type 4a box of 1909 is typical of its type. The window arrangement of four panes by three provides the signalman with a clear view, but in a box with an open vista facing south, there are a few problems on sunny days.

SECTION 1: NETWORK RAIL

Box Name	Quail Map	Box:- Type	Date	Frame/Equipment:- Design	Date	No. of Levers	Lock'g	Notes
Abbey Foregate	4/22A	GW 7d	1914	GW HT3 4"	1914	93	T	
Abercynon	3/29A	GW 27c 2h	1932	GWVT5/IFS NX pnls	1932/77/89	35R	T/E/SSI	2
Aberdeen	1/17A	BR(ScR)PB	1981	NX panel	1981	-	E	
Abergavenny	3/27C	GW 28b	1934	GW VT3	1934	52	T	
Abergele	L 4/36B	LNW 4	1902	LNW Tumbler	1902	60	B&S	
Aberthaw	3/30A	Barry 2	1897	GW VT5	1962	53	T	
Acle	2/8B	GE 3/S&F	1883	S&F Rocker 5"	1883	20	R.T	
Acton Canal Wharf	5/1A	Midland 2b	1895	LMR Standard	c1965	35	T	
Acton Wells Junction	5/1A	NL 3a+	c1892	IFS panel	1990	-	E	3
Aldershot	5/24C	LSW 4	c1900	Stevens (Stevens)	c1900	24	T	
Allerton Junction	4/40	BR(LMR) 15	1960	LMR Standard	1960	70	T	
Allington Junction	2/25B	GN 1	1875	S&F Rocker	1882	22	R.T	4,53
Alnmouth	2/23A	NE N3	1907	NX panel	1990	-	E	292
Alresford Station (G)	2/6A	GE Hut+	nk	IFS	nk	-	E	
Alrewas	4/18	LNW 4+	1899	IFS panel	1982	-	E	267
Alstone Crossing (G)	3/15D	Midland 2a	1891	IFS	c1982	-	E	
Amberley (NNM)	L 5/19C	SR B.O. Extn	1934	Stevens Knee (Tyer)	1934	14	T	
Ancaster	2/25B	GN 1	u1873	S&F Rocker 4"	1887	30	Rk	
Annan	1/1C	GSW 1	1876	Stevens/Cal.recon.	1973	20	T	6
Annat (G)	1/22A	BR(ScR) N/S	1963	Stevens/Cal.	1963	16	T	
Appleby (Lincs)	2/34C	Portakabin	2003	IFS panel	2003	-	E	183
Appleby North	4/34B	LMS 11c+	1951	REC	1951	25	T	179
Arbroath	1/16C	NB 7	1911	Stevens GNP (Stev)	1911	72	T	
Arnside	4/31A	Furness 4	u1897	LMR Standard	1957	35	T	
Arpley Junction	4/26B	LNW 5	1918	LNW Tappet	1918	54	T	
Arundel	5/19C	SR 13	1938	NX panel	1979	-	E	
Ascott-under-Wychwood	3/13B	GW 4b	1883	GW VT5	1949	25	T	
Ash Vale Junction	5/24C	LSW N/S	1879	IFS panel	1984	-	E	
Ashburys	4/45A	GC 5	1906	NX panel	1984	-	E	
Ashford ASC	5/11B	PB	1993	VDUs	1993	-	SSI	
Ashington	2/23C	NE N1+	1896	McK&H16 recon.	1938	25R	T	8
Ashton Moss North Junction	4/45A	L&Y+	1911	L&Y	1911	56	T	179
Ashwell	4/3B	Midland 4a+	1912	LMR Standard 6"	1958	25	T	179
Askam	L 4/31B	Furness 2	1890	RSCo Tappet	1890	22	T	
Astley	4/46A	BR(LMR) 15 2h	1972	LMR Standard 2h	1972	15	T	173
Aston	4/16	BR(LMR) 15+	1957	NX panel	1992	-	SSI	179/82
Atherton Goods Yard	4/48A	BR(LMR) 15	1956	LMR Standard	1956	35	T	
Attleborough	2/13B	GE 4/McK&H	1883	McK&H 4"	1912	36	T	
Auchterarder	1/16C	Caledonian N2	1895	Stevens GOP(Stev)	1895	16	T	
Aviemore	1/19D	McK&H 3/High	1898	McK&H12 rec/NX pnl	1971/79	30R	T/E	299
Awre (E,G)	3/20A	GW 7d+	1909	None	-	-	-	11
Axminster (G)	3/17C	**	-	IFS panel	1973	-	E	67
Aylesford	5/7	SR 11a	1921	EOD 2h	1921	26	T	
Ayr (E)	1/3	BR(ScR) PR	1985	NXpnl(HWmsDom'o)	1985	-	E	300/1
Baguley Fold Junction	4/45A	RSCo [L&Y]	1890	IFS panel	1998	-	E	
Balne (G)	2/18A	BR(NER) 17	1957	McK&H16 recon.	1957	5R	T	317
Bamber Bridge Station LCF (G)	4/33A	L&Y *	1904	IFS Panel	1972	-	E	
Banavie	1/22A	BR(ScR) N/S	1987	RETB VDUs/panel	1987	-	SSI	12
Banbury North	3/13B	GW 7b	1900	GW VT5	1957	95	T	
Banbury South	3/13B	GW 7d	1908	GW VT5 / NX panel	1944/1992	u64R	T/SSI	13
Bangor	4/36D	LNW 5	1923	LNW Tappet	1923	60R	T/E	
Barassie (E)	1/3	BR(ScR) PR	1982	NXpnl(SwissincoD'o)	1982	-	E	301
Barcroft (G)	2/18A	Portakabin	nk	IFS	nk	-	E	
Bardon Hill	4/7B	Midland 2b	1899	IFS	1979	-	E	
Bardon Mill (NNM)	2/46C	NE N1	c1874	McK&H16 recon.	1966	20	T	
Bare Lane	4/28B	LMS 11c+	1937	REC	1937	32	T	179
Bargoed	3/28B	BR(WR) 37b 2h	1970	GW VT5 2h	1970	51	T	14
Barkston East Junction	2/16C	GN 1	1882	Gloucester Wagon	1882	29	R.T	53
Bar!by (G)	2/38A	NE S1a	u1898	McK&H16 recon/IFS	1932/72	7R	T/E	
Barnby (E,G)	2/16C	BR(ER) 20	1977	IFS panel	1977	-	E	276

SECTION 1: NETWORK RAIL

Box Name		Quail Map	Box:- Type	Date	Frame/Equipment:- Design	Date	No. of Levers	Lock'g	Notes
Barnby Moor & Sutton (E,G)		*2/17B*	GN 1	1872	None	-	-	-	276
Barnetby East		2/31C	GC 5+	1914	GC (McK&H)	1914	72	T	179
Barnham		5/20C	LBSC 3b	1911	LBSC 1905 Patt./IFS	1911/85	75	T	245
Barnhill		1/16A	Caledonian N1	u1874	Stevens GOP (Stevens)	nk	20	T	
Barnsley		2/36A	2-high Por'kabins	1998	NX panel	1998	-	E	
Barrhead		1/4B	Caledonian S4+	1894	Stevens/Cal.recon.	1973	25	T	
Barrhill		1/2B	GSW 7 2h	1935	Stevens GNP/GSW 2h	1935	18	T	17
Barrow-in-Furness		4/31B	Furness 4	1907	RSCo Tap (Atkinson)	1907	67	T	
Barrow Road Crossing (G)		2/32B	RSCo [MS&L]	1885	RSCo Tappet	1885	28	T	
Barry		3/30B	Barry 1	c1897	GW VT5	1957	77R	T	
Barton Hill		2/18C	LNER 13	1936	McK&H16 recon.	1936	16	T	
Basford Hall Junction		4/13	LNW 4	1897	LNW Tumbler	1897	48R	B&S	
Basingstoke		5/27B	BR(SR) 19 PB	1966	NX panel	1966	-	E	
Bathley Lane (E,G)		*2/16C*	GN 4b+	1930	IFS panel	1976	-	E	276
Batley		2/41B	LNW 4	1878	IFS panel	1966	-	E	20
Bearley West Junction		4/15A	GW 7d+	1907	LMR Std 2h/NX panel	1974/98	30	T/E	273
Beckingham	L	2/27B	GN 1	1877	NX panel (Whse)	1977	-	E	
Bedale (G) **NNR**	L	*2/45E*	NE S1a	1875	McK&H 16	1909	31	T	
Bedford St Johns No.1		4/2C	BR(LMR) 15	1977-	LNW Tappet	1911	34R	T	21,268
Bedlington North		2/23C	NE N4	1912	McK&H16	1912	60R	T	
Bedlington South		2/23C	NE N1	nk	McK&H16 recon.	1940	30R	T	
Beeston Castle & Tarporley		4/35A	LNW 5	1915	LNW Tappet	1915	26	T	
Beighton Station		2/29	GC N/S	nk	McK&H 1886 4" 2h	1962	49	R.T	
Belasis Lane		2/48A	NE S4+	1929	McK&H16 recon.	1929	25	T	289
Bellwater Junction		2/26A	GN 4a	1913	S&F Rocker 5" 2h	1913	25	Rk	
Belmont (G)		2/42D	NE S5	1914	McK&H16 recon.	1968	5	T	
Bentley Heath Crossing (G)		4/15A	GW 28b+	1932	IFS	nk	-	E	1,179
Berwick		5/17A	S&F 5 [LBSC]	1879	S&F Rocker 5"	1879	17	R.T	
Bescot Down Tower		4/19	BR(LMR) PB	1965	NX panel	1965	-	E	
Bescot Up Hump (NBP) (OOU)		*4/19*	BR(LMR) 15	1963	LMR Standard	1963	20	T	
Betley Road		4/12C	LNW 3+	1875	LNW Tumbler	1904	12R	R.T	143
Beverley Station	L	2/39A	NE S4	1911	McK&H16	1911	20R	T	
Bexhill		5/17B	S&F 5 [LBSC]	1876	S&F Rocker 5"	1876	19	R.T	
Billingham		2/48A	NE C2a	1904	McK&H17 recon.	1945	50R	T	
Billingshurst	L	5/19C	S&F 1b [LBSC]	u1876	S&F Rocker 5"	1876	19	R.T	
Bingham		4/6B	GN 1+	1875E	McK&H C&T 4"	1922	40	C&T	24,179
Bishton Crossing (G)		3/20C	GW 12a	1941	GW VT5	1941	2R	T	26
Blackford		1/15B	LMS 12	1933	REC	1933	25		
Blackpool North No.1		4/49A	BR(LMR) 15+	1959	LMR Standard	1959	65	T	179
Blackpool North No.2		4/49A	L&Y	1896	L&Y	1896	72R	T	124
Blackrod Junction		4/48A	GWCo [L&Y]	1881	L&Y	1890	37	T	
Blair Atholl		1/19B	McK&H 3/High	u1890	McK&H 4" 2h/IFS	1969/78	18	T/E	
Blakedown		4/20C	GW 4c+	1888	IFS panel	1980	-	E	179
Blankney		2/27A	GN 4b	1928	Tyer Direct Tappet	1928	30	T	321
Blaydon		2/21B	NE N2	nkE	McK&H17 recon.	1929	43R	T	27
Blea Moor		4/34A	LMS 11c+	1941	REC	1941	30	T	179
Bletchley		4/9B	BR(LMR) PB	1965	NX panel/VDUs	1965/2003	-	E/SSI	319
Blotoft		2/26D	N/S	c2002-	Stevens (Stevens)	1882	16	T	10
Bloxwich		4/20C	BR(LMR) 15	1959	LMR Std/NX panel	1959/81	30	T/E	293
Bognor Regis		5/20c	SR 13	1938	Westinghouse A2	1938	66	T	
Bollo Lane Junction	L	5/1A	LSW 2	1878	NX panel	1983	-	E	
Bootle		4/31C	Furness 1	c1871	LMR Standard 2h	1977	15	T	29
Boston Dock Sw/Bge (G,B) **NNR**	L	*2/26A*	Boston Corp.	by1887	uGN - EL	1913	12	T	251
Bopeep Junction		5/17B	SE*	c1912	Whse A2 recon.	1973	24	T	
Bottesford West Junction		2/25B	GN 1+	1876	S&F Rocker 5"/IFS	1876/nk	38	R.T/E	179
Bounds Green Car.Sdgs GF (NBP)		2/14B	BR(ER) hut	c1978	gf	c1978	24	T	
Bounds Green S. End CC (NBP)		2/14B	BR(ER) hut	by1994	IFS panel	1994	-	E	252
Bournemouth ASC		*5/31A*	**	2003	VDUs	2003	-	CBI	
Bournemouth Car.Sdgs GF (NBP)		5/31A	LSW 3a	1888	Stevens(Stevens)	1888	14	T	32
Bowesfield		2/47C	NE N/S	1905	3 x IFS panels	1969/73/84		E	284

SECTION 1: NETWORK RAIL

Box Name		Quail Map	Box:-		Frame/Equipment:-		No. of Levers	Lock'g	Notes
			Type	Date	Design	Date			
BP Tmnl LC [Grangemouth] (G) **NNR**		1/12	Hut	1970	IFS panel	1970	-	E	
Brampton Fell		2/46A	NE N4	1918	McK&H16	1918	20R	T	
Brandon		2/13A	LNER 11c	1931	GN Duplex	1931	40	T	
Bransty		4/32A	LNW 4	1899	LNW Tumbler	1899	60	B&S	
Brereton Sidings		4/21A	LNW 5+	1908	LNW Tappet	1908	20	T	179
Bridlington		2/39B	NE S1a+	1875E	McKH16/IFS panel	1912/98	65R	T/E	34
Brierfield Station (G)		4/33B	S&F 8 [L&Y]	1876	IFS panel	1986	-	E	35
Brigg		2/31C	RSCo [MS&L]	1885	GC (uRSCo)	1923	30	T	
Brightside (RR,E)		2/29	BR(ER) N/S+	1965	NX panel	u1965	-	E	307
Bristol		3/5B	BR(WR) PB	1970	NX panels	1970	-	E	
Brockenhurst		5/30B	BR(SR) 18	1964	NX panel	1978	-	E	
Brocklesby Junction	L	2/32A	GC 5	1914	NX panel	1998	-	E	
Bromfield		3/27A	LNW/GW Jt 1	1873	GW VT5	1956	29	T	
Bromley Cross (G)		4/48A	Yardley1 [L&Y]	1875	L&Y	1902	16R	T	37
Broomfleet		2/38B	NE S2	1904	McK&H16	1904	60R	T	
Brough East		2/38B	NE S2	1904	McK&H16	1904	52R	T	
Brundall		2/8	GE 3/Stevens	1883	McK&H 4" 2h	1927	35	T	39
Buildwas Power Stn CR **NNR**		*4/21D*	**	c1965	-	nk	-	-	279
Burscough Bridge Junction		4/42A	L&Y+	1922	IFS panel	1993	-	E	179
Bury St Edmunds Yard		2/12D	GE 7/McK&H	1888	McK&H u 1886 5"	1888	53	R.T	
Butterwell Bunker **NNR**		2/22B	**	1977	IFS panel	1994	-	E	261
Butterwell TP Hut		2/22B	Hut	1994	None	-	-	-	262
Buxton		4/44A	LNW 4	1894	LNW Tumbler	1894	45R	B&S/T	113
Caersws (G)	L	4/23D	Dutton 1[Cambrian]	1891	Dutton combination	1891	18	T	
Caldicot Crossing GF (G,NBP)		3/20B	BR(WR) hut	c1979	gf/IFS	c1979	10	T/E	43
Cambridge		2/11C	BR(ER) PB	1982	NX panel	1982	-	E/SSI	44
Camden Road Junction		4/1R	NL 3b	1896	NX panel	1987	-	E	
Canning Street North (OOU)		4/39A	LNW 4	1900	LNW Tumbler	1900	18	B&S	45
Canterbury East		5/9B	SEC	c1911	LCD	c1911	28	T	
Canterbury West	L	5/9B	Overhead 2h	1928	SEC NP 2h	1928	72R	T	46
Canterbury Wye ASC		5/9B	Portakabin	2003	NX panel	2003	-	E	
Cantley		2/8	GE 7	1887	S&F 1905 Duplex	1913	22	Dx	
Cardiff		3/22	BR(WR) PB	1966	NX panel	1966	-	E	
Carleton Crossing		4/49A	LNW 5	1924	L&Y	1924	12	T	
Carlisle		4/29C	BR(LMR) PB+	1973	NX panel	1973	-	E	48
Carlton (ELC,G)		2/17A	BR(ER) 20	1977	NX panel (Whse M3)	1997	-	E	50
Carmarthen Junction		3/25B	BR(WR) 16a	1956	NX panel	1985	-	E	
Carmont		1/16D	Caledonian N1	c1876	Stevens/Cal	1907	18	T	
Carmuirs East Junction		1/9A	NB 4	1882	Stevens GOP (Stevens)	u1901	28	T	
Carmuirs West Junction		1/9A	Caledonian N/S	1881	Stevens/Cal	1912	20R	T	
Carnforth Station Junction	L	4/28B	Furness 4	1903	RSCo Tappet (EOD)	1903	59R	T	
Carnoustie		1/16B	Caledonian N2	1898	Stevens/Cal 2h	1984	20	T	51
Carterhouse Junction		4/38A	LNW 4	1896	LNW Tumbler	1896	30	B&S	
Castleford		2/42A	2-high Por'kabins	1997	NX panel	1997	-	E	
Castleton East Junction		4/47A	BR(LMR) 15	1963	LMR Standard	1963	65	T	
Cathcart		1/7R	BR(ScR) PB	1961	OCS panel	1961	-	E	311
Cattal		2/42E	NE S5	c1892	McK&H16 recon.	1934	15	T	
Causeway Crossing (G)		3/4A	BR(WR) hut	1975	IFS	1975	-	E	
Cave (G)		2/38B	NE S2	1904	McK&H16	1904	16R	T	
Caverswall		4/25B	LMS 11c+	1942	REC	1942	35	T	179
Cemetery North		2/48A	NE C2a	1905	McK&H17 recon.	1955	20R	T	281
Chapel-en-le-Frith		4/44A	BR(LMR) 15	1957	LMR Standard	1957	20	T	
Chapel Lane Crossing (G)		4/42A	Hut	2002	LMR Standard	1952	5	T	256
Chard Junction		3/17B	BR(WR) N/S	1982	NX panel	1982	-	E	
Charlton Lane Crossing (G)		5/5	S&F 12a [SE]	1894	S&F1888Duplex	1894	7	E	
Chartham (G)		5/9B	SE	c1880	SE Brady 5"/IFS	1880/2003	2R	T/E	
Chathill (RR)	L	*2/23A*	NE N1	c1873E	-	-	-	-	255
Chelford Frame (NBP, NNM)		4/43B	BR(LMR) N/S	1959	LMR Standard	1959	20	T	320
Chester		4/35A	BR(LMR) PB	1984	NX panel	1984	-	E	
Chichester		5/20D	S&F 5 [LBSC]	1882	NX panel	1991	-	E	

SECTION 1: NETWORK RAIL

Box Name		Quail Map	Box:- Type	Date	Frame/Equipment:- Design	Date	No. of Levers	Lock'g	Notes
Chinley		4/44A	BR(LMR) 15	1980	LMR 'OCS' panels	1980/82	-	E	
Chippenham Junction		2/12D	GE 7*	u1921	McK&H 4"	u1921	16	T	
Chitts Hill [Colchester] (G)		2/5E	GE Hut	nk	IFS	nk	-	E	
Clachnaharry (B)		1/18C	McK&H 3/High	1890s	McK&H 4"	1912	4R	T	57
Clacton		2/6A	GE 7	1891	S&F 1888Duplex	1891	52R	R.T	
Clapham Yard Shunters Pnl (NBP)		5/2L	**	(1990)	ML NX panel	1990	-	E	58
Clarbeston Road		3/26A	GW 7c	1906	NX panel	1988	-	E	
Clarence Road		2/48A	NE N/S	1904	McK&H17 recon.	1933	36R	T	
Claydon L&NE Junction		3/13A	Portakabin	1985	NX panel	1985	-	E	
Claypole (ELC,G)		2/16C	BR(ER) 20	1977	Panel	1977	-	E	50
Cliff House		2/48A	BR(NER) 17	1958	McK&H16 recon/IFS	1958/61	70R	T/E	86
Clipstone Junction		2/30A	GC 5	1917	GC(RSCo)/NX panels	1917/86/97	u26R	T/E	15
Codsall	L	4/21C	GW 28+	1929	GW VT3 2h	1929	25	T	59,179
Colchester		2/6A	BR(ER) PB	1983	NX panel	1983	-	E	
Colchester Road [Alresford] (G)		2/6A	GE Hut	nk	IFS	nk	-	E	
Colthrop Crossing (G)		3/11A	GW 7c+	1912	gf/IFS	1978	2	T/E	85
Colwich		4/12A	BR(LMR) 15	1961	LMR Std/NX panel	1961/74	30R	T/E	61
Corby Gates		2/46A	BR(NER) 17	1955-	McK&H16 recon.	1955	26	T	62
Corkerhill SP (NBP)		!/5A	Hut	1984	IFS panel	1984	-	E	
Corus Redcar NNR		2/50B	BSC	1972	Panel (INTEGRA)	1972	-	E	
Cosford		4/21C	GW 12+	1939	GW VT5	1939	39	T	179
Coundon Road Station		4/14B	LNW 4+	1876	LNW Tumbler	1876	22	B&S	179
Coventry		4/14B	BR(LMR) PB	1962	NX panel	1962+	-	E	278
Cowbridge Road		3/23A	BR(WR) hut	1965	IFS	1965	-	E	
Cowlairs SC		1/7L	Relay Room Bldg	(1998)	NX panel (Whse)	1998	-	SSI	272
Crabley Creek		2/38B	NE S1b+	1891E	McK&H17 recon.	c1956	14R	T	64
Crag Hall		2/51A	NE C1+	1878	McK&H16	1906	30	T	65
Craigentinny CSD Panel (NBP)		1/11A	Hut	1976	IFS panel	1976	-	E	
Craigo		1/16D	Cal N1	c1877	Stevens/Cal	1907	21	T	
Craven Arms Crossing		3/27A	GW 34	u1947	GW VT5	nk	30	T	66
Crediton	L	3/10C	LSW 1	1875	NX panel	1984	-	E	168
Crewe Coal Yard		4/13	LMS 13	1939	REC	1939	65	T	267
Crewe		4/13	BR(LMR) PB	1985	NX panel	1985	-	E	
Crewe Sorting Sidings North		4/13	BR(LMR) 15	1962	IFS panel	1962	-	E	
Crewe Steel Works		4/13	LMS 11c	1935	REC	1935	20	T	
Cricklewood Depot (NBP)		4/1L	BR(LMR) PB	1979	OCS panel (Whse)	1979	-	E	
Croes Newydd North Fork		4/22D	GW 27c+	1905E	GW VT5	1940	83	T	315
Croft Sidings		4/3B	LNW 4	1901	LNW Tumbler	1901	30	B&S	
Crosfields Crossing		4/26B	LNW 4*	1906	LNW Tumbler	1906	18	B&S	
Crow Nest Junction		4/48A	BR(LMR) 15	1972	LMR Standard	1972	25	T	
Crown Point Depot CC (NBP)		2/7A	BR(ER) 20	1982	Panel	1982	-	E	
Culgaith		4/34C	Midland 4a+	1908	Mid Tum Wks Rlk	1908	16	T	179
Cupar		1/14C	NB 7	nk	Stevens GNP (Stevens)	nk	32	T	
Cutsyke		2/39D	BR(ER) N/S	1975	IFS panel	1975	-	E	
Cuxton		5/7	SE	nk	SE u Brady 5"	nk	29	R.T	
Daisyfield Station		4/33B	S&F 6 [L&Y]+	1873	L&Y recon.	1943	16	T	69
Dalston Junction		2/1B	NL 3a	1891	NX panel	1987	-	E	271
Dalton Junction		4/31B	Furness 4	1902	RSCo(EOD)	1902	20	T	
Dalwhinnie		1/19C	Highland+	1909	McK&H16 recon/IFS	1966/78	20	T/E	179
Daventry IRFT CC (NBP)		4/11A	N/S	1997	nk	1997	-	E	
Dawdon		2/48B	NE N3*	1905	IFS panel	1986	-	E	
Deal		5/9A	SR 13	1939	Westinghouse A2	1939	42	T	
Deansgate Junction		4/46A	BR(LMR) 15	1957	NX panel (Whse)	1991	-	SSI	70
Dee Marsh Junction		4/37E	GC 5	1930	RSCo-LNER Std	1930	25R	T	
Deganwy		4/36C	LNW 5+	1914	LNW Tappet	1914	18	T	179
Denton Junction		4/45A	LNW 4	1888	LNW Tumbler	1888	18R	B&S	
Derby		4/4B	BR(LMR) PB+	1969	NX panel (Whse)	1969	-	E	48
Diggle Junction		4/45C	LNW 4+	1885	nk	nk	26R	T	102
Dinting Station		4/45D	GC 5+	1905	GC(RSCo)	1905	43	T	22
Ditton Junction		4/38A	PB	2000	NX panel	2000	-	E	

SECTION 1: NETWORK RAIL

Box Name	Quail Map	Box:- Type	Date	Frame/Equipment:- Design	Date	No. of Levers	Lock'g	Notes
Doncaster	2/17C	BR(ER) PB	1979	NX panel	1979	-	E	
Dorchester	5/31D	BR(SR) 16	1959	NX panel	1985	-	E/SSI	72
Dorking	5/19A	SR 13	1938	Westinghouse A2	1938	44	T	
Dorrington	4/23B	LNW/GW Jt 1	c1872	GW VT5	1941	33	T	
Dover Priory (E)	5/13	SR12	1930	Panel	1980	-	E	
Downham Market	2/12A	GE 2	1881	S&F Rocker 5"	1881	13R	R.T	
Driffield	2/39B	NE S1a+	1875	McK&H16 re./IFSpnl	1957/87	3R	T/E	152
Drigg	4/31C	Furness 1	u1871	RSCo 1877 Pat.	1882	13	T	
Droitwich Spa	3/14A	GW 7d+	1907	GW HT3 5¼"	1907	79	T	28
Dudding Hill Junction	5/1A	Midland 3a+	1902	Midland Tumbler	1902	16	Tum	73
Dullingham	2/11C	GE 4/Stevens	1883	IFS panel	1978	-	E	
Dumfries Station	1/1C	BR(ScR) 16c	1957	OCS panel	1997	-	E	
Dunblane	1/15A	Caledonian N3	1902	Stevens/Cal	1955	60	T	
Dundee SC	1/16B	BR(ScR) PB	1985	NX panel (Whse)	1985	-	E	
Dunkeld	1/19A	Highland	1919	McK&H C&T 4"	1919	23R	T	
Dunragit	L 1/2A	LMS 12	1927	Stevens/Cal	1942	32R	T	
Dyce	1/17B	GNS 1	1880E	Stevens GNP	1928	26R	T	
Earles Sidings	4/44B	Midland 4e+	1929	REC	1929	35	T	74
East Farleigh	5/10C	SE	1892	SE Brady 5"	1892	25	T	
East Gate Junction [Colchester]	2/6A	LNER N/S	1924	McK&H 4"/panel	1924/83	35	T/E	77
East Holmes [Lincoln]	2/27A	GN 1	1873	McK&H 4"	1910	35	R.T	
East Usk	3/21A	BR(WR) 37	1961	GW VT5	1961	39	T	78
Eastbourne	5/17A	S&F 5 [LBSC]	1882	NX panel	1991	-	SSI	75
Eastfield (NBP)	L 2/16A	GN 1	1893E	RSCo Tappet	1893	65	T	76
Eastleigh	5/28A	BR(SR) PB	1981	NX panels	1981/95	-	E/SSI	249
Eastleigh (RR)	5/28A	BR(SR) 19 PB	1966	-	-	-	-	250
Eastleigh DEMU Depot GF (NBP)	5/28A	BR(SR) 16	1968	Westinghouse recon.	1968	24	T	
Eastleigh GF 'C' (NBP)	5/28A	LSW hut	1918	Stevens Knee (RSCo)	u1918	29	T	
Eccles	4/46A	LMS 11b	1933	NX panel	1998		E	
Eccles Road	2/13B	GE4/McK&H	1883	McK&H u1873 5"	1883	21	R.T	
Edale	4/44A	Midland 2b	1893	Midland Tumbler	1893	20	Tum	
Edge Hill	4/40	BR(LMR) PB	1961	NX panel (Whse)	1985	-	E	
Edgeley Junction No.1	4/44A	LNW 4	1884	LNW Tumbler	1884	54R	B&S	323
Edgeley Junction No.2	4/44A	LNW 4	1884	LNW Tumbler	1884	54	B&S	
Edinburgh SC	1/11A	BR(ScR) PB	1976	NXpnls(HWmsDom')	1976/97	-	E/SSI	257
Egginton Junction	4/25C	NS 1+	1877	McK&H 1873 Pat. 6"	1877	14R	R.T	179
Elgin	1/18A	Highland* 2h	1951	Stevens/Cal recon.	1973	26	T	79
Elland	2/41A	BR(NER) 17	1958	McK&H16 recon.	1958	60	T	100
Ellesmere Port	4/35A	BR(LMR) 15	1972-	LNW Tappet	1924	64	T	80
Elmton & Creswell	2/30A	LMS 11c	1946	LMS 1938 Patt.	1946	48	T	81
Elsenham (G)	2/11B	Brick Hut	nk	IFS	nk	-	E	
Elsham	2/34C	Portakabin	2003	Panel	2003	-	E	183
Errol	L 1/16A	Caledonian N1	c1877	Stevens/Cal	1911	20	T	
Eurotunnel RCC **NNR**	5/12A	**	1994	VDUs etc.	1994	-	SSI	253
Everton (E,G)	2/15C	BR(ER) 20	1976	IFS panel	1976	-	E	276
Evesham	3/13D	BR(WR) 37a	1957	GW VT5	1957	42R	T	267
Exeter	3/7A	BR(WR) PB	1985	NX panel	1985	-	E	
Exmouth Junction	3/18B	BR(SR) 18*	1959	NX panel	1988	-	E	
Falkland Down Yard (NBP) **NNR**	1/3	Yard Insp's Office	1985	IFS panel	1985	-	E	304
Falsgrave [Scarborough]	L 2/18D	NE S4	1908	McK&H16	1908	120	T	312
Farncombe	5/26A	LSW 4	1897	IFS	1986	-	E	
Farnham	5/24C	LSW 4	1901	Stev(RSCo)/NX Pnl	1901/85	35	T/E	82
Faversham	5/8B	BR(SR) 17 PB	1959	NX panel	1959	-	E	
Fawley GF (NBP)	5/30A	BR(SR) hut	1950	gf (Stevens)	1950	5	T	
Felixstowe N.Quay F'lt Dpt **NNR**	2/9A	nk	1987	Shunter's panel	1987	-	E	83
Feltham	5/25A	BR(SR) PB	1974	NX panel	1974	-	E	
Feniton (G)	3/17C	BR(WR) SB+BO	1974	IFS	1974	-	E	
Fenny Compton	4/14A	BR(WR) 17+	1960	GW VT5	1960	77	T	179
Fenny Stratford	4/9C	LNW4	1883	LNW Tumbler	1883	22	B&S	268
Ferme Park CC (NBP, OOU)	2/14B	BR(ER) hut	1976	Panel	1976	-	E	

SECTION 1: NETWORK RAIL

Box Name	Quail Map	Box:- Type	Date	Frame/Equipment:- Design	Date	No. of Levers	Lock'g	Notes
Ferrybridge	2/35B	BR(NER) 16b	1956	IFS panel	1982	-	E	202
Ferryhill	2/20C	BR(NER) 13	1952	IFS	1992		E	84
Ferryside	3/25B	GW 3	1880s	GW DT	1898	24	R.T	291
Fidlers Ferry Power Station	4/38B	BR(LMR) 15	1967	LMR Standard	1967	45	T	
Finningley (G)	2/17C	GN1	1877	NX panel	1977	-	E	
Fiskerton (G)	4/6B	Midland 3a+	1902	Midland Tumbler	1902	15R	Tum	179
Fiskerton Junction	4/6B	Midland 4e+	1929	REC	1929	30	T	179
Foley Crossing	4/25B	NS 2	1889	McK&H 1873 Pat 5"	1889	37	HCS	
Folkestone East	5/13	BR(SR) 18 PB	1962	NX panels	1962/98	-	E/SSI	19
Folkestone Harbour (NNM)	5/13	S&F 5 2h	1933	Westinghouse A2 2h	1933	22	T	
Forders Sidings	4/9C	LMS 11*	1930	REC	1930	40	T	268
Forres	1/18A	McK&H3/High	1896	McK&H 1886 4" 2h	1967	24	R.T	
Fort William Junction	1/22A	NB 6b	1894E	Stev/Cal recon/NX pnl	1973/75	30	T/E	131
Fouldubs Junction	1/12	Caledonian N3	1908	Stevens/Cal	1951	40R	T	
Foxfield	4/31B	Furness 3*	1879E	RSCo Tappet	1909	52	T	40
Foxton (G)	2/24C	GN 1	1878	IFS	1983	-	E	87
Fratton GF 'A' (NBP)	5/26C	BR(SR) 19 hut	1968	Stev. Knee (RSCo) 2h	1968	24	T	88
Freemans	2/23C	BR(NER) 16b	1956	IFS panel	1982	-	E	18
Frinton (G)	2/6A	LNER hut	u1924	gf 3¾"	1936	15	T	89
Frisby Station	4/3B	LMS 11c+	1941	IFS	1987	-	E	179
Frodsham Junction	4/26B	LNW 5+	1912	LNW Tumbler 2h	1893	32	B&S	90
Furness Vale	4/44A	LNW 4+	1887	LNW Tumbler	1909	22	B&S	94
Gaerwen	4/37A	LNW 4+	1882	LNW Tumbler	1882	20	B&S	179
Gainsborough Central	2/31B	MS&L 2	1885	MS&L Iron brackets	1885	26	R.T	
Gainsborough Lea Road	2/27B	GN 1+	u1877	EOD	1895	35	T	179
Gainsborough Trent Junction	2/31B	BR(ER) 19	1964	RSCo - GNI	1964	40	T	
Garsdale	4/34B	Midland 4c+	1910	Midland Tappet	1910	33R	T	179
Gascoigne Wood	2/37B	NE S4	1908	NX panel	1982	-	E	
Gidea Park EMU Sdgs (NBP)	2/5B	Hut	1997	Panel	1997	-	E	
Gilberdyke Junction	2/38A	NE S2	1903	McK&H16/IFS	1903/nk	55	T/E	148
Gillingham [Dorset]	5/33C	BR(SR) 16	1957	Westinghouse A3	1957	30	T	
Gillingham [Kent]	5/8A	SEC	1913	SEC NP	1913	44	T	
Girvan	1/2B	GSW 3	1893E	Stevens/Cal recon.	1973	30	T	92
Glasgow Central SC	1/7R	BR(ScR) PB	1961	NXpnl(HWmsDom'o)	nk	-	E	305
Glazebrook East Junction	4/46A	BR(LMR) 15	1961	LMR Standard	1961	80	T	
Glenwhilly	1/2A	GSW 7	c1905	Stevens GNP/GSW	1905	20	T	
Gloucester	3/15D	BR(WR) PB	1968	NX panel	1968	-	E	
Gobowen North	4/22B	McK&H 3 [GW] +	1884	GW Stud	1912	16	T	93
Godnow Bridge (G)	2/33B	GN	1999	IFS Panel 2h	1999	-	E	233
Goole	2/40B	NE S4	1909	NX panel	1975	-	E	95
Goole Bridge	L 2/40B	NE N/S	1869	McK&H 1886 Pat/pnl	1933/33	5	T/E	96
Goonbarrow Junction	3/9B	GW 7d	c1909	GW VT3	1924	25	T	
Gosberton	2/26D	GE 2	1882	Stevens(Stevens)	1882	30	T	
Gospel Oak	4/1	BR(LMR) N/S	1985	IFS panel	1985	-	E	
Goxhill	2/32B	GC N/S	1910	GC (McK&H)	1910	36	T	
Grain Crossing (G)	5/7	Stevens [SE]	1882	SE Tappet	nk	9	T	97
Grangemouth Junction	1/9A	Portakabin	1997	NX panel (Whse)	1997	-	SSI	
Grange-over-Sands	4/31A	BR(LMR) 15	1956	LMR Standard	1956	25	T	
Grangetown	2/50B	LNER 15	1954	NX panel	1984	-	E	
Great Coates No.1	2/32A	MS&L 3 2h	1909	RSCo Tappet 2h	1909	23	T	
Great Rocks Junction	4/44A	Midland 4d+	1923	Midland Tappet	1923	34	T	74
Greatham	2/48A	NE N1+	1889	McK&H16 recon.	1941	21	T	127
Greenbank	4/43B	BR(LMR) 15	1975	NX panel	1980	-	E	
Greenford East	3/19A	GW 27c	1904E	GW VT5	1956	76	T	98
Greenhill Junction	1/9A	Relay Room Hut	(1990)	NX panel	1990	-	E	99
Greenloaning	1/15B	Caledonian N2	1891	Stevens GOP (Stevens)	1891	32	T	
Greetland	2/41A	LMS 13	1941	REC	1941	55	T	100
Gresty Lane No.1	4/13	LNW 4 *+	1899	IFS panel	1978	-	E	179
Grindleford	4/44B	LMS 11c	1938	REC	1938	25	T	
Gristhorpe (G)	2/39C	NE S1b	1874	McK&H 1873 6" 2h	1910	15R	R.T	

SECTION 1: NETWORK RAIL

Box Name	Quail Map	Box:- Type	Date	Frame/Equipment:- Design	Date	No. of Levers	Lock'g	Notes
Grove Road (E,G)	2/17A	GN 1+	c1880	Panel	1976	-	E	276
Guide Bridge	4/45A	GC 5+	1906	NX panel	1984	-	E	101
Guildford ASC	5/23	N/S	1998	NX panel	1998	-	E	
Hademore Crossing	4/12A	LNW 4	1899	IFS	1979	-	E	
Hale (RR)	L 4/46A	S&F 8 [CLC]	c1875	-	-	-	-	269
Halifax	2/43	RSCo [L&Y]	1884	IFS panel	1970	-	E	55
Hall Dene	2/48B	NE N3*	1905	McK&H16 recon.	1942	21	T	
Halton Junction	4/26B	LNW 4	1897	LNW Tumbler	1897	25	B&S	
Haltwhistle	2/46C	Portakabin	1993	IFS panel	1993	-	E	318
Hammerton	2/42E	Platf'm cupboard	1972	McK&H16	1914	10	T	103
Hampden Park	5/17A	LBSC 2b	1888E	EOD	c1930	24	T	104
Hamworthy	5/31B	LSW 3b	1893	Stevens (Stevens)	1893	59	T	
Harlescott Crossing	4/23A	LNW 4	1882E	LNW Tumbler	1882	38R	B&S	
Harling Road	2/13B	GE 4/McK&H	1883	McK&H 1873 Pat.5"	1883	25	R.T	
Harringay Park Junction	2/1B	BR(ER) N/S	1959	RSCo - GN1	1959	25	T	
Harrogate	2/42D	LNER 15	1947	McK&H16 recon.	1947	45R	T	33
Hartlebury	4/20C	McK&H 2 [GW]+	1876	IFS panel	1982	-	E	179
Haslemere	5/26A	LSW 4	1895	Stevens (RSCo)	1895	47	T	
Hastings	5/18C	SR 12	1930	Westinghouse A2	1930	84	T	
Havant	L 5/20D	S&F 5 [LBSC]	1876E	Westinghouse A2	1938	64R	T	105
Havensmouth [Normans Bay] (G)	5/17A	Portakabin	c1999	IFS panel 2h	c1999	-	E	
Hawkesbury Lane	4/11B	LNW 4+	1896	LNW Tumbler	1896	26	B&S	179
Haydon Bridge	2/46E	NE N1	1877	McK&H17 recon.	1964	31	T	
Haymarket Dpt Pnl (NBP) **NNR**	*1/11A*	Shunter's Bldng	nk	uIFS panel	nk	-	E	
Hazel Grove	4/44A	LNW 4	1877	LMR 'OCS' panel	1986	-	E	
Healey Mills	2/41B	BR(ER) PB	1963	NX panel	2003	-	E	106
Heath Junction	3/28B	Portakabin	1984	OCS panel	1984	-	E	
Heaton Car. Depot C/T (NBP)	2/22A	BR(ER) CT	1977	IFS panel	1977	-	E	
Heaton Norris Junction	4/44A	BR(LMR) 14	1955	LMR Standard	1955	125	T	
Hebden Bridge	2/41A	L&Y	1891	L&Y	1891	38	T	
Heckington	L 2/25C	GN 1	1876	S&F Rocker 4" 2h	1925	18	Rk	
Hednesford	4/21A	LNW 4	1877	LNW Tumbler	1877	38	B&S	
Heighington	2/47A	NE C1+	c1872	McK&H16	1906	11R	T	127
Hellifield South Junction	4/33C	Midland 4c	1911	Midland Tappet	1911	58R	T	298
Helpston (G)	2/16B	GN 1	1898	IFS panel	1997	-	E	237
Helsby Junction	4/35A	LNW 4	1900	LNW Tumbler	1900	45	B&S	239
Henley-in-Arden	4/15A	GW 7d+	1907	GW HT3 5¼"	1907	57	T	179
Hensall Station	2/40A	Yardley 1 [L&Y]	1875	McK&H16rec/IFSpnl	1964/nk	8R	T/E	
Henwick	3/14A	McK&H 1 + [GW]	c1875E	GW DT	1897	25	R.T	107
Henwick Hall (G)	2/18A	NE S1b	1912	IFS panel	1973	-	E	
Hereford	3/27B	LNW/GW Jt 2	1884	GW VT5/panel	1938/84	60R	T/E	108
Hessle Road	2/38B	BR(NER) PB	1962	NX panel	1962	-	E	
Hest Bank LCF (G)	4/28B	BR(LMR) 15	1958	IFS	1982	-	E	
Hexham	L 2/46E	NE N5 overhead	u1918	Stevens (McK&H28)	1918	60	T	318
Heyworth (G)	2/18A	Portakabin	nk	IFS	nk	-	E	
Hickleton	2/33A	LMS 11b+	1931	REC	1933	50	T	127
High Street [Lincoln]	2/27A	GN 1	1874	McK&H C&T 4"	1892	36	C&T	
Hilton Junction	1/14C	Caledonian N1	1873	Stevens GNP/GSW 2h	nk	20	T	109
Hinckley	4/3B	LNW 4+	1894	LNW Tumbler	1894	20	B&S	179
Hither Green (RR)	5/3B	BR(SR) 18 PB	1962	None	-	-	-	
Holme (E,G)	2/15D	BR(ER) 20	1975	NX panel	1975	-	E	276
Holmes Chapel Frame (NBP,NNM)	4/43B	BR(LMR) Hut	1959	LMR Standard	1959	10	T	110
Holmwood (NNM)	5/19A	S&F 5 [LBSC]	1877	S&F Rocker 5"	1877	18	R.T	
Holton-le-Moor	2/28A	MS&L 3	1890	Panel	1989	-	E	
Holyhead	4/37B	LMS 11c+	1937	REC	1937	100	T	111
Holywell Junction	L 4/36A	LNW 4	1902	LNW Tumbler	1902	54	B&S	239
Holywood	1/2D	GSW 7	nk	Stevens GNP/GSW	nk	23	T	
Honiton	3/17C	BR(SR) 16	1957	Westinghouse A3	1957	24	T	
Hooton	4/38C	Presco P'kabin	1985	NX panel	1985	-	E	
Horbury Junction	2/42A	LNW 5+	1927	REC	1927	65	T	22

SECTION 1: NETWORK RAIL

Box Name		Quail Map	Box:- Type	Date	Frame/Equipment:- Design	Date	No. of Levers	Lock'g	Notes
Hornsey Carriage Sidings (NNM)		2/14B	BR(ER) N/S	1976	Panel	1976	-	E	
Horrocksford Junction		4/33B	S&F 6 [L&Y]	1873	L&Y	1928	8	T	
Horsforth		2/42C	NE S1b	1873	McK&H16	1916	15R	T	
Horsham		5/19B	SR 13	1938	Westinghouse A2	1938	90	T	
Howe & Co's Siding		4/34C	Midland 4a	1916	REC	1943	30	T	
Howsham (G)		2/18C	NE S1b	c1873	McK&H 1873 Pat 6"	1891	7	R.T	
Hubberts Bridge		2/25C	BR(ER) N/S	1961	RSCo-GNI	1961	25	T	
Huddersfield		2/41A	BR(NER) PB	1958	NX panel	u1993	-	SSI	
Hull Bridge (B)		2/38C	S&F+	1885	S&F/IFS panel	1885/1964	5	R.T	112
Hull Paragon		2/38C	LNER 13 PB	1938	NX panel	nk	-	E	
Huncoat Station LCF (G)		4/33B	L&Y+	1902	L&Y	1902	8R	T	179
Hunterston (E)		1/4A	BR(ScR) PR	1978	NX panel	nk	-	E	306
Hunterston H/Level (NBP) **NNR**		1/4A	CT	c1980	NX panel (Whse)	c1980	-	E	275
Huntly		1/17D	GNS 2b	1890	Stevens/Cal recon.	1970	25	T	114
Hunts Cross		4/40	BR(LMR) PR	1982	NX panel	1982	-	E	
Hurlford		1/3	LMS 2	1920s	Stevens/Cal recon.	1976	20	T	
Huyton		4/42B	LNW 4	1899	LNW Tumbler	1899	36	B&S	
Ilford Carr. Sheds CC (NBP)		2/5A	nk	1997	Panel	1997	-	E	
Immingham East Junction		2/32B	GC 5	1912	British Pneu.pf/pnl	1912/81	60	T/E	
Immingham Rec'pt'n Sdgs **NNR**		2/32B	GC 5	1912	Brit.Pn.pf/NX&IFSpnl	1912/67	91R	T/E	116
Immingham West Junction **NNR**		2/32B	GC 5	1912	IFS panel	1972	-	E	115
Ingatestone (G)		2/5C	GE 7+	1905	Panel	1996	-	E	267
Insch		1/17C	GNS 2a	1886	Stevens/Cal recon.	1969	20	T	235
Inverkeilor		1/16C	NB 1	1881	Stevens GOP (Stevens)	1881	22	T	
Inverness SC		1/18B	BR(ScR) PB	1987	NX pnl/RETB VDUs	1987/88	-	E/SSI	117
Inverurie		1/17C	GNS 3b	1902	Stevens/Cal recon.	1970	30	T	
Joan Croft Junction (G)		2/18A	Portakabin	nk	IFS	nk	-	E	
Keadby Canal Junction (B)		2/34A	LNER 11a	1926	IFS panel	2003		E	118
Keith Junction		1/17D	GNS 3b	1905	Stevens/Cal recon.	1969	40	T	
Kennethmont		1/17C	RSCo hip. [GNS]	1888E	Stevens/Cal recon.	1969	20	T	235
Kennett		2/12D	GE 2	1880	McK&H 1873 Pat 5"	1880	17R	R.T	
Ketton		2/24D	Midland 2b+	1900	Midland Tumbler	1900	20	Tum	179
Kew East Junction		5/1A	NL 3b	c1900	NL Tappet	c1900	50	T	
Kidderminster Junction		4/20C	BR(WR) 16+	1953	GW VT5	1953	66	T	179
Kidwelly		3/25b	BR(WR) 35	1950s-	NX panel	1983	-	E	119
Kilkerran		1/2B	GSW 3	1895	Stevens/Cal recon.	1973	20	T	
Kilmarnock		1/3	BR(ScR) PB	1976	NXpnl(HWmsDom'o)	1976	-	E	
Kingmoor (RR)		4/29C	BR(LMR) PB	1963	None	-	-	-	
Kings Cross		2/14A	BR(ER) PB	1971	NX panel	1976	-	E	
Kings Dyke		2/13C	GE 7/Dutton	1899	Dutton 1893 pat.	1899	19	T	
Kings Lynn Junction		2/12B	GE 2	1881	S&F1888Duplex	u1918	48R	R.T	
Kingsbury SF (NBP)		4/18	BR(LMR) 15	1969	LMR Standard	1969	30	T	
Kingsferry Bridge (NBP) **NNR**		5/8B	**	1960	IFS	1960	-	E	120
Kingswinford Junction South		4/20C	N/S	2003	WR HT gf	2003	14	T	308
Kingussie	L	1/19C	McK&H 3/High	nkE	McK&H C&T 4"	u1922	17	T	121
Kintbury Crossing GF (G)		3/11B	BR(WR) hut	1978	IFS	1978	-	E	
Kirkby Stephen		4/34B	BR(LMR) 15	1974	LMR Standard 2h	1974	20	T	287
Kirkby Summit		4/5	2-high Por'kabins	1995	NX panel	1995	-	E	
Kirkby Thore		4/34C	2-high Por'kabins	1994	IFS panel	1994	-	E	
Kirkcaldy (E)		1/13	BR(ScR) PR	1980	NXpnl(HWmsDom'o)	1980	-	E	274
Kirkconnel		1/2E	GSW 7	1911	Stevens GNP/GSW	1911	42	T	
Kirkham		4/49	L&Y	1903	L&Y	1903	76R	T	91
Kirkham Abbey	L	2/18C	NE S1a	c1873	McK&H16 recon.	1926	16	T	
Kirton Lime Sidings	L	2/31C	RSCo [MS&L]	1886	RSCo Tappet	1886	15	T	
Kiveton Park		2/31A	GC 5	nk	IFS panel	1980	-	E	
Knaresborough	L	2/42D	NE N/S	c1873	McK&H17 recon.	1950	12	T	
Knottingley		2/40A	BR(NER)17	1967-	IFS	1967	-	E	122
Lakenheath		2/13A	GE 4/S&F	c1885	S&F Rocker 5"	c1885	25	R.T	
Lancing		5/20A	BR(SR)16*	1963	NX panel	1988	-	E	
Langham Junction		4/3B	Midland 2a*+	1890	Midland Tumbler	1890	20	Tum	179

SECTION 1: NETWORK RAIL

Box Name	Quail Map	Box:- Type	Date	Frame/Equipment:- Design	Date	No. of Levers	Lock'g	Notes
Langworth	2/28A	MS&L 3	1890	IFS panel	1990	-	E	
Larbert Junction	1/9A	Caledonian N/S	c1871	Stevens/Cal	1915	40	T	
Larbert North	1/15A	Caledonian N2+	1892	Stevens GNP	nk	59	T	179
Laurencekirk	1/16D	Caledonian N2	1910	Stevens/Cal	1910	40	T	
Leamington Spa	4/14A	BR(LMR) PB	1985	NX panel	1985	-	SSI	
Ledbury	3/14B	McK&H 3 [GW]	1885	GW DT	nk	42	R.T	123
Leicester	4/3B	BR(LMR) PB	1986	NX panel/VDUs	1986	-	E	
Leominster	3/26d	LNW/GW Jt	c1875	GW VT5	1941	30	T	
Leuchars	1/14C	NB 8	1920	Stevens GNP (Stevens)	1920	38R	T	
Lewes	5/16	S&F 5 [LBSC]	1888	NX panel	1976	-	E	
Lichfield Trent Valley No.1	4/12A	LNW 5+	1911	LNW Tappet	1911	80	T	179
Lichfield TV Junction	4/12A	LNW 4	1897	LNW Tumbler	1897	45	B&S	
Lightmoor Junction	4/21D	BR(WR) 15+	c1951	GW VT5	c1951	31	T	179
Lime Kiln Sidings (G,OOU)	3/28A	GW 3	1887	GW VT3	1918	29	T	
Lincoln Road [Enfield] (G)	2/10B	Portakabin	2003	IFS/gf	2003/nk	2	E,T	
Liskeard	3/9A	GW 27c	1915	GW HT3 5¼"	1915	36	T	
Little Mill Junction	3/27D	McK&H 3 [GW]	1883E	GW VT5/panel	1938/79	17R	T/E	126
Littlehampton	5/20C	LBSC 2a	1886	LBSC Bosham patt.	1901	44	T	125
Littlehaven (G)	5/19B	SR SB + BO	1938	Stevens Knee [Whse]	1938	8	T	
Littleport	2/12A	GE 2	1882	S&F Rocker 5"	1882	25	R.T	
Littleworth	2/26C	GN 1+	1875	McK&H 1873 Pat 5"	1875	30	R.T	127
Litton's Mill Crossing	4/26B	LNW 4	1890	LNW Tappet	1922	18	T	
Liverpool Lime Street	4/40	LMS 13+	1948	Westinghouse L pf	1948	95	E	179
Liverpool Street IECC	2/2A	PB	1989	VDUs	1989/99	-	SSI/E	5
Llandarcy GF (NBP)	3/24A	GW 7d	1920	GW VT3	1920	20R	T	128
Llandudno	4/36C	LNW 4+	1891	LNW Tumbler	1891	34R	B&S	179
Llandudno Junction	4/36C	BR(LMR) 15+	1985	NX panel	1985	-	E	179
Llanelli West (G)	3/25A	GW 2	1877E	IFS	u1973	-	E	129
Llanfair LC (G)	4/37A	LNW C&H+	c1871	Panel	nk	-	E	179
Llanrwst & Trefriw	4/37C	LNW 4+	1880	LNW Tappet 2h	c1954	20	T	130
Llantrisant West GF (NBP)	3/23A	BR(WR) Hut	1966	WR gf	u1966	5R	T	
Lock Lane Crossing (G)	4/6C	BR(LMR) 15	c1955	LMR Standard	c1955	10R	T	
London Bridge	5/3A	BR(SR) PB	1975	NX panel	1975	-	E/SSI	132
Longannet	1/14A	BR(ScR) N/S	1969	Stevens/Cal	1969	30	T	
Longbeck	2/51A	LNER 12	1932	IFS	1970	-	E	
Longbridge East (NBP) **NNR**	4/17E	Midland 4a	1916	Midland Tappet	1917	36	T	133
Longforgan	1/16A	LMS 12	1929	Stevens/Cal recon.	1929	20	T	
Lostwithiel	3/9B	GW 5	1893	GW VT3/NX panel	1923/91	63	T/SSI	134
Lovers Walk Depot (NBP)	5/16	Portakabin	1985	IFS panel	1985	-	E	
Low Gates	2/20B	BR(NER) 16b+	1956	Panels	1992/97	-	SSI/E	266
Low House Crossing	4/34C	Midland 2b+	1900	Midland Tumbler	1900	12	Tum	179
Low Row	2/46B	NE N1	c1874	McK&H17 recon.	1957	29	T	
Lowdham	4/6B	Midland 2b+	1896	Midland Tumbler	1896	16	Tum	179
Lowestoft	2/8A	GE 6	1885	S&F1888Duplex	1905	61	R.T	
Lugton	1/4B	LMS 12	1929	REC	u1938	35R	T	
Lydney Crossing GF (G)	3/20B	GW 27c+	c1918	IFS	1969	-	E	135
Lynemouth **NNR**	2/23C	NCB	1956	IFS panel	1995	-	E	263
Macclesfield	4/43B	BR(LMR) 15+	1965	LMR Standard	1965	55	T	127
Machynlleth	4/23E	BR(WR) 37*	1960	GWVT5/RETB VDUs	1960/88	50	T/SSI	136
Madeley	4/12C	LMS 11b	1930	REC	1930	40	T	
Madeley Junction	4/21C	BR(LMR) 15+	1969	LMR Stnd/Westcad VDU	1969/2002	40	T/SSI	296
Magdalen Road	2/12B	GC 5 2h	1927	IFS panel	1992	-	E	137
Maidstone East	5/7	BR(SR) 18+	1962	Whse L pf /NX pnl	1962/83	47	E/E	138
Maidstone West	5/7	EOD [SE]	1899	EOD	1899	115	T	
Maltby Colliery South	2/35A	GC 5	1912	GC (McK&H)/IFS pnl	1912/84	36	T/E	
Malton	2/18C	NE S1a	c1873	IFS panel (extended)	1966/nk	-	E	
Malvern Wells	3/14B	GW 7d	1919	GW VT3	1919	40	T	
Manchester North	4/45A	PB	1998	VDUs	1998	-	SSI	
Manchester South	4/44A	PB	2003	VDUs	2003	-	CBI	175
Manchester Piccadilly	4/45A	**	1988	NX panels	1988/99	-	E/SSI	139

SECTION 1: NETWORK RAIL

Box Name		Quail Map	Box:- Type	Date	Frame/Equipment:- Design	Date	No. of Levers	Lock'g	Notes
Manea		2/13C	GE 3/McK&H	1883	McK&H 1873 Pat. 5"	1883	25R	R.T	
Mantle Lane		4/7C	Midland 4c+	1910	Mid Tap/IFS/OCS pnl	1910/79/85	28	T/E	140/79
Manton Junction		4/3B	Midland 4c*+	1913	NX panel	1988	-	E	179
March East Junction		2/13C	GE 5/S&F	1885	S&F1888Duplex	1897	61R	uDx	141
March South Junction		2/13C	LNER 11a	1927	S&F1888Duplex 2h	1927	51	R.T	
Marcheys House		2/23C	NE N2	1895	McK&H16 recon.	1960	15R	T	
Marchwood		5/30A	**	1925	Stevens(Stevens) 2h	1943	24	T	142
Margate		5/9A	SEC	1913	SEC NP	1913	80	T	
Marsh Brook		4/23B	LNW/GW Jt 1	1872	LNW Tumbler	nk	18	B&S	
Marsh Junction		2/32A	GC 5+	1908	GC(RSCo)	1908	44	T	179
Marston Moor (G)		2/42E	NE S5	1910	McK&H 1873 6" 2h	1910	16	R.T	9
Marylebone IECC		3/18C	**	1990	VDUs	1990	-	SSI	144
Maryport		4/32B	LMS 11b	1933	REC/IFS panel	1933/79	50R	T/E	
Mauchline		1/3	GSW 1+	1877	Stevens/Cal recon.	1978	35	T	179
Medge Hall (G)		2/33B	RSCo [MS&L]	1886	RSCo Tappet	1886	7R	T	
Melton Lane		2/38B	NE S4	1921	McK&H16/IFS	1921/80	26R	T/E	16
Melton Station		4/3B	LMS 11c+	1942	REC/IFS/IFS	1942/78/86	45	T/E	294
Merseyrail		4/41A	PB	1994	VDUs	1994	-	SSI	145
Mickle Trafford		4/35A	BR(LMR) 15	1969	LMR Standard	1969	35	T	239
Middlesbrough		2/50A	NE C1	1877	IFS panel	1978	-	E	
Midge Hall		4/49C	BR(LMR) 15	1972	LMR Standard	1972	20	T	
Milford		2/42B	BR(NER) 17	1958	NX panel	1982	-	E	
Mill Green		2/26C	GE 2	1882	S&F1888Duplex 2h	1931	21	R.T	
Mill Lane Junction		2/43	RSCo [L&Y] +	1884	IFS panel	1973	-	E	
Millbrook Dock Gates (G) **NNR**		*5/29A*	Dock gate house	u1936	IFS	nk	-	E	248
Millbrook Station		4/9C	LNW hut	u1870	LMR Std (outside)	1990	11	T	42,268
Millerhill		1/11A	BR(ScR) PB	1988	NX panel (Whse)	1988	-	SSI	
Millom		4/31C	Furness 1	1891	RSCo Tappet	1891	31	T	147
Milner Royd Junction		2/41A	Yardley 2 [L&Y]	1874	RSCo Tappet	1903	20	T	
Milton (G)		2/46A	NE N2	1893	Stevens (Stevens)	nk	10	T	224
Minety Crossing (G)		3/15A	Portakabin	2000	IFS	2000	-	E	
Minster		5/9A	SR 12	1929	Westinghouse A2	1929	70	T	
Mobberley		4/46A	CLC 1b+	1886	IFS	1991	-	E	179
Moira West Junction		4/7C	Midland 2b+	1896	IFS panel	1986	-	E	179
Mold Junction		4/36A	LNW 4+	1902	LNW Tumbler	1902	30R	B&S	179
Monks Siding		4/38B	LNW 3	1875	LNW Tumbler	1875	20	B&S	
Montrose North		1/16C	NB 1	1881	Stevens/Cal	1953	51	T	
Montrose South		1/16C	NB 1	1881	Stevens GOP (Stevens)	1914	42	T	
Moorthorpe		2/33A	Midland 4c	1908	Mid Tumbler Wks Rlk	1908	36	R.T	260
Moreton-in-Marsh		3/13D	GW 4b+	1883	GW VT3	1911	40	T	267
Moreton-on-Lugg		3/27D	GW 12a	1943	GW VT5	1943	44	T	
Morpeth		2/22B	BR(ER) 20	1978	NX panel	1991	-	SSI/E	277
Moss (G)		2/18A	NE S1a	1873	McK&H16 recon./IFS	1940	11R	T/E	149
Mossend EWS Shunters (NBP) **NNR**		*1/8L*	Yard Office	2003	IFS panel	2003	-	E	
Mostyn	L	4/36A	LNW 4	1902	LNW Tumbler	1902	40	B&S	
Motherwell SC		1/8R	BR(ScR) PB	1972	NX panels	1972-2003	-	E/SSI	150
Mouldsworth		4/35A	CLC 1a+	1894	CLC	1894	34	T	151
Mountfield GF (NBP)		5/18B	BR(SR) hut	1975	Stevens Knee (Stev) 2h	1975	11	T	
Nairn		1/18B	**	-	VDU (Westcad)	2000	-	CBI	153
Nantwich		4/23A	LMS 11c 2h +	1948	REC 2h	1948	30	T	71
Narborough		4/3B	LNW 3+	1875	IFS panel	1986	-	E	179
Neasden Junction		5/1A	Mid 2b	1899	Mid Tumbler	1899	24	Tum	
Neath & Brecon Junction		3/24A	GW 5	1892	GW VT5	1957	14R	T	
Netherfield Junction		4/6B	BR(ER) N/S	1960	RSCo-GNI	1960	40	T	
Neville Hill Depot (NBP)		2/43A	Hut	2001	NX panel	2001	-	E	
New Cumnock		1/2E	GSW 7	1909	Stevens GNP/GSW	1909	40	T	
New Hythe		5/7	SR 13*	1939	Stevens (Stev) 2h	1939	20	T	
New Mills Central		4/44A	Midland 4d	1924	REC	1924	30	T	
New Mills South Junction		4/44A	Midland 3b+	1903	LMR Standard 6"	1962	55	T	179
New Street [Birmingham]	L	4/16	BR(LMR) PB	1966	NX panel	1966	-	E	

SECTION 1: NETWORK RAIL

Box Name		Quail Map	Box:- Type	Date	Frame/Equipment:- Design	Date	No. of Levers	Lock'g	Notes
Newark Castle		2/27D	Midland 4a	1912	Midland Tappet	1912	16	T	
Newhaven Harbour		5/17A	S&F 5 [LBSC]	1886	S&F Rocker 5"	1886	42	R.T	
Newhaven Town		5/17A	S&F 5 [LBSC]	1879E	Westinghouse A2	1953	40	T	
Newland East		3/14B	GW 7a	1900	GW VT3	nk	33	T	155
Newport		3/21A	BR(WR) PB	1962	NX panels	1962/68	-	E	
Newsham		2/23C	NE N1	nk	McK&H17 recon.	1945	20R	T	146
Newtonhill		1/17A	Caledonian N1	c1876	Stevens/Cal	1907	30	T	
Noblethorpe (G)		2/18A	Portakabin	nk	IFS	nk	-	E	316
Norbury Crossing (G)		4/44A	BR(LMR) 15+	1977	SK 446 gf	1977	5R	T	179
North Pole Intern'l DCC **NNR**		5/1A	**	1994	NX panel	1994	-	SSI	288
North Seaton (G)		2/23C	NE N/S	u1872	McK&H17 recon.	1950	21	T	
North Sdgs GF [Worc'ster] (NBP)		3/14A	Hut	nk	GW gf	nk	11	T	
Northampton Bridge St LC (OOU)		4/10A	LNW 5	1907	LNW Tumbler	1907	15R	B&S	
Northenden Junction		4/46A	Stevens N/S [CLC]	nk	CLC	nk	25	T	
Northorpe		2/31C	RSCo [MS&L]	1886	RSCo Tappet	1886	17	T	
Norton		4/26B	BR(LMR) 15	1972	LMR Standard	1972	10	T	
Norton (G, NBP)		2/40A	BR(ER) 20	1980	NX panel	1980	-	E	156
Norton Bridge		4/12B	BR(LMR) PB	1961	NX panel (Whse)	1961	-	E	
Norton East		2/47C	NE early Ctl Divn	1870	McK&H17 recon.	1959	25	T	281
Norton Junction		3/14A	GW 7d	1908	GW HT3 5¼"	1908	19R	T	
Norton-on-Tees		2/48A	NE C2a	1897	McK&H16 recon.	1957	26	T	
Norton South		2/47C	NE early Ctl Divn	1870	McK&H17 recon.	1955	20	T	
Norton West		2/47C	NE S4	1910	McK&H16	1921	41	T	
Norwood Crossing (G)		2/30A	BR(ER) hut	nk	Midland gf 2h	1967	5	nk	158
Nuneaton		4/11B	BR(LMR) PB	1963	NX panel	1990	-	E	
Nunthorpe		2/50B	NE C2b	1903	McK&H16 recon.	1966	16	T	280
Oakenshaw		2/39D	Midland 4e	1928	IFS panel	1970	-	E	
Oakham Level Crossing	L	4/3B	Midland 2b+	1899	Midland Tumbler	1899	17	Tum	179
Oddingley (G)		3/15B	Midland 3a	1908	None	-	-	-	
Offord (E,G)		2/15C	BR(ER) 20	1976	IFS panel	1976	-	E	276
Old Dalby **NNR**		4/4C	**	2001	NX panel	2001	-	E	303
Oldham Mumps		4/47A	BR(LMR) 15 2h	1967	IFS panel	1998	-	E	
Ollerton Colliery (OOU)		2/30B	GC 5	1926	GC (Whse)/IFS panel	1926/84	30	T/E	264
Onibury		3/27A	BR(WR) 37	1977	IFS panel	1977	-	E	
Oulton Broad North Station		2/8	GE 7	1901E	McK&H C&T 4"	1928	35	T	159
Oulton Broad Swing Bridge (B)		2/8	GE 7	1907	S&F1888Duplex	1907	10	Dx	160
Oxford		3/12C	BR(WR) PB	1973	NX panel 2h	1973	-	E	161
Oxley		4/21C	BR(LMR) 15+	1969	LMR Standard 2h	1969	60	T	162
Oxmardyke (G)		2/38A	NE S1a	1901	McK&H16 recon.	1956	16	T	
Oxmarsh Crossing		2/32B	BR(ER) 16a	1959	RSCo Tappet	1885	30	T	7
Oxted		5/14B	BR(SR)	1987	NX panel	1987	-	SSI	164
Paignton		3/7C	**	1989	IFS panel	1989	-	E	165
Paisley SC		1/5A	BR(ScR) PB	1985	NXpnl(HWmsDom'o)	1985	-	E	166
Pantyffynnon	L	3/31C	GW 5	1892	GW DT	1892	49	R.T	167
Par		3/9B	GW 2	c1879E	GW VT3/IFS panel	c1913/1986	57	T/E	169
Parbold	L	4/42A	S&F 9 [L&Y]+	1877	LMR Standard	1983	20	T	63
Park Junction		3/21A	McK&H 3 [GW]	1885E	GW VT 5	1920	100	T	170
Park Lane [Cheshunt] (G)		2/10B	Portable Hut	nk	IFS	2003	-	E	
Park South		4/31B	Furness 3	1883	RSCo Tap (LY) 2h	1962	24	T	171
Parkeston		2/9B	BR(ER) PB	1987	NX panel 2h	1987	-	E	285
Parton		4/32A	LNW 4	1879	LNW Tumbler	1879	28R	B&S	36
Pasture Street		2/32A	BR(ER) 19	1962	NX panel	1993	-	E	258
Peak Forest South		4/44A	Midland 4d+	1925	LMR Standard	1974	50	T	179
Pelham Street Junction [Lincoln]		2/27A	GN 1	u1874E	GN Duplex (Tyer)	1918	100	Dx	
Pembrey		3/25A	GW 7+	1907	GW VT5	1953	83	T	172
Pencoed Crossing GF (G)		3/23A	GW 27c	c1905	IFS	nk	-	E	
Penmaenmawr		4/36D	BR(LMR) 14+	1952	LMR Standard	1952	25	T	267
Penyffordd		4/37E	BR(LMR) 15	1972	LMR Standard	1972	25	T	
Penzance		3/10B	GW 12b	1938	GW VT5	1938	75	T	
Perth		1/15D	BR(ScR) PB	1962	SGE NX panel	1962	-	E	322

SECTION 1: NETWORK RAIL

Box Name	Quail Map	Box:- Type	Date	Frame/Equipment:- Design	Date	No. of Levers	Lock'g	Notes
Peterborough	2/16A	BR(ER) PB	1972	NX panel	1972	-	E	
Petersfield	5/26B	LSW 3a	1880s	Stevens/IFS	1880s/1974	10R	T/E	
Petersfield GF (NBP,NNM)	5/26B	SR brick hut	nk	Stevens Knee (RSCo)	nk	15	T	
Pevensey	5/17A	S&F 5 [LBSC]	1876	S&F Rocker 5"	1876	14	R.T	
Pinxton	4/5	Midland 2b	1897	Midland Tumbler	1897	28	Tum	
Pitlochry	L 1/19B	Highland	1911	McK&H C&T 4"	u1911	24	T	
Plean Junction	1/15A	Caledonian N1	c1870s	Stevens/Cal	1922	26	T	
Plumley West	4/43B	CLC 2*+	1908	CLC	1908	26	T	179
Plumpton (G)	L 5/15C	LBSC 2b	1891	LBSC 1880s pattern	1891	21	T	
Plymouth	3/8C	BR(WR) PB	1960	NX panel	1960	-	E	
Polegate Crossing	5/17A	S&F 5 [LBSC]	1883	S&F Rocker 5"	1883	20	R.T	
Polmont	1/12	BR(ScR) PR	1979	NX panel	1979	-	E	309
Pontrilas	3/27C	McK&H 3 [GW]	1880	GW VT3	1910	42	T	
Poole	5/31b	LSW 4+	1897E	Stevens (uRSCo)	u1897	51	T	177
Poppleton	2/42E	NE S1	u1870s	McK&H16 recon.	1941	11	T	
Port Talbot	3/23C	BR(WR) PB	1963	NX panels	1963/73	-	E	
Portsmouth	5/26C	BR(SR) 19 PB	1968	NX panel	1968	-	E	
Portsmouth Harbour (RR)	5/26C	SR 13	1946	-	-	-	-	
Poulton	4/49A	L&Y+	1896	L&Y	1896	72R	T	179
Prees	4/23A	LNW 4+	1881	LNW Tumbler	1881	25	B&S	179
Prescot	4/42B	LNW 5*	1953	LMR Standard	1953	30	T	178
Prestatyn	4/36B	LNW 4	1897E	LNW Tumbler	1897	45	B&S	60
Preston	4/27C	BR(LMR) PB+	1972	NX panel	1972	-	E	48
Prince of Wales Colliery	2/39D	L&Y+	1912	IFS panel	1996	-	E	180
Prudhoe	2/21C	NE N1	c1872E	McK&H17 recon.	1944	45	T	181
Pulborough	5/19C	S&F 5 [LBSC]	1878	LBSC 1905 patt. 2h	1952	30	T	
Puxton & Worle (G)	3/6A	GW 7	c1916	IFS panel	1972	-	E	
Pwllheli West Frame (NBP)	4/24C	Dutton 2 [Cam] 2h	1909	Dutt 1893 Pat. 2h	1909	4R	R.T	297
Pyewipe Road (NNM)	2/32C	BR(ER) 16a	c1958	RSCo-GNI	c1958	20	T	
Radyr Junction	3/28B	Portakabin	1998	NX panel	1998	-	SSI	
Rainford Junction	4/41A	LMS 11c+	1933-	L&Y	1896	10R	T	184
Rainham	5/8A	BR(SR) 17 PB	1959	SGE NX panel	1959	-	E	
Rainhill	4/42B	LNW 4	1896	LNW Tumbler	1896	25	B&S	
Ramsgate	5/9A	SR 11a	1926	SEC NP	1926	96	T	
Ranelagh Rd Crossing (G, NNM)	2/6B	LNER N/S	1927	McK&H	u1927	10	R.T	
Ranskill (ELC,G)	2/17B	GN 1	1875	NX panel (Whse M3)	1975	-	E	50,192
Rauceby	2/25C	GN 1	1880	McK&H 2h/IFS	1975/75	5	T/E	190
Reading	3/3A	BR(WR) PB	1965	NX panels	1965/77	-	E	194
Rectory Junction	4/6B	GN 1+	1888	RSCo Tappet	1888	64R	T	23,267
Redcar	2/51A	LNER 13	1937	IFS panel	1970	-	E	
Redford (E)	1/13	BR(ScR) C/T	1956	NXpnl(HWmsDom'o)	1981	-	E	310
Reedham Junction	2/8	GE 7	1904	McK&H C&T 4"	1904	60	R.T	
Reedham Swing Bridge	2/8	GE 7*	1904	McK&H C&T 4"	1904	12	R.T	186
Reigate	5/15A	SR 11b	1929	Westinghouse A2/IFS	1929/nk	24	T/E	
Rhyl	L 4/36B	LNW 4	1900	LNW Tumbler	1900	90	B&S	188
Richmond	5/1A	SR 13	1940	NX panel	1980	-	E	
Ridgmont	4/9C	**	1934	LNW KI (outside)	1934	13	T	189
Rigton	2/42D	NE S1a	c1873	McK&H16 recon.	1939	6	T	
Robertsbridge	5/18B	S&F 12a [SE]	1893	S&F1888Duplex	1893	23	R.T	
Rochdale	4/47A	RSCo [L&Y]	1889	REC	c1944	30R	T	176
Rochester	5/7	BR(SR)17 PB	1959	SGE NX panel	1959	-	E	
Rockcliffe Hall	4/36A	2-high Por'kabins	1995	IFS panel	1995	-	E	
Romiley Junction	4/45A	Midland 2b*+	1899	'OCS' panel	1980	-	E	179
Roskear Junction	3/10A	GW 5	c1895	IFS	nk	-	E	
Rosyth Dockyard **NNR** (OOU)	1/12	NB 7	1917	Stevens GNP (Stevens)	u1917	45	E	191
Roxton Sidings	2/32A	MS&L2	1883	MS&L Iron Brackets	1883	18	R.T	
Rufford	4/49B	Portakabin	1988	IFS panel	1988	-	E	
Rugby	4/11A	BR(LMR) PB	1964	NX panel	1964	-	E/SSI	193
Runcorn	4/39A	LMS13	1940	REC	1940	45	T	
Ryde St Johns Road	5/35C	EOD 2h	1928	Stevens (Stev)2h/Pnl	1928/89	40	T/E	185

SECTION 1: NETWORK RAIL

Box Name		Quail Map	Box:- Type	Date	Frame/Equipment:- Design	Date	No. of Levers	Lock'g	Notes
Rye		5/18D	S&F 12a [SE]	1894	S&F 1888 Duplex	1894	30	Dx	
Ryhope Grange Junction		2/48B	NE N3	1905	McK&H17 recon.	1950	40R	T	
St Andrews Junction		3/17A	GW 27c	1910	Panels	1988/93	-	E/SSI	195
St Bees		4/32A	Furness 3+	1891	RSCo Tappet	1891	24	T	179
St Blazey Junction		3/9B	GW 7d	1908	GW HT3	1908	41	T	
St Erth		3/10B	GW 5	1899	GW VT3	1929	69	T	
St Fagans GF (G)		3/23A	BR(WR) hut	c1966	IFS panel	c1966	-	E	
St Helens Station		4/42B	LNW 4	1891	LNW Tumbler/IFS	1891/1995	24	B&S/E	54
St James Deeping		2/26C	GN 1	1876	uWestinghouse 17A	1941	32	T	
St Mary's Crossing (G)	L	3/15A	GW 2*	1870s	None	-	-	-	197
Salisbury		5/32B	**	1981	NX panel	1981	-	E	198
Salop Goods Junction		4/13	LNW 4	1901	REC	1936	65	T	
Saltley		4/16	BR(LMR) PB+	1969	NX panel	1969	-	E/SSI	48
Saltmarshe		2/40C	NE S2+	1905	McK&H16	1905	19R	T	179
Salwick		4/49A	RSCo [L&Y]	1889	RSCo Tappet	1889	33R	T	199
Sandbach		4/43B	BR(LMR) PB	1959	OCS panel (Whse)	1959	-	E	
Sandwich		5/9A	SR 11b	1938	IFS panel	1977	-	E	
Sandycroft (NNM)		4/36A	LNW 4	1900	LNW Tumbler	1900	60	B&S	
Saxby Junction (OOU)		4/3B	Midland 2a	1892	LMR Standard	1962	60	T	
Saxilby		2/27B	LNER 11b	1939	McK&H 1886 Pat. 4"	2h1939	30	R.T	
Saxmundham		2/9A	GE 2+	1881	IFS pnl/RETB VDUs	1986	-	E/SSI	200
Scopwick		2/27A	LNER 11a	1937	McK&H C&T 2h	1937	25	R.T	201
Scropton		4/25C	NS 2+	1880s	McK&H 1873 Pat. 5"	1880s	22	HCS	179
Scunthorpe		2/34A	BR(ER) PB	1973	NX panel	1973	-	E	
Scunthorpe Hump (NBP,OOU)		2/34A	BR(ER) N/S	1972	IFS panel	1972	-	E	283
Seaham		2/48B	NE N3+	1905	McK&H16 recon.	1950	23R	T	267
Seamer		2/18D	NE S4+	1910	NX panel	2000	-	E	313
Selby		2/38A	NE S1*+	c1870E	NX panel	1973	-	E	203
Selby Swing Bridge (B)		2/38A	NE N/S	1891	gf + 2 panels	1970s	2	nk	204
Selhurst Depot (NBP)		5/14C	**	(1985)	IFS panel	1985	-	E	205
Sellafield		4/31C	Furness 4*	1918	RSCo Tappet	1918	49	T	
Settle Junction		4/34A	Midland 4c+	1913	LMR Standard 6"	1960	31	T	179
Seymour Junction		2/30A	BR(ER) 19+	1963	RSCo-GNI	1963	30R	T	179
Shaftholme Junction (RR,ELC)		2/18A	BR(NER) PB	1958	Panel	nk	-	E	206
Shaw Station		4/47A	L&Y 2h +	1941	L&Y 2h	1941	24	T	30
Sheerness Dockyard GF (NBP)		5/8B	SR hut	n/k	Stevens Knee recon.	nk	5	T	207
Sheffield		2/28E	BR(ER) PB	1973	NX panel	1973	-	E	
Shepherdswell		5/13	LCD	c1878	LCD	c1878	23	T	
Sherborne (G)		5/33C	**	nk	IFS panel	nk	-	E	295
Shildon		2/47B	NE C2a	1887	McK&H16 recon.	1928	42R	T	
Shippea Hill		2/13A	GE 4/McK&H	1883	McK&H u 1873 Pat.	u1883	30	R.T	
Shirebrook Junction		2/30A	Midland 2b+	1899E	Midland Tappet	1928	40	T	
Shirley		4/15A	GW 7d+	1907	GW HT3 5¼"	1907	31	T	179
Shrewsbury Crewe Bank		4/22A	LMS 13	1943	REC	1943	45	T	
Shrewsbury Crewe Junction	L	4/22A	LNW 4	1903	LNW Tumbler	1903	120	B&S	208
Shrewsbury Severn Bridge Jn	L	4/22A	LNW 4*	1903	LNW Tumbler	1903	180	R.T	209
Sibsey		2/26A	GN1	1888	IFS panel	1989	-	E	
Silecroft		4/31C	Furness 4	1923	RSCo Tappet	1923	15R	T	
Sittingbourne		5/8B	BR(SR)17 PB	1959	SGE NX panel	1959	-	E	
Skegness		2/26B	GN 1	1882E	RSCo Tappet	1900	80	T	210
Slade Green CR		5/5	PB	1992	NX panel	1992	-	SSI	259
Sleaford East	L	2/25C	GN 1	1882	S&F Rocker 5"	1882	50	R.T	
Sleaford North		2/25C	GE 2	1882	Stevens(Stevens)	1882	18	T	
Sleaford South		2/25C	BR(ER) 16a	1957	RSCo-GNI	1957	25	T	
Sleaford West		2/25C	GN 1	c1880	S&F Rocker 5"	c1880	46R	R.T	
Sleights Sidings East		4/5	Midland 2a	1892	IFS	1980	-	E	
Slough		3/2C	BR(WR) PB	1963	NX panel	1963	-	E	
Slough New		3/2C	PB	1992	VDUs	1992	-	SSI	211
Smithy Bridge		4/47A	L&Y	1903-	IFS panel	1981	-	E	212
Sneinton Crossing SF (G)		4/6A	Midland 4c+	1914	Midland Tappet	1914	10R	T	179

SECTION 1: NETWORK RAIL

Box Name		Quail Map	Box:-		Frame/Equipment:-		No. of Levers	Lock'g	Notes
			Type	Date	Design	Date			
Snodland		5/7	SE	1870s	SE Brady 5"	1870s	26	R.T	
Snowdown Colliery (OOU)		5/13	BR(SR) N/S	1953	Stevens (RSCo) 2h	1953	18	T	290
Somerleyton Swing Bridge		2/8	GE 7*	1904	McK&H C&T 4"	1904	14	R.T	186
South Tottenham		2/10B	GE 7	1894	NX panel	1977	-	E	
Spalding		2/26C	GN 4b+	1921	IFS panel	1984	-	E	179
Speke Junction		4/40	LNW 5	1907	LNW Tappet	1907	86R	T	
Spooner Row		2/13B	GE 2	1881	McK&H 5"	u1881	15	R.T	
Stafford No.4		4/12B	BR(LMR) 15+	1960	LMR Standard	1960	105	T	179
Stafford No.5		4/12B	BR(LMR) 14+	1952	LMR Standard	1952	150	T	202
Stallingborough		2/32A	MS&L 2	1884	MS&L Iron Brackets	1884	20	R.T	
Stalybridge		4/45A	Stevens/MS&L +	1886	Stevens GNP/GSW	1942	70R	T	213
Stanley Junction		1/19A	BR(ScR) N/S	1961	Stevens/Cal	1961	45	T	
Stanlow & Thornton		4/35A	LMS 11c	1941	REC	1941	50	T	
Stanton Gate SF (NBP,OOU)		4/7A	BR(LMR) 15	1969	LMR Standard	1969	50	T	
Stapleford & Sandiacre (NBP)		4/7A	BR(LMR) 14	1949	LMR Stnd/Panel	1949/nk	115	T	
Starbeck		2/42D	NE S1a+	nkE	McK&H16	1915	26R	T	31
Staythorpe Crossing		4/6B	LMS 11c+	1950E	REC	1960	35	T	179
Stirling Middle	L	1/15A	Caledonian N2	1901	Stevens GNP(Stev)	1901	96	T	
Stirling North	L	1/15A	Caledonian N2	1900	Stevens/Cal	1950	48R	T	
Stockport No.1		4/44A	LNW 4	1884	LNW Tumbler	1884	98R	B&S	38
Stockport No.2		4/44A	LNW 4	1890	LNW Tumbler	1890	90R	B&S	41
Stoke-on-Trent		4/25A	BR(LMR) PB	1966	VDUs	2003	-	SSI	
Stone Crossing (G)		5/7	SE*	u1904	Stev. Knee (Tyer) 2h	1971	5	T	
Stonea		2/13C	Portakabin	1984	IFS panel	1984	-	E	
Stonehaven		1/17A	Caledonian N2	1901	Stevens/Cal	1901	40	T	
Stourbridge Junction		4/20C	GW 7b	1901	NX panel	1990	-	SSI	
Stow Park	L	2/27B	GN 1	1877	S&F Rocker 5"	1877	32	R.T	
Stowmarket (G)		2/6C	GE 3	c1882	IFS panel	1985	-	E	
Stranraer Harbour		1/2A	GSW 3	1897	Stevens GNP (Stevens)	u1897	56	T	
Stranton		2/48A	NE N4	1911	McK&H16 recon.	1950	30R	T	
Strensall		2/19	NE S2*	1901	IFS panel	1988	-	SSI	
Sturry (G)		5/9B	S&F 12a [SE]	1893	S&F1888Duplex	1893	19R	Dx	68
Sudbury	L	4/25C	NS 1	1885	McK&H 1873 Pat. 5"	1885	25	HCS	
Sudforth Lane		2/40A	BR(NER) 17+	1961	IFS Panel	1968	-	E	127
Sutton Bridge Junction		4/23B	GW 7	1913	GW VT3	1913	61	T	
Swinderby		2/27E	Midland 3a	1901	Midland Tumbler	1901	16	Tum	
Swindon		3/4B	BR(WR) PB	1968	NX panel	1968	-	E	
Swindon 'B'		3/4B	PB	1993	VDUs	1993	-	SSI	
Talacre		4/36B	LNW 4 2h	1903	LNW Tumbler 2h	1903	24	B&S	52
Tallington (E,G)		2/16B	BR(ER) 20	1975	NX panel	1975	-	E	276
Tamworth Low Level		4/11B	LNW 5	1910	LNW Tappet	1910	35	T	
Tay Bridge South		1/14D	NB 2a	1887	Stevens GOP (Stevens)	1887	27	T	
Tees		2/49C	BR(NER) C/T	1962	NX panel	1962	-	E	216
Templecombe		5/33C	SR 13	1938	Westinghouse A2	1938	16R	T	
Teynham Crossing (G)		5/8B	Hut	nk	Stevens Knee (Whse)	nk	5	-	217
Thetford		2/13A	GE 4/McK&H	1883	McK&H u1873Pat. 5"	u1883	33	R.T	
Thoresby Colliery		2/30A	GC 5	1926	GC (Westinghouse)	1926	30	T	
Thornhill		1/2E	LMS 13*	1943	REC	1943	30	T	
Thorpe Culvert		2/26B	GN1	2003	IFS panel (TEW)	2003	-	E	174
Thorpe Gates (G)		2/37B	NE S1a	c1873E	IFS	1973	-	E	218
Thorpe-le-Soken		2/6A	GE 2	1882E	IFS panel	1989	-	E	219
Thorrington (G)		2/6A	GE Hut+	nk	gf	nk	3	T	302
Three Bridges		5/15B	BR(SR) PB	1983	NX panel	1983	-	E	
Three Horse Shoes		2/13C	GE 7	1901	McK&H 5"	1901	30	R.T	
Three Spires Junction		4/14B	Portakabin	2003	NX panel	2003	-	E	
Thrumpton [Retford]		2/31B	MS&L 3	1889E	NX panel	1965	-	E	187
Tinsley Yard		2/29	BR(ER)18 PB	1965	NX panel	1965	-	E	
Tisbury (RR)		5/33B	BR (SR) 16	1958	-	-	-	-	163
Tonbridge		5/10B	BR(SR) 18 PB+	1962	NX panel	1962	-	E	221
Tondu		3/29B	GW 3+	1884	GW VT5	1963	65	T	222

SECTION 1: NETWORK RAIL

Box Name		Quail Map	Box:- Type	Date	Frame/Equipment:- Design	Date	No. of Levers	Lock'g	Notes
Totley Tunnel East		2/28E	Midland 2b	1893	Midland Tumbler	1893	12	Tum	
Towneley LCF (G)		4/33B	S&F 9 [L&Y]+	1878	IFS panel	1979	-	E	127
Tram Inn		3/27C	GW 5	1894-	GW VT5 2h	1978	23	T	223
Trent		4/6A	BR(LMR) PB	1969	NX panels	1969/c2003	-	E	48
Tring Sidings Frame (NBP)		4/9A	BR(LMR) 15	1964	LMR Standard	1964	10	T	225
Trinity Lane [Waltham X] (G)		2/10B	Portable Hut	nk	IFS	2003	-	E	
Trowse Swing Bridge		2/7A	N/S	1987	NX panel/VDU	1987/2000	-	E	254
Truro		3/10A	GW 7a	1899	GW VT5 2h	1971	54	T	226
Tutbury Crossing	L	4/25C	McK&H 1 [NS]+	c1872	McK&H 1886 Pat. 5"	1897	9R	R.T	179
Tweedmouth		2/23B	BR(NER) PB +	1961	NX panel	1990	-	SSI	227
Ty Croes (G)	L	4/37A	LNW C&H	1872	LNW Tumbler 2h	1901	6R	B&S	228
Tyneside		2/22A	PB	1991	VDUs	1991/2002	-	SSI	157
Tyseley No.1		4/15B	GW 14	1949	GW VT5	1949	30	T	229
Uffington & Barnack		2/24D	Midland 4a+	1909	Midland Tappet	1909	16	T	267
Ulceby Junction		2/32B	GC 5	1910	GC(McK&H)/panel	1910/88	30R	T/e	282
Ulverston		4/31A	Furness 4+	1900	RSCo Tappet	1900	22R	T	179
Upminster IECC		2/3B	PB	1994	VDUs	1994	-	SSI	
Upper Holloway		4/1	2-high Portakabins	1985	NX panel	1985	-	E	
Urlay Nook		2/47C	NE C2a	1896E	McK&H17 recon.	1943	41	T	230
Usan		1/16C	NB N/S	1906	Stevens GOP(Stev)	u1906	16	T	
Uttoxeter		4/25C	BR(LMR) 15 2h	1981	LMR Standard 2h	1981	40	T	
Valley	L	4/37A	LNW 5+	1904	LNW Tumbler	1904	25	B&S	179
Victoria		5/2	BR(SR) PB	1980	NX panel/panel	1980/92	-	E/SSI	231
Vitriol Works		4/47A	BR(LMR) 14	1954	LMR Standard	1954	65	T	
Wainfleet		2/26B	GN 1	1899	RSCo Tappet	1899	25	T	
Wakefield Kirkgate		2/42A	Portakabin	1982	NX panel	1982	-	E	
Walkden		4/48A	RSCo [L&Y]+	1888	RSCo Tappet	1888	24	T	179
Walsall		4/19	BR(LMR) PB	1965	NX panel (Whse)	1965	-	E	
Wareham		5/31C	LSW 4	1928	Stevens (Tyer)	1928	30	T	
Warnham		5/19A	S&F 5 [LBSC]	1877	S&F Rocker 5"	1877	20	R.T	
Warrington		4/26B	BR(LMR) PB+	1972	NX panel	1972	-	E	48
Warrington Central		4/46B	BR(LMR) 15 2h	1973	LMR Standard 2h	1973	55	T	232
Washwood Heath No.1 (NBP)		4/16	Midland 3b	1899	REC	1924	60R	T	
Wateringbury		5/10C	S&F 12a [SE]	1893	S&F1888Duplex/IFS	1893	9R	Dx	246
Watery Lane Shunt Frame (G)		4/19	LMS 13	1942	IFS	nk	-	E	
Watford Junction		4/8B	BR(LMR) PB	1964	NX panel	1964	-	E/SSI	154
Weaver Junction (RR)		4/26A	BR(LMR) N/S	1961	-	-	-	-	
Weaverthorpe	L	2/18D	NE S1a	c1873	McK&H16 recon.	1933	16	T	
Welton (G)		2/38B	NE S2	1904	McK&H16	1904	R6	T	
Wem		4/23A	LNW 4	1883	REC	1943	35	T	
Wembley Main Line SCC		5/1B	N/S	2000	NX panel	2000	-	SSI	
Wembley Yard		5/1B	PB	1993	Panel	1993	-	SSI	270
Wennington Junction (NNM)		4/28B	Midland 2a	1890	Midland Tumbler	1890	27	Tum	286
West Burton		2/31B	BR(ER) 18 PB	1965	IFS panel	1965	-	E	
West Hampstead		4/1	BR(LMR) PB	1979	NX panel (Whse)	1979	-	E	
West Holmes [Lincoln]		2/27A	GE 2/GN	1882	RSCo Tappet/IFS	1907/88	69	T	247
West Street Junction [Boston]	L	2/26A	GN 1	1874	McK&H C&T 4"	1894	36R	R.T	
Westbury		3/11C	BR(WR) PB	1984	NX panel	1984	-	E	
Whissendine		4/3B	Midland 4d 2h	1940	REC	1940	20	T	
Whitchurch (NNM)		4/23A	LNW 4	1897	LNW Tumbler	1897	55	B&S	
Whitehouse		2/50B	NE C1	1874E	McK&H17 recon.	1940	40R	T	
Whitland		3/26A	BR(WR)37b 2h	1972	GW VT5 2h	1972	39	T	234
Whittlesea		2/13C	GE 7	1887	S&F Rocker 5"	1887	23R	R.T	215
Whyteleafe South (G)		5/14C	**	(1982)	Panel	1982	-	E	196
Wickenby		2/28A	MS&L 3	1890	IFS panel	1990	-	E	
Wigan Wallgate		4/27A	LMS 13*	1941	LMR Standard 2h	1977	75	T	236
Wigton		4/32C	BR(LMR) 15+	1957	LMR Standard	1957	40	T	179
Willesden Carr. Shed Middle (NBP)		5/1B	N/S	1998	REC/panel	1953/84	3R	T/E	25
Willesden Carriage Shed North		5/1B	LMS 11c	c1953	REC/panel	1953/85	42	T/E	238
Willesden Carr. Shed South		5/1B	LMS 11c	c1953	REC	c1953	30	T	238

SECTION 1: NETWORK RAIL

Box Name	Quail Map	Box:- Type	Date	Frame/Equipment:- Design	Date	No. of Levers	Lock'g	Notes
Willesden High Level Junction	5/1A	LNW 5	1930	NX panel	1985	-	E	
Willesden Suburban	5/1A	2-high Portakabins	1988	NX Panel	1988	-	SSI	
Wilmslow	4/43B	BR(LMR) PB	1959	OCS panel (Whse)	1959	-	E	
Wimbledon	5/21A	PB	1990	NX panel	1990	-	E	
Wimbledon Pk TopYd Sh'rs (NBP)	5/21A	Hut	1976	Panel	nk	-	E	
Winning	2/23C	NE N2	1895	McK&H16 recon.	1963	15	T	
Winsford	4/26A	LNW 4+	1897	LNW Tumbler/panel	1897/1997	41R	B&S/E	214
Woburn Sands	4/9C	LNW 4	1904	LNW Tumbler	1904	25	B&S	268
Woking ASC	5/23	**	1997	NX panel	1997	-	E	
Wokingham	5/25B	SR 12	1933	Whse A2 (Tyer)	1933	40	T	
Wolverhampton	4/19	BR(LMR) PB	1965	NX panel (Whse)	1965	-	E	
Woodburn Junction	2/29	Portakabin	1992	IFS panel	1992	-	SSI	
Woodhouse Junction	2/29	LNER 11a	1926	GC (RSCo)	1926	84	T	
Woofferton Junction	3/27A	LNW/GW Jt 1+	c1875E	GW HT3 4"	1914	39R	T	240
Wool	5/31C	LSW 3b+	c1890	Stevens (Stevens)	c1890	19	T	241
Woolley Coal Siding (NNM)	2/36A	Relay Room	(1996)	IFS panel 2h	1996	-	E	242
Worcester Shrub Hill	3/14A	GW 11+	1935	GW VT5	1935	84	T	267
Worcester Tunnel Junction	3/14A	GW 7	1905	GW VT5	1960	58R	T	265
Workington Main No.2	4/32B	LNW 4	1889	LNW Tumbler	1889	58R	B&S	49
Workington Main No.3	4/32B	LNW 4	1886	LNW Tumbler	1886	25R	B&S	47
Worksop	2/31A	Portakabin	1997	NX panel	1997	-	E	
Wrawby Junction	L 2/31C	GC 5+	1916	GC (McK&H)	1916	137	T	179
Wrenbury	4/23A	LNW 4+	1882	LNW Tumbler	1882	17R	B&S	22
Wye (G)	5/11B	**	(2003)	IFS panel	2003	-	E	243
Wylam	L 2/21C	NE N5 overhead	c1897	IFS panel	1969	-	E	318
Wymondham	2/13B	GE 2*	1877	McK&H 4"	nk	42	R.T	314
Yarmouth Vauxhall	2/8	GE 4/S&F	1884	S&F Rocker 5" 2h	1905	63	R.T	
Yeovil Junction	5/33D	LSW 4+	1909	GW VT5	1967	45R	T	244
Yeovil Pen Mill	3/17B	GW 11	1937	GW VT5	1937	65	T	
Yoker SC	1/6A	**	1989	VDUs	1989	-	SSI	220
York	2/19	BR(ER) PB	1989	VDUs	1989	-	SSI	
Ystrad Mynach South	3/28B	McK&H 3 [Rhym]	nk	GW VT5	nk	45	T	

Notes

1   Base of frame (GW HT3 of 1932 now with VT5 locking) only (no levers) retained in box.

2   Box 2h, originally at Birmingham Moor St (1909) then at Didcot Foxhall Jn (1915). Now BTF. Frame shortened 1971. First panel (IFS 1977, relay locking) controls Stormstown Jn area. Second panel (1989, SSI) controls Aberdare line.

3   Box re-windowed 1990.

4   Frame made 1882 but no definite evidence installed in this box at that date.

5   Control area extended: 'Stratford North London Line Signal Box' as separate room in IECC (1999); West Anglia lines (2000-2003).

6   Frame contains some RSCo-made parts.

7   Box (RSCo,1885) destroyed by fire 1959 and present box built around existing frame.

8   Formerly 'Hirst'; re-windowed in the 2000s.

9   Ceased to be a block post in 1972 when Hammerton-Poppleton singled.

10   GE 2* of 1882 largely reconstructed and extended in 2002.

11   Last regularly used 1974, crossing now CCTV from Lydney and box used only as accommodation for gatekeeper in emergencies. Box was re-windowed but is now boarded.

12   2 RETB workstations/2 SSIs - one controlling Helensburgh Upper to Oban/Upper Tyndrum, one controlling Upper Tyndrum to Mallaig (excl. Fort William Jn/station area). Also works swing bridge adjacent to box. IFS panel controls signals protecting swing bridge and LC.

13   Panel controls Aynho Jn area. Frame reduced from 87 levers c1982.

14   Box (and probably frame) 2h ex Cymmer Afan (1960).

15   Formerly 'Clipstone West Jn'. 1986 panel controls Rufford Jn area. Additional PGW Mosaic NX panel 1997 for Welbeck Colliery Jn.

16   IFS is for Ferriby.

17   Box 2h ex Portpatrick (1908 there). Frame 2h ex previous Barrhill box (1907 there) and refurbished with many new parts in the 1940s. Tablet instruments located in Booking Office.

18   Still manned two shifts but only traffic now is Alcan trips to/from North Blyth (since power station and diesel depot closures).

19   1998 panel to control Dover area.

20   Former Gate Box ('Lady Anne's Crossing'), made BP 1952. Now a fringe box to York IECC (Leeds West Work Station).

21   LNW Type 5 box of 1911 burnt out June 1977 and present BR(LMR) top built on existing brick base.

22   Box re-windowed c1990.

23   Frame is 84 levers downstairs with portion between 24 and 42 floored over upstairs and partition installed.

24   Box extended 1922.

25   New box built around floor/frame of original LMS 11c box believed erected c1946 (not BIU until c1953).

26   Also has small 2-lever frame for wickets.

27   Box extended u1911.

28   Now VT 5 locking. Box refurbished/re-windowed in the 2000s.

29   Frame 2h ex Nethertown (1958 there). Box built c1871 in preparation for line's doubling (1873).

30   Box and frame ex-LMS Emergency Reserve (World War 2). Box renovated/re-windowed in the 2000s.

31   Formerly 'Starbeck South'.

32   Formerly 'Bournemouth West Jn' and recent nameplate on box has this (unofficial) name. Abolished 1965, re-opened as G.F. 1967.

33   Formerly 'Harrogate North'.

34   Opened 1875 as 'Bridlington South' and renamed on closure of Quay Crossing Box in 1998. Extended, and replacement windows, 1903. Frame reduced to 65 levers in 1974.

35   Disused frame (L&Y, 1902, 12R, T) remains in box dismantled (nothing visible upstairs).

36   Frame has spaces for 36 levers below floor.

37   Four working levers, for wickets and slots on Manchester Piccadilly signals. Box also serves to transcribe train details between incompatible Preston PB and Manchester Piccadilly train describer systems.

38   Ex-L&Y tappet locking added for conditional locking. Lever nos.16-113 above floor.

39   Frame incorporates some Tyer-made parts.

40   Box originally built into station buildings. Frame originally 52T levers but highest lever filled is no. 51.

41   Ex-L&Y tappet locking added for conditional locking. Lever nos.31-120 above floor.

42   Pre-interlocking signal box. Instruments in box, frame outside (as it always has been), now however under perspex shelter.

43   Controls level crossing and Caerwent and Sudbrook branch connections. IFS slot main signals.

44   SSI for Ely area, 1992.

45   Line from Rock Ferry is mothballed pending possible decision to re-open.

46   Claimed that box and/or frame are 2h from Blackfriars Jn.

47   Frame originally 55 levers; nos. 19-43 in use.

48   Box provided with new hipped roof 1980s in lieu of original flat roof.

49   Frame originally 60 levers.

50   Normally Gate Box only but can assume full local control in emergencies (and is regularly so used, for practice).

51   Frame 2h ex Slateford Jn (part) (1960 there).

52   Box/frame ex-Gronant; frame re-locked 1984 using levers ex-Llysfaen.

53   New box 'Allington Jn.' with panel (TEW type) planned for 2004-5; will also replace Barkston East Jn. box.

54   IFS panel (12 switches) added 1995 to control Ravenhead Oil Terminal.

55   Formerly 'Halifax East'.

56   On Mersey Docks & Harbour land. Telephone link to Merseyrail IECC. Delivers TS to trains going to Seaforth.

57   Former BP, Bridge control cabin only since RETB 1988.

58   Located on upper floor of previously existing shunters' office building.

59   Frame 2h ex previous Codsall box (1926 there).

60   Box extended 1931 when frame extended from 30 to 45 levers.

61   Panel controls Rugeley and Armitage areas.

62   Built on base of previous (NE) box.

63   Totally rebuilt 1983.

64   Box extended 1904 and re-windowed c1990.

65   Re-opened 31.3.1974 after previous abolition; re-windowed.

66   Formerly 'Long Lane Crossing'. Re-clad box as now exists believed 1947 but may be 1931 frame (1931 box damaged and reconstructed).

67   Panel in station office works signals protecting level crossing.

68   Under the Canterbury (Wye Area) CC scheme, the frame at Sturry will be replaced by an IFS panel early in 2004.

69   Often referred to as 'Daisyfield LC' since 1960s. Re-windowed 1980s.

70   Also acts as box for Metrolink line.

71   Box/frame ex-Wem North. Box re-windowed c1990.

72   Previously abolished as BP 1970 but retained as GF. Re-opened as BP 1985. Relay locking for Dorchester area, SSI for Weymouth area (added to panel in 1987).

73   New brick base 1950s.

74   Re-built with flat roof after 1976 fire.

75   Disused frame (72-lever Westinghouse A2, 1934) in box. VDUs vice panel in 1998 but panel in situ for use in emergency.

76   Box (and frame) extended 1940.

77   Panel controls St Botolphs area.

78   BTF construction. Ground floor is a relay room for Newport box. Since 2000 controls traffic to Fifoots Power Station.

79   Box top 2h ex Mosstowie, 1902 there.

80   New top on LNW Type 5 base following fire.

81   Frame made 1938 but not used due to World War 2.

82   Panel controls Bentley and Alton.

83   Felixstowe Dock & Railway Co. box.

84   Formerly 'Ferryhill No.2'; still a BP (with IFS panel) to Norton West; now a fringe box to Tyneside IECC.

85   Box re-windowed in 1999.

86   Switched out; only manned for occasional nuclear flask train to/from Hartlepool Power Station (on Seaton Snook branch).

87   Box built by GN at cost of GE, on GE line worked by GN.

88   Frame manufactured in 1900.

89   Box probably 1924 when previous box abolished; no Block Post here 1924-36, made BP 1936, since reduced to GB again.

90   Frame 2h ex previous Frodsham Jn box, 1893 there. Box refurbished/re-windowed in the 2000s.

91   Formerly 'Kirkham North Jn'; frame originally 105 levers; lever nos. 1-29 removed, 30-86 used, 87-105 spare.

92   Formerly 'Girvan Station', then 'Girvan No.3', then 'Girvan No.2'. Box extended 1907.

93   Box re-windowed 1987.

94   Frame (1887) extended and significantly altered 1909. Box refurbished/re-windowed in the 2000s.

95   Formerly 'Boothferry Road'.

96   Originally a bridge control cabin only; became BP 1933.

97   Box also houses NSKT instrument.

98   Box extended 1956.

99   Built as Relay Room only, became SB 1990. Operating room is former RR technician's accommodation.

100   From NNM to regularly open following restoration of Dryclough Jn curve (1999).

101   Formerly 'Ashton Junction'; box refurbished/re-windowed in the 2000s.

102   Replacement frame ex-Ordsall Lane. Box refurbished and re-windowed in the 2000s.

103   Instruments in station buildings, frame (open until 1972) on platform.

104   Box extended u1930.

105   Box extended 1938.

106   In yard control tower. New NX panel in 2003 in former hump control room. Previous operating floor now disused.

107   Box extended and altered 1897. Now VT5 locking.

108   Formerly 'Ayleston Hill'. Panel controls Shelwick Jn area.

109   In view of GSW locking, frame probably LMS period.

110   Works emergency crossover only.

111   Levers 1 - 15 removed 1968 for adjacent Freightliner depot GF, then frame extended (101 - 115) 1974; box refurbished/re-windowed in 2000s.

112   Box built 1885, top re-built 1940 after bomb damage. No pre-1940 photographs known so original type uncertain. Box controls river swing bridge - 6-lever non-standard (ie no catch-handles or blocks) S&F frame remains for this (one spare); also IFS panel of 1964 for signals. Box open for period either side of high tide for ships needing to pass. Permission required from Hessle Road SB; bridgeman operates slot controls on two of Hessle Road's signals before swinging bridge.

113   Frame for 60 levers below floor; lever nos. 4-48 retained and in use.

114   Formerly 'Huntly South'. From 1901 to 1970 was Gate Box only.

115   Owned by Associated British Ports. Staffed by Network Rail.

116   Owned by Associated British Ports. Staffed by Network Rail. NX panel 1967; IFS panel added 1981.

117   RETB control centre (1 workstation) for Kyle of Lochalsh and Thurso/Wick lines. Controls 4 SSIs - Inverness/Kyle/Lairg; Lairg/Wick/Thurso; Inverness East; Inverness West.

118   Box controls bridge and protecting signals, slotted by Scunthorpe PB. IFS panel is combined switch and indication facility.

119   New top on GW Type 3 base of 1885.

120   Road/rail bridge control cabin. Staffed by Network Rail, but bridge is owned by highway authority.

121   Box extended 1922 or 1928 (frame may be 1928).

122   New top (1967) on base of 1876 S&F box 'Knottingley Depot East'.

123   Now all 3-bar locking.

124   Frame originally 120 levers; nos. 11-90 retained but 8 spares subsequently removed.

125   Re-locked with modern tappet locking.

126   Box extended 1938.

127   Re-windowed.

128   Formerly 'Lon Las South'.

129   Formerly 'Llanelly No.4'. Box extended 1904. Frame (GW DT, 1904) remains in box but all levers are removed.

130   Frame 2h ex Brundritts Sidings (1909 there); only 4 working levers, points are train-operated. Box refurbished/re-windowed 2000s.

131   Formerly 'Mallaig Junction'. Panel controls Fort William station area.

132   SSI for Cannon Street 1991.

133   Owned by BMW and maintained/staffed by the company. Has slots on Saltley signals for trains coming on to branch.

134   Panel controls Largin area via SSI located at Par S&T depot.

135   Formerly 'Lydney West'. Re-windowed.

136   Box is BTF construction. Machynlleth station area worked from frame. Line to Dovey Jn controlled direct by TCB. 'East Workstation' controls RETB Sutton Bridge Jn to Machynlleth. 'West Workstation' controls RETB Dovey Jn to Pwllheli/Aberystwyth.

137   Box retains original name, adjacent station renamed Watlington.

138   Frame controls station area; box re-windowed in the 2000s.

139   Located in station office block. Also VDUs but these act as train describers only. 'South' panel section renewed 1999.

140   IFS (1979) for west end of layout, also OCS Panel (1985) for Coalville Crossing and Coalfields Farm area.

141   Box raised in height 1897. Frame re-locked 1987 when March West area taken over.

142   Frame in station office. Opened 1925 as NBP with 5-lever frame; made BP 1943.

143   Box totally rebuilt in original form 1991/92.

144   Located in station office buildings.

145   Located at Sandhills.

146   Formerly 'Newsham South'.

147   Box/frame 1891 but box hit by train early 1913 and largely re-constructed, reopened May 1913. Box refurbished/re-windowed in 2000s.

148   Formerly 'Staddlethorpe West'.

149   IFS for signals for Fenwick Crossing.

150   Panel 1 is NX (Westinghouse); Panels 2,3,5&6 are NX (Henry Williams Domino); Panel 4 is NX (TEW). Controls remote RRs at Abington, Beattock, Carmyle, Fauldhouse, Hamilton, Holytown, Lanark Jn, Law Jn, Lockerbie, Summit, Uddingston, Whifflet, and Wishaw. Controls SSIs - 2 for Newton area (1991), 2 for Motherwell area (1998), 1 for Gartsherrie area (1999), 3 for Mossend area (2003). Interfaced SSIs - 2 for Carstairs area (1996).

151   Lower parts of box re-built 1989 and re-windowed. (Roof is only original part left!)

152   3R to work mechanical barriers + two wicket gate locks; box re-windowed in the 1990s.

153   Westcad with 'Westrace' CBI; located in station office which has been the Block Post since the line opened.

154   SSI for remodelled/resignalled Watford North/South Junction area (date nk).

155   Formerly 'Stocks Lane'. Frame (which is the second frame in this box) now has VT5 locking.

156   Works points and signals for siding/crossover, as well as being Gate Box.

157   Control area extended 2002: Pelaw (excl.)-Sunderland (dual running with Nexus Metro LRT); Sunderland-South Hylton (LRT only).

158   Signals off when levers normal.

159   Box extended 1928 and new frame installed at that date.

160   Now controls swing bridge only. Controls released from Oulton Broad North Station.

161   Panel 2h ex Twyford.

162   Frame 2h ex Denbigh, 1957 there. Box refurbished/re-windowed in the 2000s.

163   Relay Room for Salisbury box; brought into use as such when passing loop installed at Tisbury (previously, no use).

164   Crossover and signals at Woldingham are relay locked in cabinets on site, not SSI.

165   In station building behind Booking Office.

166   Controls remote RRs at Ayr, Barassie, Dunrod, Elderslie, Glengarnock, Gourock, Hunterston, Kilwinning, Ladyburn, and Wemyss Bay Jn. The adjacent 1966 Paisley box still contains relay equipment in use but is without its operating floor. Ayr, Barassie, Hunterston and Kilwinning RRs have emergency panels

167   Supervises No Signalman Token working (NSTR) on Central Wales line between Pantyffynnon and Craven Arms. Frame now has VT5 locking. Box was previously 'Pantyffynon South'.

168   Supervises No Signalman Token working (NSTR) Crediton - Eggesford - Barnstaple.

169   Box extended 1893. Now VT5 locking. Panel controls Burngullow/Probus area. TCB within Par box area to Probus, then AB Probus to Truro. Start made in 2003 to re-instate double line Burngullow-Probus.

170   Box extended 1899.

171   Frame 2h ex Coniston Station box (1897 there).

172   Box repaired after accidents in 1912 and 1964.

173   Frame 2h ex-Fylde area (stored 1954-1972).

174   New structure built on foundation of previous GN 1 box of c1888 in similar style to the original.

175   Ansaldo Keyboard/Tracker Ball control with VDU back-projection screen; only controls Cheadle Hulme area at present.

176   Formerly 'Rochdale Goods Yard'.

177   Frame originally 27 levers, extended to 51 in 1934 and/or 1940. Box extended, probably 1934. Re-windowed.

178   Built from 2h LNW 5 parts on BR(LMR) 15 base.

179   Box refurbished/re-windowed in the 2000s.

180   Out of use 10.1995 after fire. Repaired and re-opened 1996; re-windowed, but main structure remains as before.

181   Box extended 1908.

182   The 20 levers remaining of the shortened frame (LMR Std, 1957) in situ but OOU as Vauxhall Up/Down goods line abolished.

183   Operation currently in Portakabin pending decision regarding original 1885-built RSCo[MS&L] Grade II listed structure.

184   New top 1933 on base of S&F (1874) box. Full 56-lever frame still in situ below floor. Remaining levers are 21-30 (renumbered 1-10). Box re-windowed in 1990s.

185   Box 2h ex Waterloo East (SE). Panel includes integral Tokenless Block instruments for working to Sandown (all under the control of St Johns Road). Owned by Network Rail but managed and staffed by Island Line train company (aka 'Island Line SC').

186   Box also contains swing bridge control equipment.

187   Box extended 1927.

188   Formerly 'Rhyl No.1'.

189   Instruments in station office, open frame. New 'Marston Vale' SC (with VDU work station) to replace this box in 2004.

190   Formerly 'Broadwater Siding'. Frame works wickets and detonators only.

191   Owned by Property Services Agency, but staffed by Network Rail. Abolished February 1923, re-opened June 1941.

192   Also additional panel 1997 to control Grove Road LC.

193   SSI for Northampton line (1991).

194   1977 panel controls Berks & Hants line.

195   Second panel controls coal sidings (NX+VDUs/SSI). Frame (below floor level), disused, remains in box.

196   Panel in station building.

197   Abolished as BP 1970 and frame removed. Crossing normally worked by resident keeper in adjacent house. Controls on Gloucester PB signals worked by turning the gates' Annett's Keys. SB used only as shelter for relief signalmen as necessary.

198   In former Parcels Office.

199   Formerly 'Salwick No.2'; RSCo 30-lever frame extended (A - E) 1942 with L&Y parts; subsequently reduced by two (29&30).

200   New concrete blocks base to box in LNER period. Re-windowed c1985. Panel controls Saxmundham Station area. RETB control centre for East Suffolk Line from Westerfield (excl.) to Oulton Broad South (fringe to Oulton Broad North Station SB).

201   Frame made 1894.

202   Frame re-locked 1995. Box refurbished/re-windowed in the 2000s.

203   Originally 'London Road', then 'Wistow Junction' (1904), then 'Selby West' (1945), now 'Selby' (1973). Box extended 1904. New frame 1945, removed 1973; NX panel 1973, altered 1983 and 1997.

204   Swing bridge cabin. Frame works bridge bolt. One panel for signalling, second panel for hydraulics.

205   In top floor of (pre-1985) Yardmaster's office building.

206   Box now a relay room for Doncaster PB, with panel for Emergency Local Control. Was BP SB 1958 - 80.

207   Frame has both Westinghouse - and RSCo - made parts. GF worked by traincrew.

208   VT3 locking added to bottom of original locking.

209   Re-locked as VT5 1952.

210   Box extended 1900.

211   SSI cubicles are located in Slough 1963 PB.

212   1903 L&Y top on 1874 Yardley base. Formerly 'Smithy Bridge East'.

213   Frame made by LMS at Irvine. Box refurbished/re-windowed in the 2000s.

214   Panel added 1997 for Hartford and Weaver Jn areas; box refurbished/re-windowed in the 2000s.

215   Frame refurbished 1996.

216   In Yard Control Tower; disused 'Tees Down Hump' yard control room in same tower.

217   Formerly 'Teynham East Crossing'. No functional mechanical locking.

218   Box extended 1907.

219   Box extended u1941.

220   Located in room within Yoker depot management building 'Matthew House'. Controls remote RR at Craigendoran. Controls SSIs for Dumbarton, Finnieston, Hyndland, Sunnyside, and Yoker.

221   Now controls Hastings line only. Box refurbished in the 2000s.

222   Formerly 'Tondu Middle'. Box re-windowed and brickwork re-faced.

223   Built on base of previous box (1880). Frame 2h ex (part of) Corporation Road.

224   Frame installed in box at opening was 6-lever tappet locking; date nk for replacement with 10-lever frame.

225   Officially re-named 'Tring Sidings Frame' 1988, but nameplates remain as before.

226   Frame 2h ex Bristol East Depot Main Line (1960 there).

227   Box re-windowed and re-clad 1990.

228   Frame 2h ex Rhyl No.2 (1892 there). Box re-windowed 1998 in similar style to original.

229   Controls rolling stock depot only; works TCB to Saltley on main line connection.

230   Box extended 1943.

231   Box located at Clapham Jn. Panel 2A, added 1992 for West London line, is SSI.

232   Box and frame 2h ex Platt Bridge.

233   RSCo[MS&L] box of 1885 replaced in 1999 by brick structure built to GN pattern; IFS equipment (1981 in old box) transferred.

234   Box and frame 2h ex Danygraig (c1960 there).

235   Box extended 2000.

236   Frame (most or all) 2h ex Bamfurlong Jn.

237   Gate box; 1975 panel replaced in 11.1997, covers Tallington, Lolham and Greatford LCs; interlocking renewed 7.2000.

238   These boxes believed erected c1946 but not BIU until c1953.

239   Refurbished and also re-windowed in traditional style of box in the 2000s.

240   Re-locked VT5 1992. Re-windowed 1996.

241   Flat-roof extension 1988. Re-windowed.

242   Panel installed in SB 1982, removed to (pre-existing) RR which became the 'signal box' in lieu 1996, but now switched out.

243   IFS panel in B.O.; can only be operated when LC gates closed, 2-lever gf locked by removing key and inserting it in panel.

244   Re-windowed with GW Type 7 windows; frame 2h ex-Newport, 55 levers with 46-55 boarded over.

245   IFS for Woodgate Crossing.

246   IFS for Teston Crossing.

247   IFS for Boultham Crossing.

248   Owned by Associated British Ports.

249   No.1 Panel (Eastleigh – Wallers Ash) renewed with SSI for SIMBIDS in 1995.

250   Former panel box, attached to new (1981) box. Houses relay equipment.

251   Box taken over from Boston Corporation by GN 1892. Re-windowed 1980s. Box bolt locks swing bridge.

252 Panel installed 1994 in previously-existing hut.

253 Eurotunnel box. (Shown as 'Cheriton PSB' in Quail). Controls Folkestone (Cheriton) terminal and the tunnel. Signals, where provided, are to SNCF patterns. Works TCB to Ashford and Frethun PRCI (SNCF). Also controls Coquelles Terminal in normal circumstances. There is a 'duplicate' RCC at Coquelles which can perform all the functions of (Folkestone) Eurotunnel RCC in emergency and is sometimes switched in for testing.

254 1997 panel for Swing Bridge area for which box acts as Bridge Box only. Box contains Emergency Panel for Norwich interlocking (normally, Colchester SB) and has VDU (Vaughan Harmon Modular Control System) for sole control of Whitlingham Jn (inclusive) to Cromer line.

255 Locking room used as Relay Room. Upper floor used as S&T mess room. (Note – the bases only of Benton, Stannington, Longhirst and Widdrington are also retained as Relay Rooms).

256 New hut built around 1952 frame in 2002.

257 Controls remote RRs at Burntisland, Charlestown Jn, Cowdenbeath, Dalmeny, Drem, Dunbar, Grantshouse, Inverkeithing, Kirkcaldy, Ladybank, Linlithgow, Markinch, Midcalder, Monktonhall, Newbridge, North Queensferry, Oxwellmains, Portobello, Prestonpans, Redford, Slateford, Thornton, Townhill, and Winchburgh. Controls interfaced SSIs for Haymarket area (2) since 1997. All of these (except Grantshouse and Linlithgow) have emergency panels.

258 Panel originally installed 1985 for Cleethorpes – Pasture St. area, altered 1993 when Grimsby area added.

259 Controls rolling stock depot (down side only).

260 Formerly 'Moorthorpe South'. Frame relocked 1979.

261 Room in Loading Bunker Tower. Owned by R.J. Budge Mining. Block Post to Morpeth. (Butterwell effectively signalled as a terminus from both directions; no interface between Butterwell Bunker and Butterwell TP Hut).

262 Network Rail box but on NNR property. Works Train Staff & Ticket (+telephone) to Ashington. Tickets permitted northbound only.

263 Owned by Alcan (formerly by NCB). Panel is rebuild of earlier panel (1986) which itself incorporated earlier parts. Also controls Alcan Branch Jn. When Lynemouth box is unstaffed, the points are set for the Alcan Branch with OTW on the Down line from Ashington to Alcan. When Lynemouth box open, Telephone Block from Ashington (double line), ie 'Absolute'.

264 IFS Panel for Boughton Jn area.

265 South end of box partly rebuilt 1970s after being hit by a derailed train.

266 New NX panel (1997) for Low Gates-Eaglescliffe resignalling. This panel installed alongside 1992 panel (for Low Gates LC; Boroughbridge Road CCTV LC; Romanby Road CCTV LC; and Springwell Lane AHBs). Box re-windowed in the 2000s.

267 Re-windowed and refurbished in the 1990s.

268 Boxes Bedford St Johns to Bletchley (excl) scheduled to be replaced by new box at Marston Vale (Ridgmont) SC Autumn 2004.

269 Box is an integral part of listed station building; operating floor OOU but frame (CLC, date nk, 18 levers) still in situ; locking room used as a Relay Room for Deansgate Junction.

270 Also controls Royal Mail Terminal area (1996).

271 Formerly 'Western Junction'.

272 In building originally opened as Relay Room, 1986. SSI Interlocking at Queen Street, Cowlairs, Eastfield, Gartshore, and Garnqueen.

273 Panel controls Stratford-upon-Avon station. Box refurbished/re-windowed in the 2000s.

274 Located at former Sinclairtown Yard. Temporary Block Post SB Feb-June 1980, relay room controlled from Edinburgh SC since June 1980; acts as emergency signalling panel.

275 Abolished 1992, re-opened 1996. Box belongs to Clydeport.

276 Previously staffed gate boxes, now closed but used as accommodation for emergency gatekeeper if barriers/CCTV fail.

277 Relay locking for Butterwell line signals.

278 Main operating panel renewed c1980, but 'indication panel' at back is original of 1962/66. Panel extended on closure of Tile Hill and Canley gate boxes (1979).

279 Works double line telephone block to Lightmoor Jn.

280 Signalman at Nunthorpe supervises NSKT working Nunthorpe-Battersby-Glaisdale-Whitby. At Battersby there are colour light signals and the signals and junction points are worked automatically on a 'first come first served' basis by trains (not controlled from Nunthorpe).

281 Boarded up but opened once/twice in most weeks for Cemetery North-Thrislington trains.

282 Panel controls Habrough area.

283 Panel no longer in use.

284 1969 panel for Eaglescliffe; 1986 panel for Stockton (this panel was formerly in North Shore box, 1973); third panel (1989) for Stockton Cut, Hartburn (previously on Eaglescliffe panel 1973-1989), and Bowesfield.

285 Panel 2h ex temporary Portakabin box (1985, abol. 1987 and removed 1989).

286 Box and frame extended 1941.

287 Frame 2h ex-Kendal (1955); re-windowed (uPVC type) 1996.

288 Owned by Eurostar (UK) Ltd.

289 NSKT instrument for Seal Sands now located at Phillips Siding GF. Belasis Lane SB re-windowed in the 2000s.

290 Frame possibly 2h ex-old box. Box now boarded up and points disconnected.

291 Re-locked VT5 1996.

292 Formerly 'Alnmouth North' (until 1957).

293 Panel controls Essington Wood area.

294 1978 IFS for Brentingby Jn; circa 1986 IFS for Pedigree Pet Foods Siding. Box refurbished/re-windowed in the 2000s.

295 IFS for protecting signals in station building; barriers operated by pedestal at level crossing.

296 Westcad VDU controls Wellington area by SSI. Box refurbished and re-windowed in the 2000s.

297 Box and frame 2h ex-Elan Valley Jn (1894 there and re-locked 1925). Full 40-lever frame remains downstairs. Released by Cab Display Unit Key which drivers can only remove after obtaining a 'Shunt Token' by radio from Machynlleth.

298   58 levers above floor, 61 lever frame below floor.

299   Panel controls remote RRs at Carrbridge, Kincraig, Moy, Slochd and Tomatin.

300   Located at Newton Jn.

301   Relay Room controlled from Paisley SC (former temporary SB reduced in status to emergency signalling panel in 1986).

302   Original GE Hut reclad in 1990s.

303   Controls signals on the Old Dalby Test Track; panel located in the test centre HQ.

304   A small IFS panel was provided in Falkland Down Yard Inspector's office to control signals on the single line connection between Falkland Up Yard West sidings and Ayr Harbour. This EWS installation is in daily use.

305   Controls remote RRs at Busby Jn, Busby Station, Cardonald, Cook Street, Muirhouse, Polmadie, Rutherglen and Shields (2). Muirhouse, Polmadie and Rutherglen RRs have emergency panels.

306   Former Hunterston SB now relay room controlled from Paisley SC, acts as emergency signalling panel.

307   Relay Room for Sheffield SB and emergency control panel located in previous signal box now bricked up.

308   Previous box and frame destroyed by fire; replacements made up from spare parts and commissioned 12/2003.

309   Controls remote RR at Bo'ness Jn (with emergency panel).

310   Former Thornton Yard Control Tower. Now RR (Redford RR) controlled from Edinburgh SC 1981; acts as emergency signalling panel.

311   Panel is OCS (Westinghouse) but with push buttons (Westinghouse called this 'a miniature OCS panel').

312   Box and adjacent signal gantry at Falsgrave are both Grade II-listed.

313   Formerly 'Seamer East'. Box refurbished/re-windowed in the 2000s.

314   Formerly 'Wymondham South Junction'.

315   Box extended 1940; refurbished and re-windowed in the 2000s.

316   Box also provides signalling protection for gates at Dormer Green LC.

317   Box also provides signalling protection for gates at Balne Lowgate LC.

318   Hexham and Wylam boxes (both listed buildings) have been renovated in their original style.

319   VDU/SSI for new Ledburn Jn (2003) which will be transferred to the new Rugby SCC, due to open mid-2004.

320   Original (wooden top) structure replaced by brick.

321   Box retains original name, adjacent station renamed Metheringham.

322   Operating floor designed to accommodate panel for Perth-Inverness CTC (scheme never proceeded with).

323   Ex L&Y tappet locking added for conditional locking.

324   Temporary end of branch from Park Junction.

Roxton Sidings (1997) – Essentially a gate box but retaining its block post responsibilities on the line between Grimsby and Habrough Junction, the MS&L Type 2 box of 1883 retains its 18-lever MS&L Iron Brackets frame from the same date, albeit relocked in the meantime.

Nairn West (2000) – Deprived of its operational role when a VDU workstation was established in the station building in 2000 and the bicycle issued for travelling between the East and West boxes was withdrawn, this 1891-built McK&H Type 3/ Highland box remains in situ as a listed building.

DIRECTORY SECTION TWO : LONDON UNDERGROUND

As signalling on the London Underground system has followed a somewhat different course of development since the 1900s than 'BR' signalling, the 'signal boxes' and other locations listed in the tabulation here comprise a rather different set of installations than those in the Network Rail list. The majority of them can be classified under one of the following headings:–
- 'Control Rooms' supervising those lines, or sections of lines, where the signalling is now wholly centrally controlled and local signal boxes no longer exist, these being:– Bakerloo Line; Central Line; District Line west of Tower Hill (incl.); East London Line; Jubilee Line; Metropolitan Line Harrow (excl.) to Aldgate Junctions; Northern Line; Piccadilly Line; Victoria Line.
- Staffed signal cabins on the remaining sections of the system, controlling relatively small areas only. The remaining boxes are mostly of 1920s – 1950s vintage, with Westinghouse power frames.
- Subsidiary cabins, which are capable of being operated locally if necessary but whose frames are normally controlled from another box.
- Former staffed signal cabins which have been abolished as such but remain as 'Interlocking Machine Rooms' (IMR) on lines which now have centrally controlled signalling. Some of these retain their original power frames (minus the catch handles) now acting as remote interlockings only, whilst others have Westinghouse Style V frames (a design developed specifically for this function). Note that only those IMRs which were formerly staffed signal cabins are included in the Directory; there are many other IMRs built as new structures which are not included here (on open-air sections these are generally single-storey brick structures, readily identifiable by the nameplates they bear).
- Depot Control Towers/Ground Frames.
Where staffed signal cabins also control IMRs elsewhere, this is noted in the footnotes (but not in the case of Control Rooms which control all the IMRs on the line in question).

The 'Locking' column is omitted from this tabulation as the situation is complex with many LUL installations, but power frames generally retain mechanical tappet locking, IMRs have both tappet and relay locking for different purposes, and panels have relay locking.

No 'Signalling Maps' for the London Underground are included here as the diagrams in Quail (Vol.5) will serve the purpose. However it may be of use to give a 'Line' order summary of LUL signalling/signal boxes as at 1.1.2004 and this is provided below:

BAKERLOO
- BAKER STREET SERVICE CONTROL CENTRE controls the whole line and fringes to Willesden Suburban SCC (Network Rail) at the west end of Queens Park.
  Also Stonebridge Park Depot (Control Tower).
  Also Former SB retained as IMR – Piccadilly Circus.

CENTRAL
- WOOD LANE SERVICE CONTROL CENTRE controls the whole line. There are panels located in certain Station Supervisors' Offices as emergency signalling panels.
  Also Former SBs retained as 'Signal Equipment Room' (SER) – Greenford, South Woodford.

DISTRICT
- EARLS COURT CONTROL ROOM controls the whole line as far east as Tower Hill IMR and fringes to Rayners Lane (Met) west of South Harrow; Richmond (Network Rail) between Turnham Green and Gunnersbury; Wimbledon ASC (Network Rail) south of Putney Bridge; and Edgware Road (Met) at Notting Hill Gate.
- (Aldgate Junctions controlled by Baker Street Control Room)
- Whitechapel
- Barking
- Upminster
- Also Upminster Depot (Control Tower)
- Also Former SBs retained as IMRs – Ealing Broadway, West Kensington East.
- Also Former SB retained as PMR – Earls Court West.

EAST LONDON
- NEW CROSS SIGNAL CONTROL FACILITY controls the whole line. It fringes to Whitechapel (District) on the St Mary's Curve.

JUBILEE
- BAKER STREET CONTROL ROOM controls the line from Stanmore to Green Park (and Charing Cross).
- NEASDEN SERVICE CONTROL CENTRE controls the line from Green Park (excl.) to Stratford.

METROPOLITAN/H&C/CIRCLE
- Amersham (fringes to Marylebone IECC (Network Rail) at Mantles Wood)
- Rickmansworth
- Rayners Lane (controls whole of Uxbridge line, and fringes to Earls Court Control Room west of South Harrow)
- Harrow North [subsidiary]
- Harrow-on-the-Hill (fringes to Marylebone IECC (Network Rail))
- Harrow South [subsidiary]
- BAKER STREET CONTROL ROOM controls the line from Harrow (excl.) to Aldgate Junctions (incl.) and then fringes to Earls Court Control Room east of Tower Hill, and to Whitechapel east of Aldgate East.
- Hammersmith
- Edgware Road (fringes to Earls Court Control Room at Notting Hill Gate, and Baker Street Control Room west of Baker Street)
- Also Neasden Depot Train Movements Room
- Also Former SB retained as IMR – Liverpool Street
- Also Former SB retained as GF – Ruislip.

NORTHERN
- COBOURG STREET CONTROL ROOM controls the whole line.
- Also Totteridge GF and Golders Green Depot GF
- Also Former SBs retained as IMRs – High Barnet, Finchley Central, East Finchley, Archway, Edgware, Hampstead. Former SB retained as Relay Room – Angel.

PICCADILLY
- EARLS COURT CONTROL ROOM controls the whole line.
- Also Former SBs retained as IMRs – Cockfosters, Oakwood.

VICTORIA
- COBOURG STREET CONTROL ROOM controls the whole line.
- Also Northumberland Park Depot (Control Tower).

WATERLOO & CITY
- WATERLOO & CITY signal box (at Waterloo) controls the whole line.

SECTION TWO: LONDON UNDERGROUND

Box Name	Quail Map	Box:- Type	Date	Frame/Equipment:- Design	Date	No. of Levers	Notes
Amersham	5/41C	LT N/S	1960	Push-Button & Switch Panel	1960	-	1
Angel (RR)	5/39B	CSLR	1901	-	-	-	
Archway (IMR/RR)	5/39A	**	1907	Westinghouse V	1992	12	
Baker Street Control Room	5/43A	**	1986	Panel (Jub., Met., H&C, Circle lines)	1986	-	
Baker Street Sig. & Control Centre	5/41B	**	1990	Panel (B'loo line)	1990	-	
Barking	5/45A	BR(ER) PB	1960	2 Push-Button Panels	1960	-	2
Cobourg Street Control Room	5/39B	**	1968	2 Pnls (N & Vic lines)	1969/68	-	
Cockfosters (IMR)	5/46B	UER	1933	Westinghouse V	1982	u36	
Ealing Broadway (IMR)	5/43B	LT	1952	Westinghouse N pf 2h	1952	55	3
Earls Court Control Room	5/44A	**	1965	Panel (Dist. & Picc. lines)	1965	-	
Earls Court West (PMR)	5/44A	LT N/S	1936	None	(1967)	-	4
East Finchley (IMR)	5/39A	LT	1939	Westinghouse N pf	1939	35	
Edgware (IMR)	5/39A	LT	1940	Westinghouse V	1965	u24	5
Edgware Road	5/44B	Met 4	1926	Westinghouse K pf	1926	38	
Finchley Central (IMR)	5/39A	LT	1940	Westinghouse N pf	1940	u59R	6
Golders Green Depot GF (NBP)	5/39A	Hut	Nk	Tyer 4" gf	1932	4	
Greenford (SER)	5/37B	LT N/S	1948	-	-	-	
Hammersmith [H&C]	5/44A	LT	1951	Westinghouse N pf 2h	1951	35	
Hampstead (IMR)	5/39A	**	1907	Westinghouse V	1993	12	
Harrow-on-the-Hill	5/42A	LT	1948	Westinghouse N pf	1948	95	7
Harrow North (Subsid)	5/42A	LT N/S	1948	Westinghouse N2 pf	1948	44	
Harrow South (Subsid)	5/42A	LT N/S	1948	Westinghouse N2 pf	1948	33	

High Barnet (IMR)	5/39A	LT	1940	Westinghouse N pf	1940	35	
Liverpool Street [Met.] (IMR)	5/44B	Met N/S	1875	Westinghouse K pf	1954	15	
Neasden Depot Train Movements Room	5/42B	LT N/S	1987	3 Panels	1988	-	8
Neasden Service Control Centre	5/42A	LT N/S	1999	Panel	1999	-	
New Cross Signal Control Facility	5/45C	LT N/S	1998	Panel	1998	-	
Northumberland Park Depot	5/40C	CT	1967	Switch Panel	1989	-	
Oakwood (IMR)	5/46B	UER	1933	Westinghouse V	1982	24	
Piccadilly Circus [B'loo] (IMR)	5/41B	**	1915	Westinghouse V	1991	12	9
Rayners Lane	5/42A	LT	1935	3 Switch Panels	1975/85/87	-	10
Rickmansworth	5/41C	LT N/S	1953	Westinghouse N pf	1953	47	11
Ruislip (NBP) L	5/42A	Met 2	1904	EOD (uSykes) R.T	1904	24	12
South Woodford (SER)	5/38A	LT	1947	-	-	-	
Stonebridge Park Depot	5/41A	O/H CT	1979	Switch Panel	1979	-	
Totteridge GF (E, OOU)	5/39A	Hut	1980	Westinghouse E2 gf 5"	1940	2	13
Upminster	5/45B	LT N/S	1958	Push-Button Panel	1958	-	14
Upminster Depot	5/45B	CT	1958	Switch Panel	1980	-	
Waterloo & City	5/38C	**	1993	NX Panel	1993	-	15
West Kensington East (IMR)	5/44A	LT N/S	1948	Westinghouse N pf 2h	1948	35	
Whitechapel	5/44B	**	1911	Westinghouse N pf 2h	1951	47	
Wood Lane Service Control Centre	5/37B	LT N/S	1993	VDUs Westrace Computer Based Interlocking	1993+	-	

Notes

1   Cabin has 'IMR' (Westinghouse V frame) in ground floor. Amersham box also controls Chalfont & Latimer IMR.
2   Formerly BR and LT 'boxes' in same building, but the BR box is now abolished. Cabin has 'IMR' (Westinghouse V frame) in ground floor. Barking box also controls Bromley-by-Bow, Plaistow, East Ham, Barking Sidings West, Barking Sidings East, and Dagenham East IMRs.
3   Now controls District Line routes only (until 1993 also controlled Central Line routes).
4   Programme Machine Room. Was formerly a staffed signal cabin.
5   Box was built 1940, but believed never used until equipped as an IMR in 1965.
6   Frame originally 71 levers but reduced on conversion to IMR.
7   Box controls Harrow North and Harrow South Subsidiary boxes. Also has Push-Button Panel for Northwood IMR.
8   Main route-setting panel (Comp. based interlocking) is supplemented by two emergency panels working points only, for use when main panel is disabled.
9   Cabin was disused 1939 – 1991.
10   1975 Panel for Ruislip IMR, 1985 Panel for Westinghouse V frame in separate building at Rayners Lane, 1987 Panel for Uxbridge IMR.
11   Also Push Button Panel (1955) for Watford South Junction IMR; Push Button Panel (1958) for Watford IMR; and Switch Panel (1961) for Rickmansworth Sidings South.
12   Frame fixed for through running and still connected to functional relay room, otherwise no function now. Frame re-locked tappet, u1930.
13   Frame works emergency crossover but the relevant lever is now inoperable. Hut was provided 1980 for a prolonged period of single line working.
14   Cabin has 'IMR' (Westinghouse V frame) in ground floor. Upminster box also controls Hornchurch and Upminster West IMRs.
15   In former staff gymnasium. Built by BR before transfer of line to LUL.

Kew East Junction (1997) – Considering the two levels of motorway traffic in close proximity to this NL Type 3b box, it is a veritable haven of peace for the duty signalman when working within its part-wooden and part-BTF walls. Now having just passed its century, the structure is unusual in that its locking-room windows can be unbolted and removed.

INTRODUCTION TO THE SIGNALLING MAPS

These Maps are in a near-geographical format but are not to the same scale, nor to any precise scale within each map, and congested areas are drawn at a larger size for clarity. Complex flyover/flyunder/multiple junction areas are shown in as much detail as practicable. Single lead junctions are only shown as such if there is a significant length of single track. The more significant unsignalled dead-end branches are shown, together with the method of working thereon, but some very short lines are omitted for clarity. Out-of-use lines are not usually shown except in those cases where signal boxes not yet formally 'abolished' exist on them, in which case they are shown, 'OOU'.

The method of working between signal boxes and on each dead-end branch is shown, <u>if other than Track Circuit Block</u> <u>(TCB)</u>. In cases where multiple tracks exist, this is the method of working on the main passenger running lines, if different methods are used on other lines (although there are in fact few such cases now). Where boxes (on open lines) are out of use, the method of working shown is that between the two boxes either side, in accordance with present reality. However where boxes are merely not normally open ('NNM' in the Directory listings) the working shown on the maps is as for when the box is open.

For the exact geographical points of signal box control area boundaries (in some cases there is actually a considerable difference between the up and down line boundaries) see the Quail maps. The purpose of these maps is to give an overall picture of the signalling scene for use in conjunction with the Quail maps and the Baker Atlas, not to replicate (beyond what is necessary) information already available in those publications. The signal boxes/installations shown on these maps are the <u>same</u> boxes as are listed in the Directory listings: see the Introduction to the Directory listings for the definition of what constitutes an eligible location. The maps are correct to 1.1.2004.

A key to the maps is provided at the top of the first map opposite. Owing to the mixture of colour light and semaphore signals at certain places, and the impossibility of defining whether signals can be said to exist 'continuously' between one box and the next in other cases, there is necessarily some subjectivity in deciding whether to show some lines 'black' or 'red'. The majority of double lines shown 'black' are controlled from panel boxes and have frequently-placed signals. Certain double lines worked on Absolute Block are also shown 'thick' if all running signals are colour lights and no long 'gaps' exist. Single lines controlled from remote power boxes are shown 'black', but it should be realised that in many cases there are in practice no signals for many miles between junctions/loops. Boxes on lines shown 'red' do not necessarily have semaphore signalling; the more significant 'isolated' one-box MAS areas are shown 'black', but where small boxes control a few colour-light signals, in the immediate box area only, in lieu of semaphores, lines are shown 'red'. Obviously any box shown in the listings as having a <u>panel</u> has colour light signals and not semaphores.

METHODS OF WORKING:

AB	Absolute Block
C2	Former Western Region method of single line working under control of nominated person-in-charge without Staff
ETS	(Miniature) Electric Train Staff (followed by letter A,B,C,D or E indicating the 'configuration' of the instrument, if known)
ETT	Electric Train Tablet (Tyer's No.6)
KT	Key Token
NB	No Block
NSKT	No Signalman Key Token
NSTR	No Signalman Key Token Remotely Controlled (unattended crossing loops)
OTS	One Train Working with Staff
OTW	One Train Working without Staff
RETB	Radio Electronic Token Block
TB	Tokenless Block
TBR	Tokenless Block regulations apply but not actually worked by Tokenless Block instruments (this is not officially recognised as a distinct system)
Tel	Telephone working
TS&T	Train Staff & Ticket

Note that these abbreviations are not all exactly as appear in Appendices. The term 'ET' used in Appendices for both Tablet and Key Token is not used here as it is insufficiently precise. Please note also the definitions of 'OTS' and 'OTW' here: there has been inconsistency in recent Appendices as to whether the term 'OT' is deemed to signify 'with' or 'without' Staff (unless stated to the contrary), hence that term is not used here. Lines worked under 'Single Line TCB' regulations comprise a multitude of differing installations, worked by Acceptance/Direction lever where mechanical boxes are involved, with many variations in what the signalmen actually have to do. Every effort has been made to check methods of working by reference to those with local knowledge, but it is inevitable that errors may occur in a handful of cases, owing to recent changes not having been assimilated, particularly in respect of unsignalled dead end branches where there has tended to be much 'flux' in recent years.

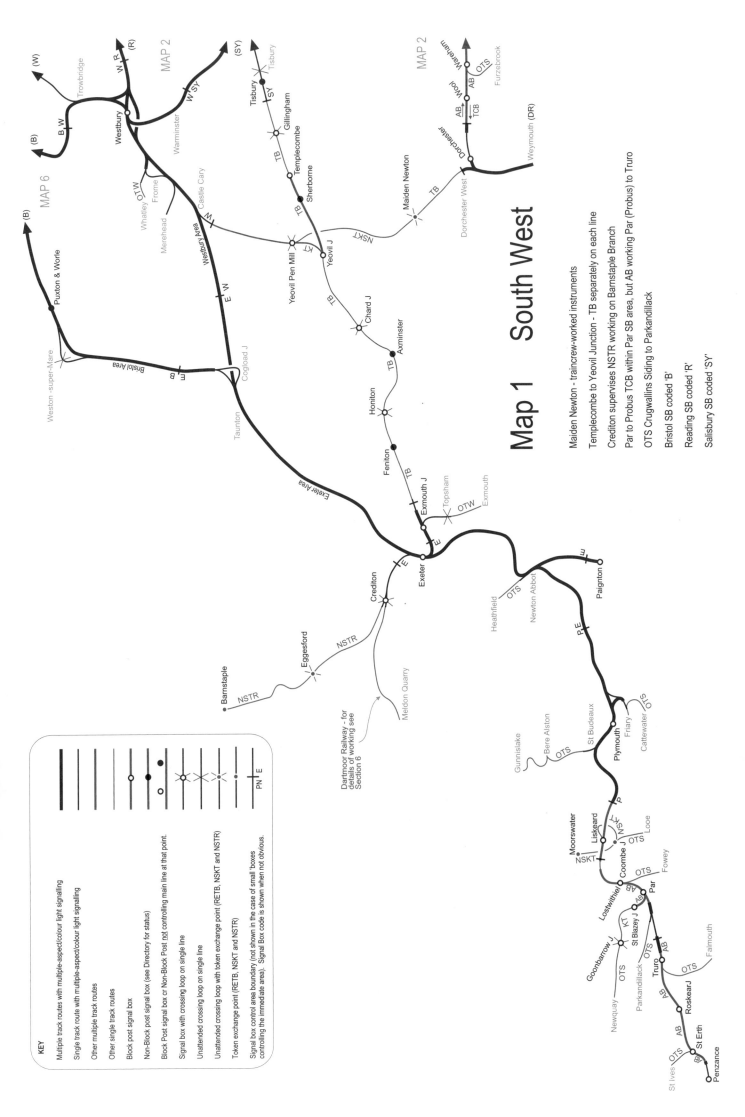

Map 1   South West

KEY

Multiple track routes with multiple-aspect/colour light signalling
Single track route with multiple-aspect/colour light signalling
Other multiple track routes
Other single track routes
Block post signal box
Non-Block post signal box (see Directory for status)
Block Post signal box or Non-Block Post not controlling main line at that point.
Signal box with crossing loop on single line
Unattended crossing loop on single line
Unattended crossing loop with token exchange point (RETB, NSKT and NSTR)
Token exchange point (RETB, NSKT and NSTR)
Signal box control area boundary (not shown in the case of small 'boxes controlling the immediate area). Signal Box code is shown when not obvious.

Maiden Newton - traincrew-worked instruments

Templecombe to Yeovil Junction - TB separately on each line

Crediton supervises NSTR working on Barnstaple Branch

Par to Probus TCB within Par SB area, but AB working Par (Probus) to Truro

OTS Crugwallins Siding to Parkandillack

Bristol SB coded 'B'

Reading SB coded 'R'

Salisbury SB coded 'SY'

Map 2 South Central

Windsor & Eton branch controlled by Slough
Henley Branch controlled by Reading
Basingstoke SB coded 'YW'
Horsham SB coded 'CBP'
Swindon 'B' coded 'SB'
Wimbledon SB coded 'W'
Ryde St Johns Road SB (coded WFP)
controls all IoW system

Map 3 South East

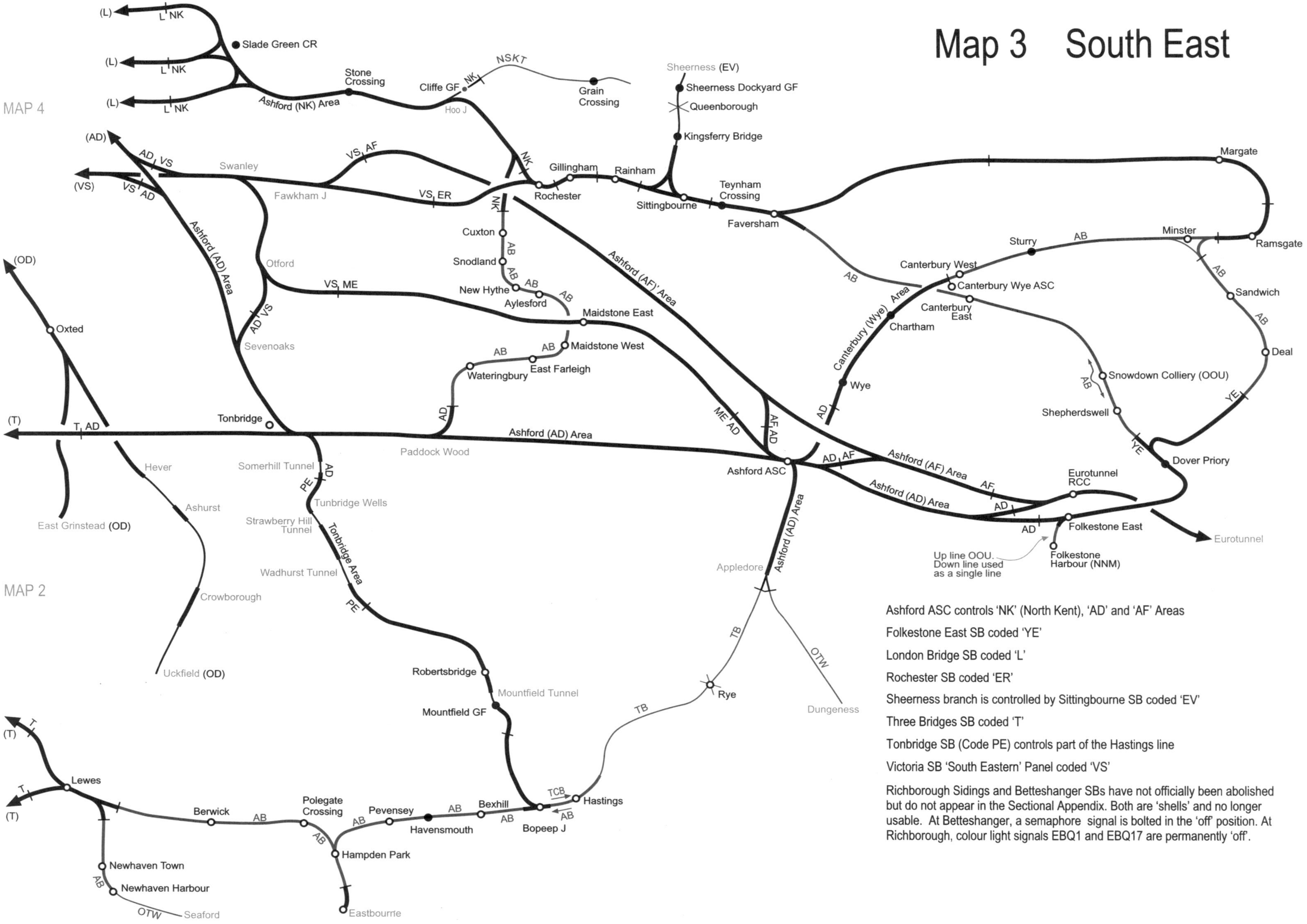

Margate

Ramsgate

Minster

Deal

Sandwich

AB

AB

AB

YE

Snowdown Colliery (OOU)

Dover Priory

Eurotunnel

AB

Shepherdswell

YE

Sturry

AB

Eurotunnel RCC

Folkestone East

AD

Canterbury West

Canterbury Wye ASC

Canterbury East

AF

AD

Folkestone Harbour (NNM)

Up line OOU
Down line used
as a single line

Chartham

Canterbury (Wye) Area

AD

Wye

AB

AD AF

Ashford (AF) Area

Ashford (AD) Area

Ashford ASC

Ashford (AD) Area

OTW

Dungeness

Sheerness Dockyard GF

Queenborough

Kingsferry Bridge

Sheerness (EV)

Teynham Crossing

Faversham

AF AD

Appledore

TB

Rye

ME AD

Grain Crossing

Sittingbourne

Rainham

Ashford (AF) Area

Maidstone East

TB

NSKT

Gillingham

Rochester

NK

NK

Maidstone West

East Farleigh

Mountfield Tunnel

Hastings

Hoo J

AB

AB

AB

AB

Wateringbury

Ashford (AD) Area

TCB

AB

Cliffe GF

NK

Cuxton

Snodland

AB

New Hythe

AB

Aylesford

AB

Bopeep J

Stone Crossing

Ashford (NK) Area

VS, ER

NK

AB

AB

Paddock Wood

Robertsbridge

Bexhill

AB

Slade Green CR

VS, AF

Fawkham J

VS, ME

Mountfield GF

Havensmouth

Pevensey

AB

L NK

Swanley

Offord

VS, ME

AD

Tunbridge Wells

Tonbridge Area

PE

Hampden Park

L NK

AD VS

Sevenoaks

Somerhill Tunnel

PE

Strawberry Hill Tunnel

Wadhurst Tunnel

Polegate Crossing

AB

Eastbourne

L NK

VS AD

AD VS

AD

Tonbridge

PE

Crowborough

Berwick

AB

Oxted

Hever

Ashurst

Uckfield (OD)

Newhaven Town

Newhaven Harbour

MAP 4

(OD)

(AD)

(VS)

East Grinstead (OD)

T, AD

(T)

MAP 2

Lewes

AB

Seaford

OTW

(L)

(L)

(L)

(T)

(T)

Ashford ASC controls 'NK' (North Kent), 'AD' and 'AF' Areas

Folkestone East SB coded 'YE'

London Bridge SB coded 'L'

Rochester SB coded 'ER'

Sheerness branch is controlled by Sittingbourne SB coded 'EV'

Three Bridges SB coded 'T'

Tonbridge SB (Code PE) controls part of the Hastings line

Victoria SB 'South Eastern' Panel coded 'VS'

Richborough Sidings and Betteshanger SBs have not officially been abolished but do not appear in the Sectional Appendix. Both are 'shells' and no longer usable. At Betteshanger, a semaphore signal is bolted in the 'off' position. At Richborough, colour light signals EBQ1 and EBQ17 are permanently 'off'.

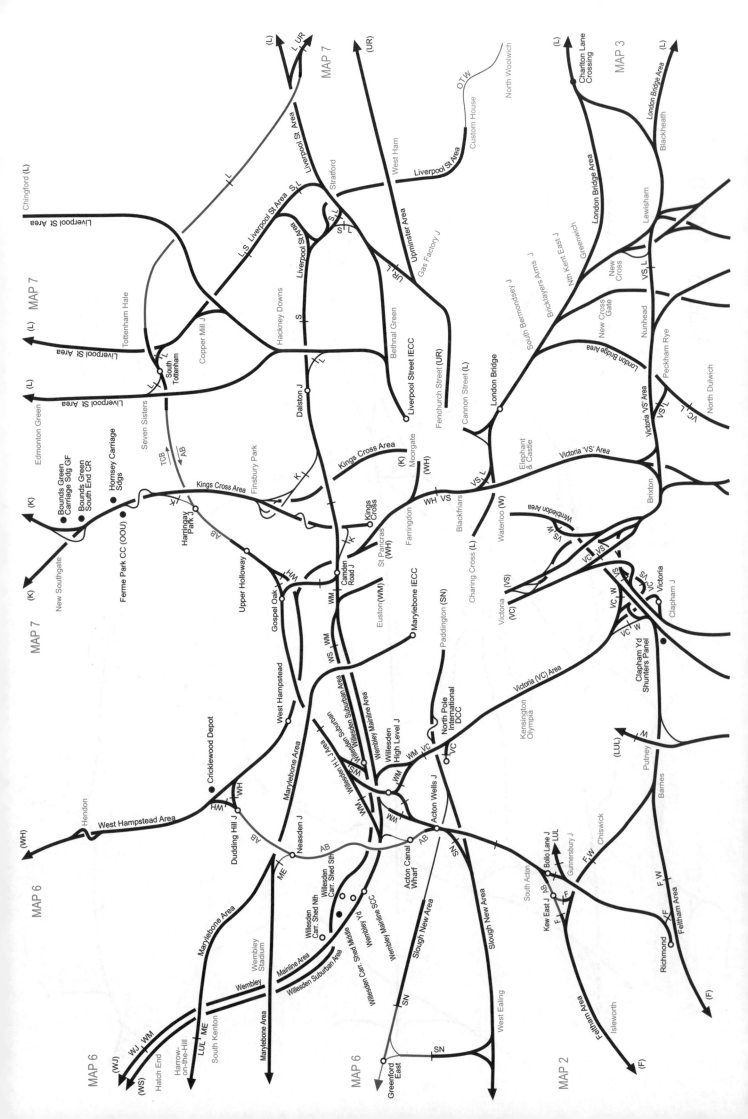

Map 4   London

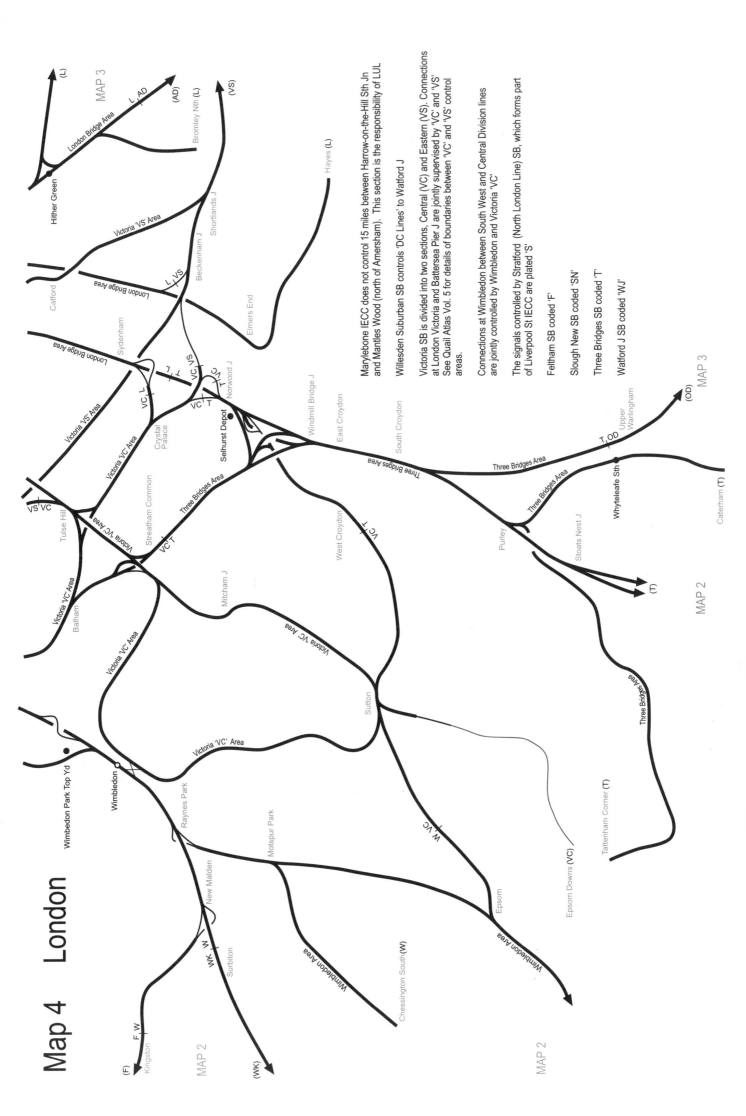

MAP 3

London Bridge Area

Hither Green

(L)

L, AD

(AD)

Bromley Nth (L)

(VS)

Shortlands J

Beckenham J

Victoria 'VS' Area

Catford

London Bridge Area

L, VS

Elmers End

Hayes (L)

Sydenham

London Bridge Area

VC, VS

T, L

Norwood J

VC, L

VC, T

Victoria 'VS' Area

VS, VC

Tulse Hill

Victoria 'VC' Area

Crystal Palace

Selhurst Depot

Streatham Common

Three Bridges Area

Windmill Bridge J

East Croydon

South Croydon

Three Bridges Area

Victoria 'VC' Area

VC, T

Mitcham J

West Croydon

VC, T

Purley

Three Bridges Area

Stoats Nest J

T, OD

Upper Warlingham

(OD)

Whyteleafe Sth

Three Bridges Area

Caterham (T)

MAP 3

(T)

Balham

Victoria 'VC' Area

Victoria 'VC' Area

Sutton

Victoria 'VC' Area

MAP 2

Wimbledon Park Top Yd

Wimbledon

Raynes Park

Victoria 'VC' Area

Motspur Park

New Malden

W, VC

Epsom

Wimbledon Area

Epsom Downs (VC)

Tattenham Corner (T)

Chessington South (W)

Surbiton

W, WK

F, W

Kingston

(F)

MAP 2

(WK)

Wimbledon Area

Marylebone IECC does not control 15 miles between Harrow-on-the-Hill Sth Jn and Mantles Wood (north of Amersham). This section is the responsibility of LUL

Willesden Suburban SB controls 'DC Lines' to Watford J

Victoria SB is divided into two sections, Central (VC) and Eastern (VS). Connections at London Victoria and Battersea Pier J are jointly supervised by 'VC' and 'VS'. See Quail Atlas Vol. 5 for details of boundaries between 'VC' and 'VS' control areas.

Connections at Wimbledon between South West and Central Division lines are jointly controlled by Wimbledon and Victoria 'VC'

The signals controlled by Stratford (North London Line) SB, which forms part of Liverpool St IECC are plated 'S'

Feltham SB coded 'F'

Slough New SB coded 'SN'

Three Bridges SB coded 'T'

Watford J SB coded 'WJ'

Map 5   South Wales

Map 6   South Midlands

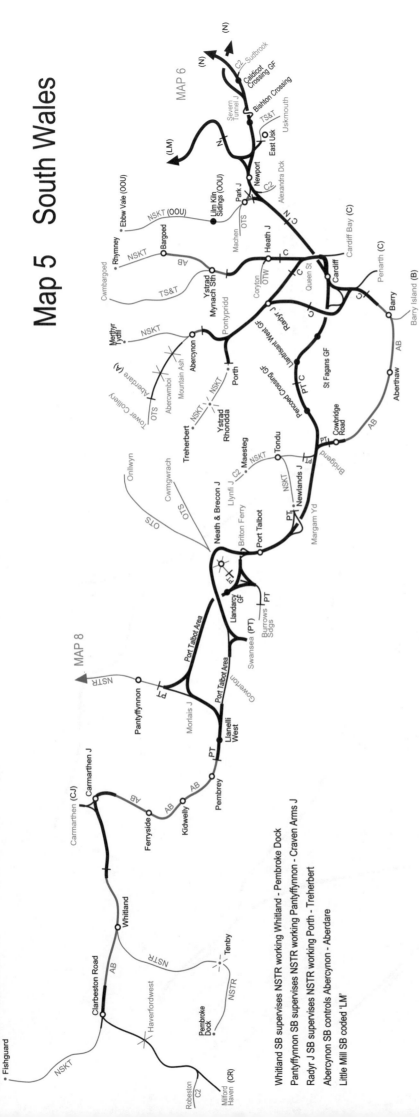

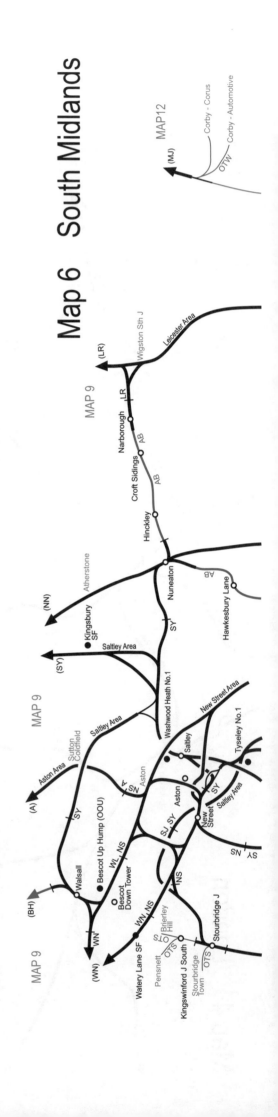

Whitland SB supervises NSTR working Whitland - Pembroke Dock

Pantyffynnon SB supervises NSTR working Pantyffynnon - Craven Arms J

Radyr J SB supervises NSTR working Porth - Treherbert

Abercynon SB controls Abercynon - Aberdare

Little Mill SB coded 'LM'

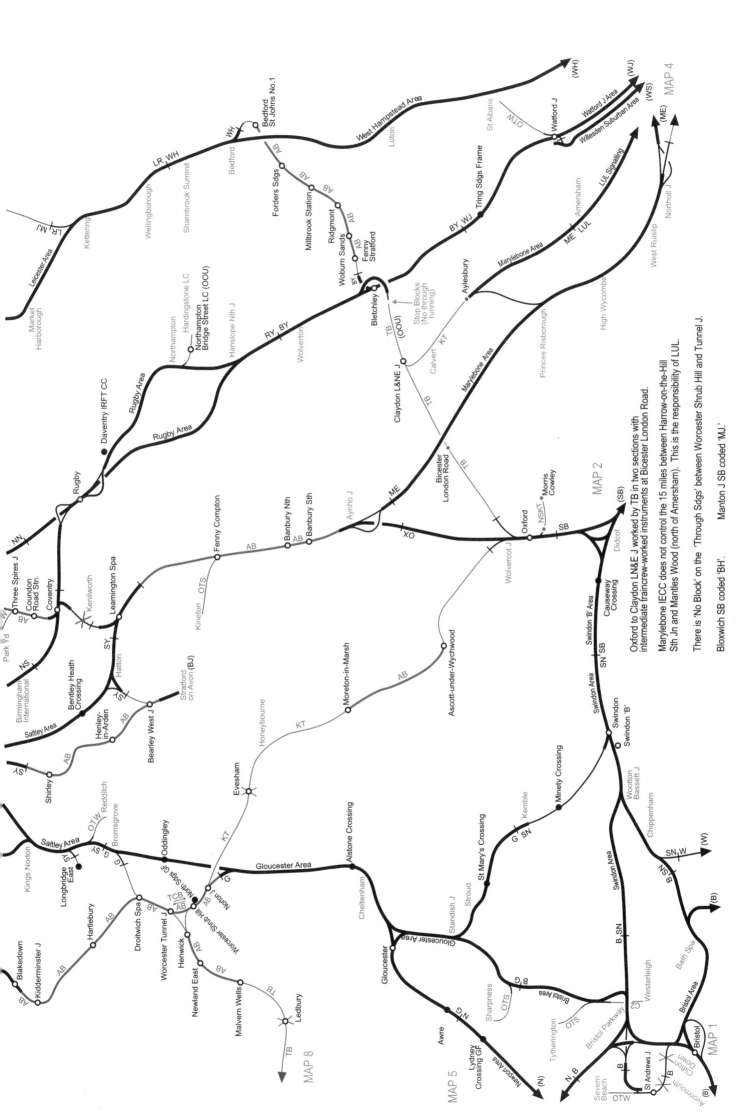

MAP 4

MAP 2

MAP 1

MAP 8

MAP 5

(WH)

(WJ)

(WS)

(ME)

West Hampstead Area

Luton

St Albans

OTW

Watford J

Watford J Area

Willesden Suburban Area

LUL Signalling

West Ruislip

Northolt J

Bedford St Johns No. 1

Bedford

WH

LR WH

Shambrook Summit

Wellingborough

Kettering

Market Harborough

Leicester Area

LR MJ

Forders Sdgs

AB

Millbrook Station

AB

Ridgmont

AB

Woburn Sands

AB

Fenny Stratford

AB

BY

Bletchley

Stop Blocks (No through running)

TB (OOU)

Tring Sdgs Frame

BY WJ

Amersham

ME LUL

Marylebone Area

High Wycombe

Princes Risborough

Aylesbury

KT

Calvert

TB

Marylebone Area

Claydon L&NE J

RY BY

Wolverton

Hanslope Nth J

Northampton Bridge Street LC (OOU)

Northampton

Hardingstone LC

Daventry IRFT CC

Rugby Area

Rugby Area

Rugby Area

Rugby

Three Spires J

Coundon Road Stn.

Coventry

NN

Park Yd

NS

AB

W

Kenilworth

SY

Leamington Spa

Hatton

SY

Bentley Heath Crossing

Birmingham International

Saltley Area

Henley-in-Arden

AB

Bearley West J

Stratford on Avon (BJ)

SY

Shirley

AB

Fenny Compton

AB

Banbury Nth

AB

Banbury Sth

Aynho J

ME

XO

Kineton

OTS

Bicester London Road

BL

Morris Cowley

NSKT

Oxford

SB

Wolvercot J

Didcot (SB)

Swindon 'B' Area

Causeway Crossing

SN SB

Swindon Area

Swindon

Swindon 'B'

Wootton Bassett J

Chippenham

SN W

(W)

NS B

Bath Spa

B SN

Bristol Area

Tytherington

OTS

Bristol Parkway

Westerleigh

Clifton Down

Bristol Area

Bristol

MAP 1

Severn Beach

OTW

St Andrews J

B

B

B

B

Avonmouth

(B)

Moreton-in-Marsh

AB

Ascott-under-Wychwood

Honeybourne

KT

Evesham

KT

Alstone Crossing

Gloucester Area

Cheltenham

Gloucester Area

Gloucester

Standish J

Stroud

St Mary's Crossing

Minety Crossing

Kemble

G SN

G SN

Sharpness

OTS

B G

Newport Area

(N)

Lydney Crossing GF

Awre

N G

Redditch

OTW

Bromsgrove

Saltley Area

G SY

Oddingley

G

Kings Norton

Longbridge East

G SY

Hartlebury

AB

Droitwich Spa

Worcester Tunnel J

Henwick

Newland East

AB

AB

AB

Worcester Shrub Hill

North Sdgs GF

TCB

AB

Norton J

G

AB

Malvern Wells

TB

Ledbury

MAP 8

Blakedown

Kidderminster J

AB

TB

Oxford to Claydon LN&E J worked by TB in two sections with intermediate traincrew-worked instruments at Bicester London Road.

Marylebone IECC does not control the 15 miles between Harrow-on-the-Hill Sth Jn and Mantles Wood (north of Amersham). This is the responsibility of LUL.

There is 'No Block' on the 'Through Sdgs' between Worcester Shrub Hill and Tunnel J.

Bloxwich SB coded 'BH'.   Manton J SB coded 'MJ.'

Map 7   East Anglia

Upminster IECC controls whole of LT&S system.
No signalling on Thames Haven branch beyond junction, except 'Stop' Board at Thames Haven.

Colchester SB controls Westerfield J. Saxmundham SB controls RETB Westerfield to Oulton Broad
South and Sizewell branch. Oulton Broad Nth SB controls Oulton Broad North J and TCB on single
line to Oulton Broad South station.

Trowse Swing Bridge SCC is coded TB. Operates swing bridge and controls Cromer branch.
Also contains emergency panel for Norwich.

Liverpool Street IECC coded 'L'.

Kings Cross SB coded 'K'.

Peterborough SB coded 'P'.

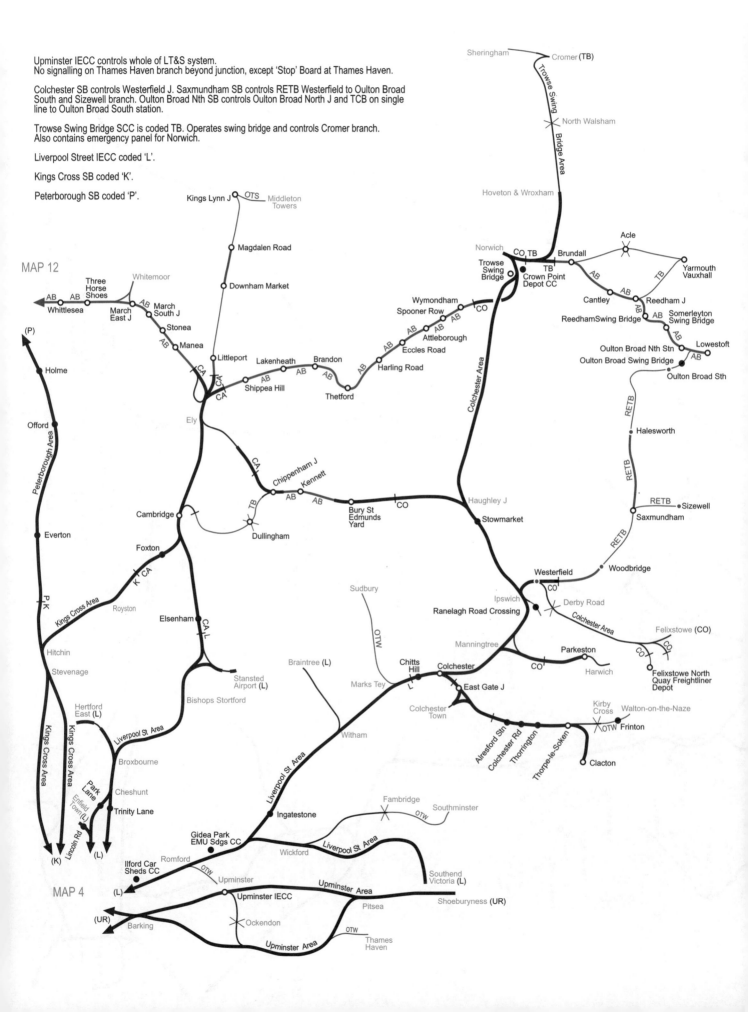

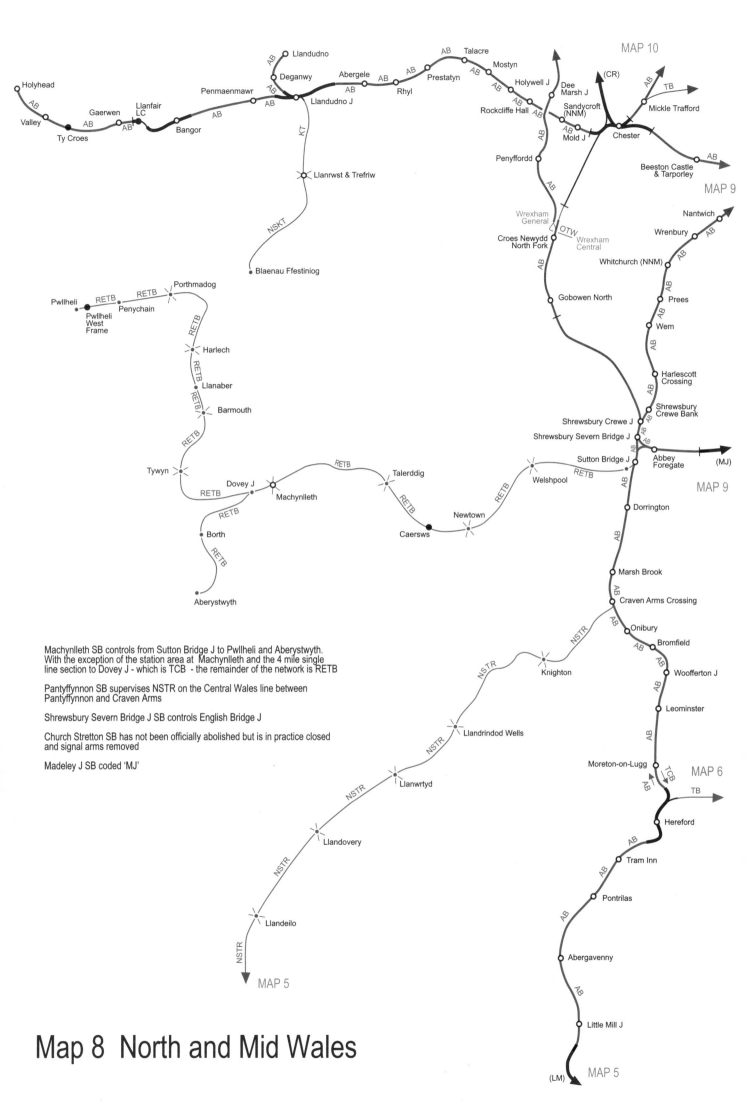

Holyhead
Valley
AB
Ty Croes
Gaerwen
Llanfair LC
AB
Bangor
AB
Penmaenmawr
AB
Deganwy
Llandudno
AB
AB
Llandudno J
Abergele
AB
Rhyl
AB
Prestatyn
Mostyn
AB
Talacre
AB
Holywell J
Dee Marsh J
Rockcliffe Hall
AB
Sandycroft (NNM)
AB
Mold J
Chester
(CR)
AB
TB
Mickle Trafford
MAP 10

Llanrwst & Trefriw
KT
NSKT
Blaenau Ffestiniog

Penyffordd
AB
Beeston Castle & Tarporley
AB
MAP 9

Wrexham General
Croes Newydd North Fork
OTW
Wrexham Central
AB
Nantwich
Wrenbury
AB
Whitchurch (NNM)
AB
Gobowen North
AB
Prees
AB
Wem
AB
Harlescott Crossing
AB
Shrewsbury Crewe Bank
AB
Shrewsbury Crewe J
AB
Shrewsbury Severn Bridge J
AB
AB
Sutton Bridge J
AB
Abbey Foregate
(MJ)
MAP 9

Pwllheli
Pwllheli West Frame
RETB
Penychain
RETB
Porthmadog
RETB
Harlech
RETB
Llanaber
RETB
Barmouth
RETB
Tywyn
RETB
Dovey J
Machynlleth
RETB
Borth
RETB
Aberystwyth
RETB
Talerddig
RETB
Newtown
RETB
Caersws
RETB
Welshpool
RETB

Dorrington
AB
Marsh Brook
AB
Craven Arms Crossing
AB
Onibury
AB
Bromfield
AB
Woofferton J
AB
Leominster
AB
Moreton-on-Lugg
TCB
MAP 6
AB
TB
Hereford
AB
Tram Inn
AB
Pontrilas
AB
Abergavenny
AB
Little Mill J
(LM)
MAP 5

NSTR
Knighton
NSTR
Llandrindod Wells
NSTR
Llanwrtyd
NSTR
Llandovery
NSTR
Llandeilo
NSTR
MAP 5

Machynlleth SB controls from Sutton Bridge J to Pwllheli and Aberystwyth.
With the exception of the station area at Machynlleth and the 4 mile single
line section to Dovey J - which is TCB - the remainder of the network is RETB

Pantyffynnon SB supervises NSTR on the Central Wales line between
Pantyffynnon and Craven Arms

Shrewsbury Severn Bridge J SB controls English Bridge J

Church Stretton SB has not been officially abolished but is in practice closed
and signal arms removed

Madeley J SB coded 'MJ'

Map 8 North and Mid Wales

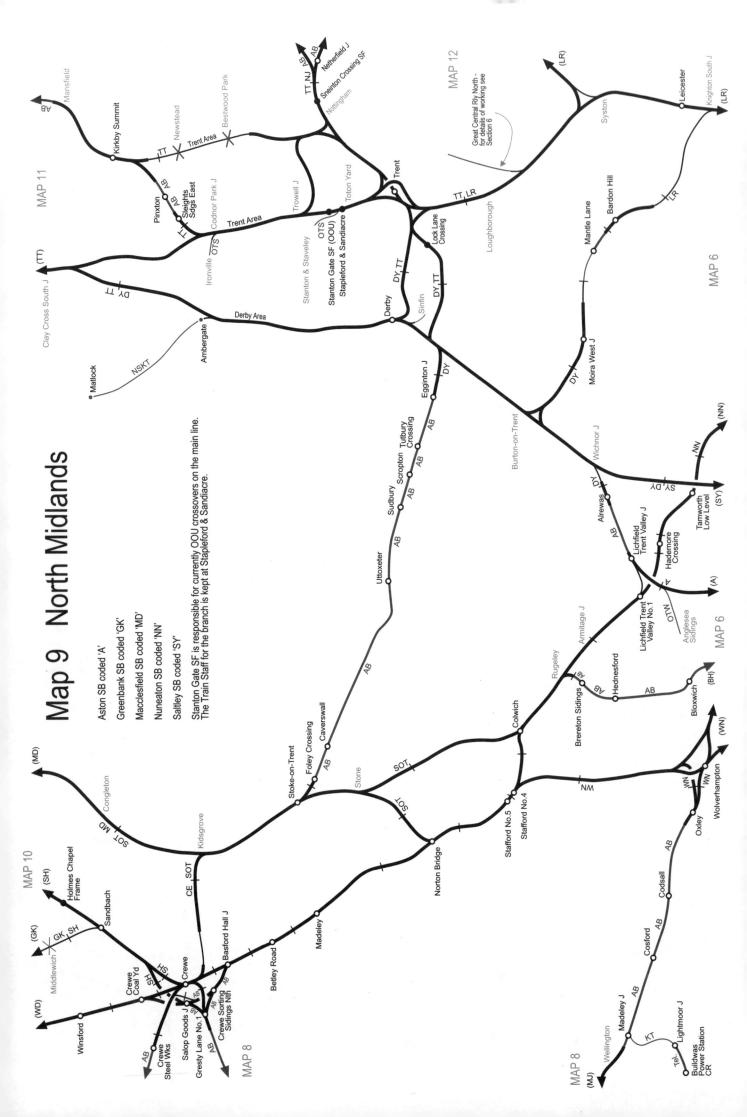

Map 9 North Midlands

Aston SB coded 'A'

Greenbank SB coded 'GK'

Macclesfield SB coded 'MD'

Nuneaton SB coded 'NN'

Saltley SB coded 'SY'

Stanton Gate SF is responsible for currently OOU crossovers on the main line.
The Train Staff for the branch is kept at Stapleford & Sandiacre.

Map 10
Liverpool & Manchester

MAP 13

Chester SB coded 'CR'
Dee Marsh J SB coded 'DM'
Diggle J SB coded 'DE'
Edge Hill SB coded 'LE'
Manchester North SB coded 'MN'
Manchester Piccadilly SB coded 'MP'
Manchester South SB coded 'MS'
Preston SB coded 'PN'
Sandbach SB coded 'SH'

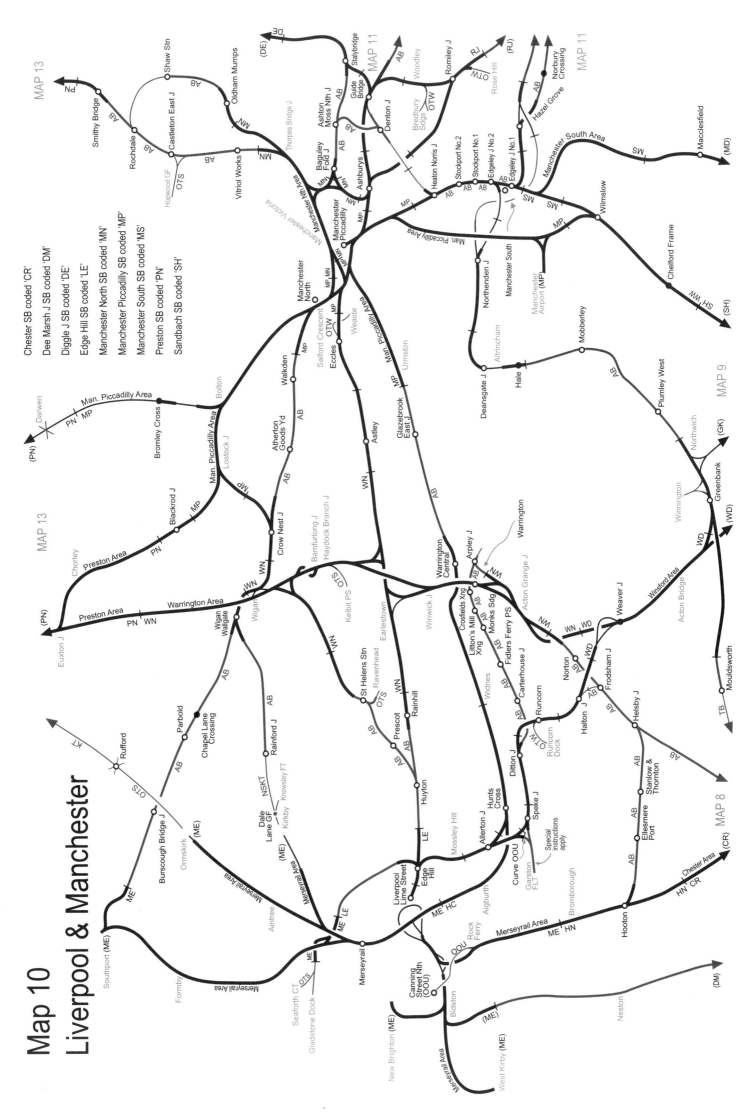

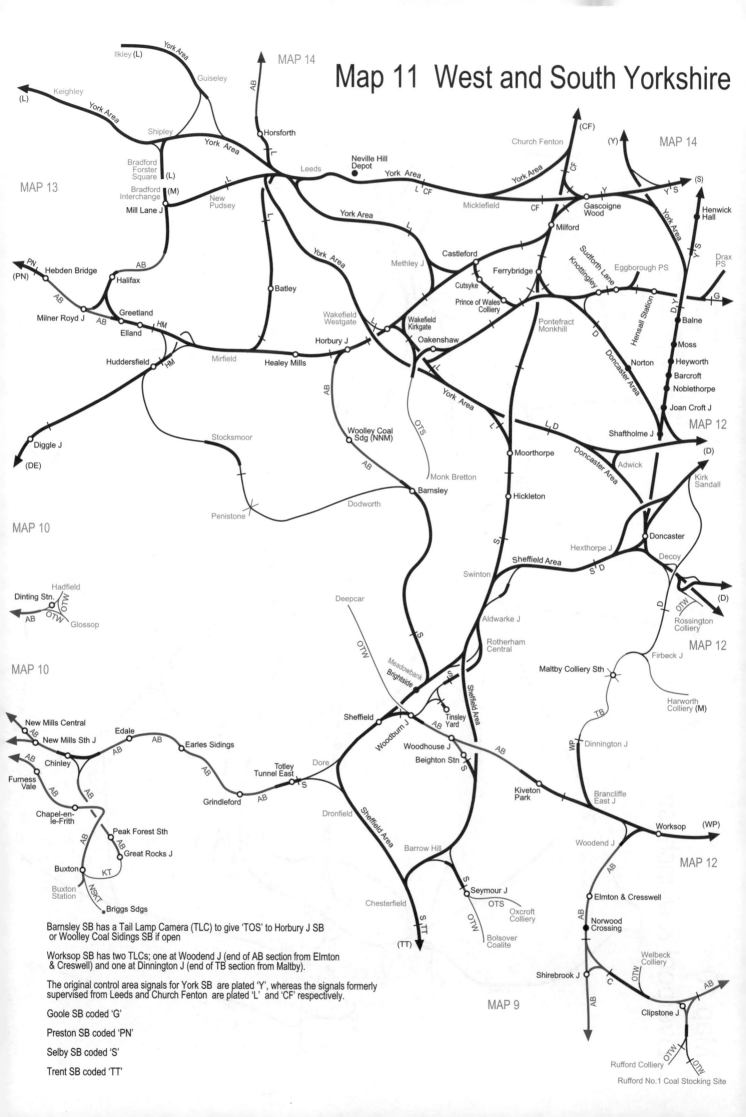

Map 11 West and South Yorkshire

Barnsley SB has a Tail Lamp Camera (TLC) to give 'TOS' to Horbury J SB
or Woolley Coal Sidings SB if open

Worksop SB has two TLCs; one at Woodend J (end of AB section from Elmton
& Creswell) and one at Dinnington J (end of TB section from Maltby).

The original control area signals for York SB are plated 'Y', whereas the signals formerly
supervised from Leeds and Church Fenton are plated 'L' and 'CF' respectively.

Goole SB coded 'G'

Preston SB coded 'PN'

Selby SB coded 'S'

Trent SB coded 'TT'

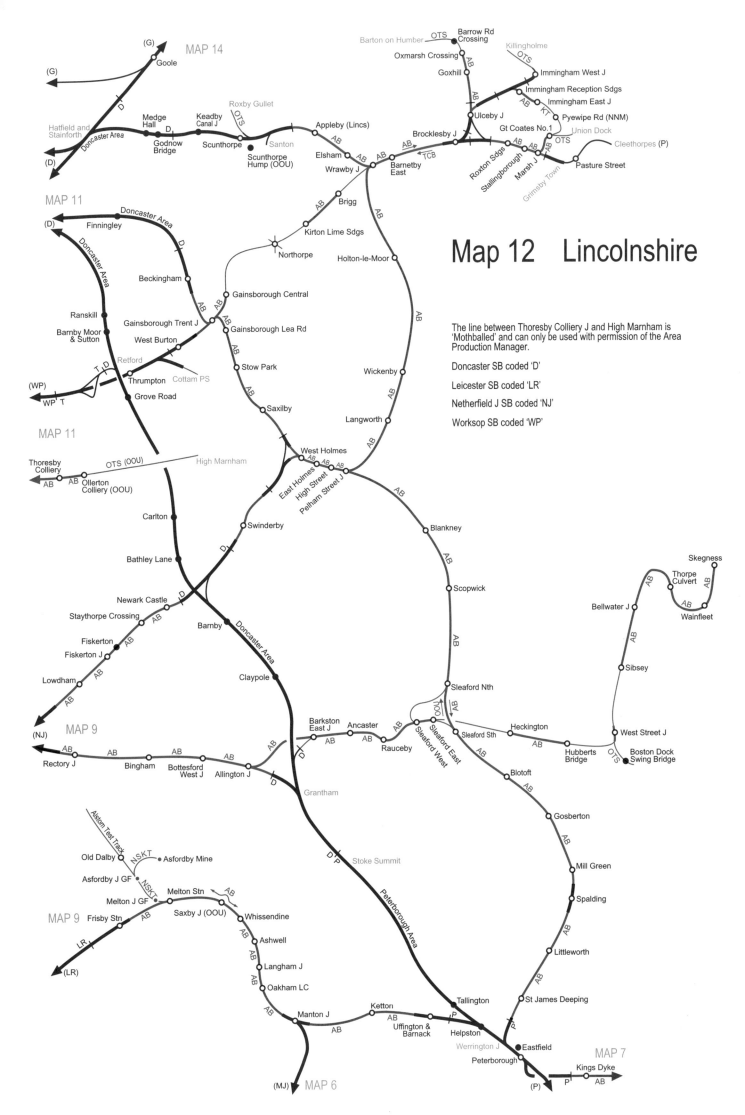

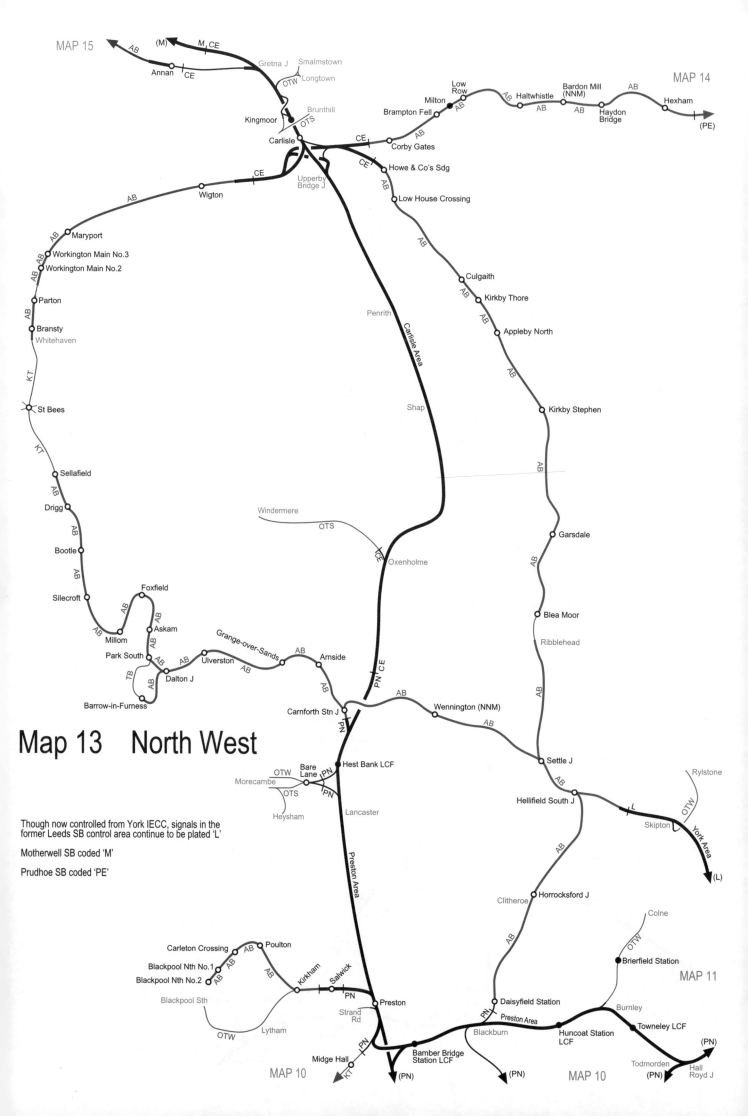

MAP 15

MAP 14

(M)

M, CE

AB

Annan

CE

Gretna J

Smalmstown

OTW

Longtown

Low
Row

Milton

Bardon Mill
(NNM)

Kingmoor

Brunthill

OTS

Brampton Fell

AB

Haltwhistle

AB

AB

Haydon
Bridge

Hexham

AB

Carlisle

Corby Gates

AB

(PE)

CE

Upperby
Bridge J

CE

Howe & Co's Sdg

CE

Wigton

AB

AB

Low House Crossing

AB

Maryport

AB

Culgaith

AB

Workington Main No.3

AB

Kirkby Thore

AB

Workington Main No.2

Penrith

AB

Appleby North

AB

Parton

AB

Bransty

Whitehaven

KT

Carlisle Area

Shap

AB

Kirkby Stephen

St Bees

KT

AB

Sellafield

AB

AB

Garsdale

Drigg

Windermere

OTS

AB

Bootle

AB

CE

Oxenholme

Blea Moor

Silecroft

Foxfield

Ribblehead

AB

AB

Askam

AB

AB

Millom

AB

Grange-over-Sands

AB

Park South

AB

AB

Arnside

Ulverston

AB

PN CE

AB

TB

AB

Dalton J

AB

Wennington (NNM)

AB

Barrow-in-Furness

Carnforth Stn J

AB

Settle J

PN

AB

Map 13   North West

Bare
Lane

PN

Hest Bank LCF

Hellifield South J

Rylstone

OTW

Morecambe

OTS

PN

Skipton

L

OTW

Heysham

Lancaster

York Area

Though now controlled from York IECC, signals in the
former Leeds SB control area continue to be plated 'L'

Motherwell SB coded 'M'

Preston Area

(L)

Prudhoe SB coded 'PE'

AB

Horrocksford J

Clitheroe

Colne

OTW

Carleton Crossing

AB

Poulton

Brierfield Station

Blackpool Nth No.1

AB

AB

Kirkham

Salwick

MAP 11

Blackpool Nth No.2

AB

AB

PN

Daisyfield Station

Blackpool Sth

Preston

Burnley

Strand
Rd

Preston Area

Towneley LCF

OTW

Lytham

Blackburn

Huncoat Station
LCF

(PN)

PN

MAP 10

Midge Hall

KT

PN

Bamber Bridge
Station LCF

(PN)

(PN)

MAP 10

Todmorden

(PN)

Hall
Royd J

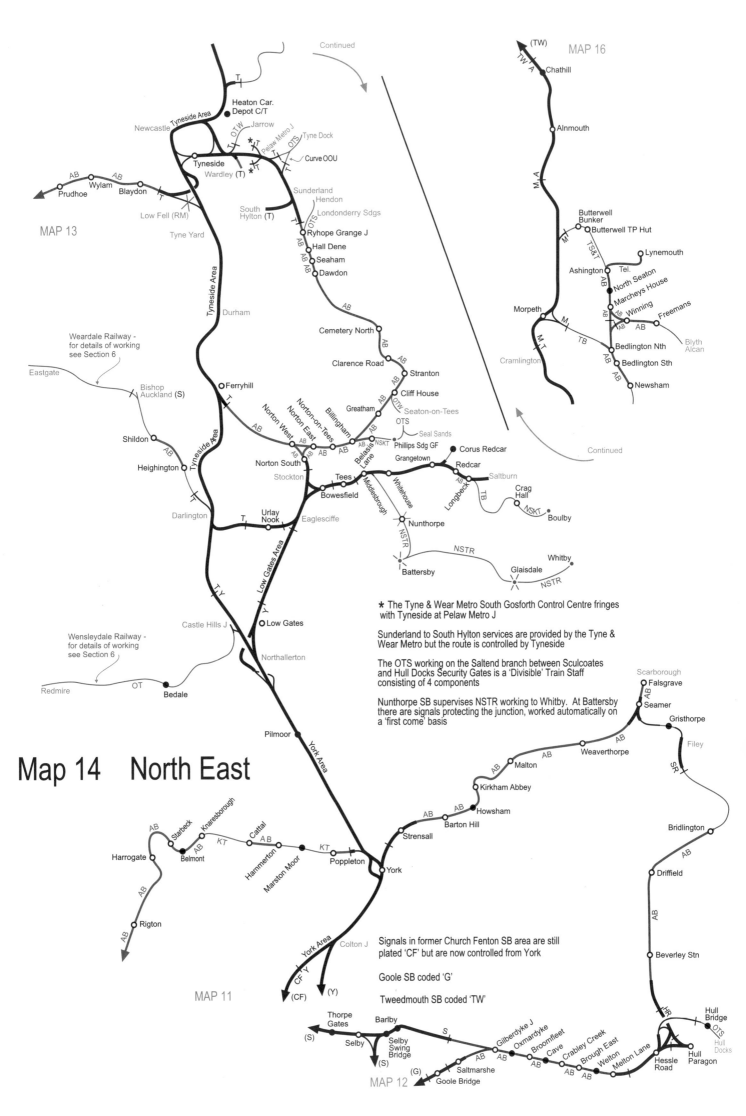

Continued

(TW)
Chathill
MAP 16

Heaton Car.
Depot C/T
Newcastle Tyneside Area
OTW Jarrow
Pelaw Metro J Tyne Dock
Tyneside Curve OOU
Wardley (T)
Prudhoe Wylam AB Blaydon
Low Fell (RM)
MAP 13 Tyne Yard

Alnmouth

Butterwell
Bunker
Butterwell TP Hut
Lynemouth
Ashington Tel.
North Seaton
Marcheys House
Morpeth Winning Freemans
Cramlington
Bedlington Nth
Blyth Alcan
Bedlington Sth
Newsham

Sunderland
Hendon
South Londonderry Sdgs
Hylton (T)
Ryhope Grange J
Hall Dene
AB Seaham
AB Dawdon

Weardale Railway -
for details of working
see Section 6

Eastgate

Bishop
Auckland (S)
Ferryhill

Durham

Cemetery North
AB
Clarence Road AB
Stranton
Cliff House
Greatham OTW Seaton-on-Tees
Billingham OTS
Norton-on-Tees Seal Sands
Norton East NSKT Phillips Sdg GF
Shildon Norton West AB Belasis Corus Redcar
Heighington AB Norton South Lane Grangetown Redcar
Stockton Whitehouse Saltburn
Tees Longbeck
Bowesfield Middlesbrough TB Crag
Hall
Urlay Nunthorpe NSKT
Darlington Nook Eaglescliffe Boulby
NSTR
NSTR
Battersby Whitby
Low Gates Area Glaisdale
NSTR

Wensleydale Railway -
for details of working
see Section 6
Castle Hills J
Low Gates

Redmire OT Northallerton
Bedale

Scarborough
Falsgrave
Seamer
Gristhorpe
Filey

Pilmoor

Nunthorpe SB supervises NSTR working to Whitby. At Battersby
there are signals protecting the junction, worked automatically on
a 'first come' basis

Weaverthorpe
Malton AB
Kirkham Abbey

Map 14 North East

York Area

Howsham
Barton Hill
Strensall
Harrogate Starbeck Knaresborough Cattal
AB Belmont KT AB
Hammerton Marston Moor KT Poppleton
York

Bridlington

AB

Driffield

Rigton AB

Beverley Stn

York Area
Colton J
CF Y

MAP 11

Signals in former Church Fenton SB area are still
plated 'CF' but are now controlled from York

Goole SB coded 'G'

Tweedmouth SB coded 'TW'

(CF) (Y)

Thorpe Barlby
Gates
Selby
Selby
Swing
Bridge
(S)

Hull
Bridge
OTS
Hull
Docks

Gilberdyke J
Oxmardyke
Broomfleet
Cave Crabley Creek
Brough East
Welton
Melton Lane
Hessle Hull
Road Paragon

Saltmarshe
Goole Bridge

MAP 12

(S)

(G)

* The Tyne & Wear Metro South Gosforth Control Centre fringes
with Tyneside at Pelaw Metro J

Sunderland to South Hylton services are provided by the Tyne &
Wear Metro but the route is controlled by Tyneside

The OTS working on the Saltend branch between Sculcoates
and Hull Docks Security Gates is a 'Divisible' Train Staff
consisting of 4 components

Map 15   West Scotland

Banavie SB controls RETB between Helensburgh Upper and Oban/Mallaig
with the exception of the section between Ft William J and Ft William
station controlled from Ft William J SB.
Fillan and Lower Crianlarich are TEPs for 'up' trains only.

Cowlairs, Motherwell, Yoker and most Paisley signal codes are two-letter
(e.g. 'PK' around Kilwinning and 'YC' around Craigendoran) according to
the interlocking but for clarity are shown as 'C', 'M', 'Y' and 'P'.

NSKT operates between Newton J (signal PA335) and Mauchline. An auxiliary
instrument is located at Annbank GF - used only by Killoch branch traffic.

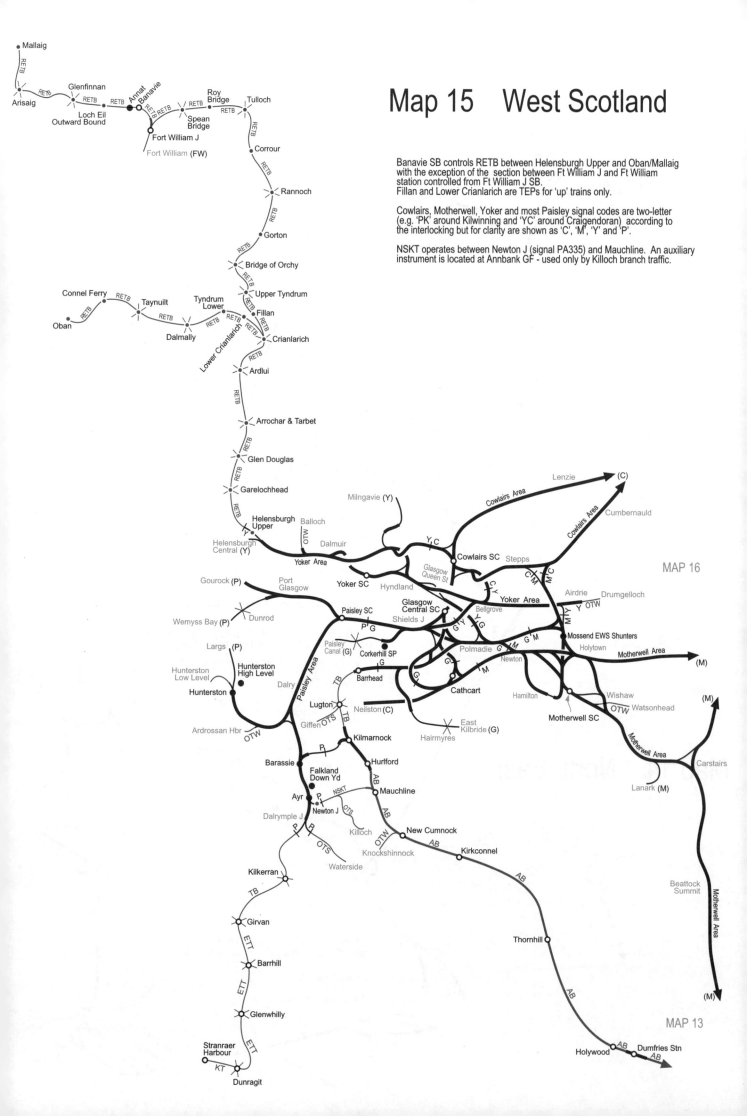

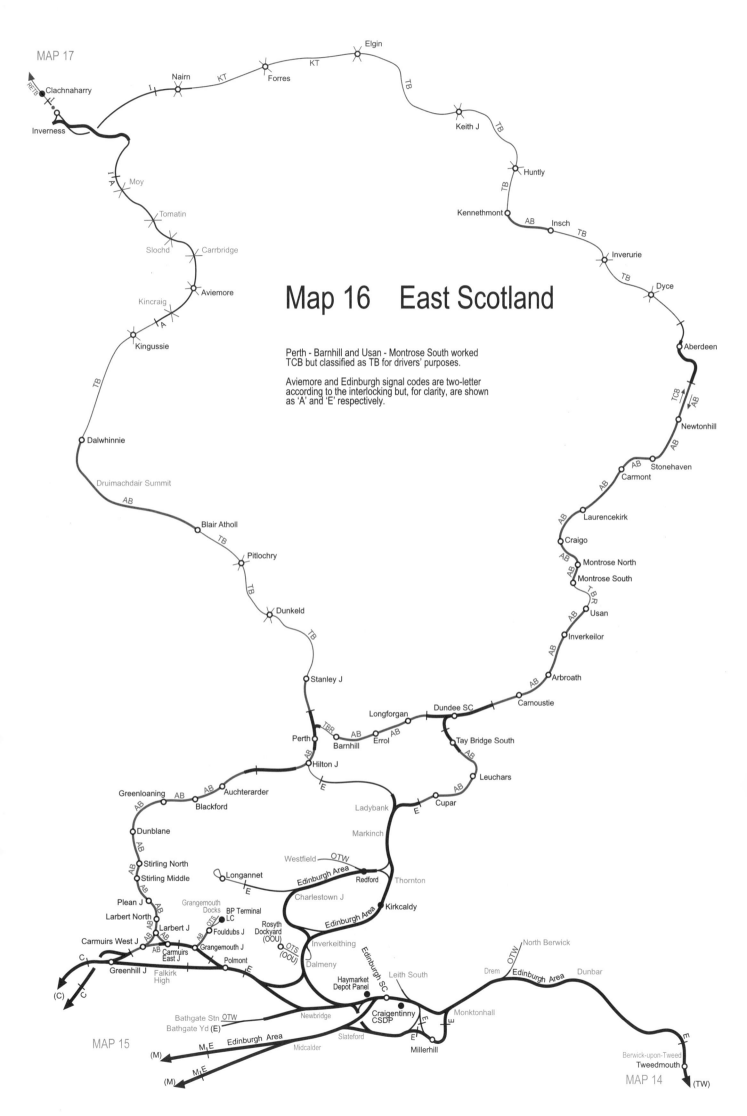

MAP 17

RETB
Clachnaharry

Inverness

Nairn
KT
Forres
KT
Elgin
TB

Keith J
TB

Huntly
TB

Kennethmont
AB
Insch
TB
Inverurie
TB
Dyce
AB

Aberdeen
TCB
AB

Newtonhill
AB
Stonehaven
AB
Carmont
AB
Laurencekirk
AB
Craigo
AB
Montrose North
AB
Montrose South
TBR
Usan
AB
Inverkeilor
AB
Arbroath
AB
Carnoustie

I
Moy
TA

Tomatin

Slochd
Carrbridge

Aviemore
Kincraig
A
Kingussie

TB

Dalwhinnie

Druimachdair Summit
AB

Blair Atholl
TB
Pitlochry
TB

Dunkeld
TB

Stanley J

Map 16   East Scotland

Perth - Barnhill and Usan - Montrose South worked
TCB but classified as TB for drivers' purposes.

Aviemore and Edinburgh signal codes are two-letter
according to the interlocking but, for clarity, are shown
as 'A' and 'E' respectively.

Perth
TBR
Barnhill
AB
Errol
AB
Longforgan
Dundee SC
Tay Bridge South
AB
Leuchars
AB
Cupar
E

Ladybank

Markinch

Westfield
OTW
Edinburgh Area
Redford
Thornton

AB
Hilton J
E
Auchterarder
Greenloaning
AB
Blackford
AB
Dunblane
AB
Stirling North
AB
Stirling Middle
AB
Plean J
AB
Larbert North
AB
Larbert J
AB
Carmuirs West J
Carmuirs East J
AB
Greenhill J
C
(C)
C
(C)
Falkirk
High

Longannet
E

Grangemouth
Docks
BP Terminal
LC
Fouldubs J
OTS
Grangemouth J
Polmont
E

Charlestown J
Edinburgh Area
Kirkcaldy

Rosyth
Dockyard
(OOU)
OTS
(OOU)
Inverkeithing
Dalmeny
Edinburgh SC
Leith South

Bathgate Stn OTW
Bathgate Yd (E)
Edinburgh Area
Newbridge
Craigentinny
CSDP
Haymarket
Depot Panel
Monktonhall

Slateford
Midcalder
E
Millerhill

North Berwick
OTW
Drem
Edinburgh Area
Dunbar
E

(M)
M E
(M)
M E

MAP 15

Berwick-upon-Tweed
Tweedmouth
MAP 14
(TW)
E

Map 17 North Scotland

All area controlled from Inverness SC

Halkirk is RETB Token Exchange Point for down trains only

Bower is RETB Token Exchange Point for up trains only

Thurso — RETB — Georgemas J — Bower — Wick
Georgemas J — RETB — Halkirk
Halkirk — RETB — Forsinard
Forsinard — RETB — Helmsdale
Helmsdale — RETB — Brora
Brora — RETB — Rogart
Rogart — RETB — Lairg
Lairg — RETB — Ardgay
Ardgay — RETB — Tain
Tain — RETB — Fearn
Fearn — RETB — Invergordon
Invergordon — RETB — Evanton
Evanton — RETB — Dingwall
Dingwall — RETB — Muir of Ord
Muir of Ord — RETB — Clunes
Clunes — RETB
Dingwall — RETB — Fodderty
Fodderty — RETB — Garve
Garve — RETB — Achnasheen
Achnasheen — RETB — Strathcarron
Strathcarron — RETB — Kyle of Lochalsh

NIR

KT between Londonderry and Castlerock worked over radio.

Coleraine to Portrush is ETT when Portrush open, OTS (actually an Annett's Key) when Portrush shut.

Antrim SB controls between Lisburn (exclusive) and Antrim (exclusive). Signals at Ballinderry are coded 'B' and at Crumlin 'C'. This line is now available for emergency diversions only. Antrim SB does not control Antrim station area.

Belfast Central SB coded 'CL'.

Coleraine SB coded 'CE'.

Portadown SB coded 'PD'.

IE

There is an unstaffed subsidiary instrument at Tara J. Trains for Kingscourt line take the Tara J - Kingscourt OTS from Navan as well as an ETS. Tara Mines is an ETS Block Post but the instrument is worked by traincrew.

Connolly control area boundaries shown as 'CY', for actual codes see Section 5 notes.

The Claremorris - Athenry Train Staff is kept at Claremorris. The line is out of use and is a 'dead-end'. The connection at Athenry was removed when the Galway Line Mini-CTC was commissioned in June 2003.

Athlone to Mullingar line is not in regular use but may be used by engineering traffic using 'Pilot Working'.

Roscrea to Ballybrophy normally worked as a dead-end branch from Roscrea. As such, the ETS is used as a one train staff from Roscrea and only put through the traincrew operated instrument at Ballybrophy when trains run to/from the main line. Connolly SB gives the 'release' to Ballybrophy North GF which works the points for main line connection.

Limerick J North - Limerick J South section worked by control levers.

Long section ETS
Arklow-Enniscorthy (E)
Castlerea-Claremorris (E)
Rathmore-Banteer (B)
(Long section normally operates as Millstreet is normally staffed as a Gate Box only)

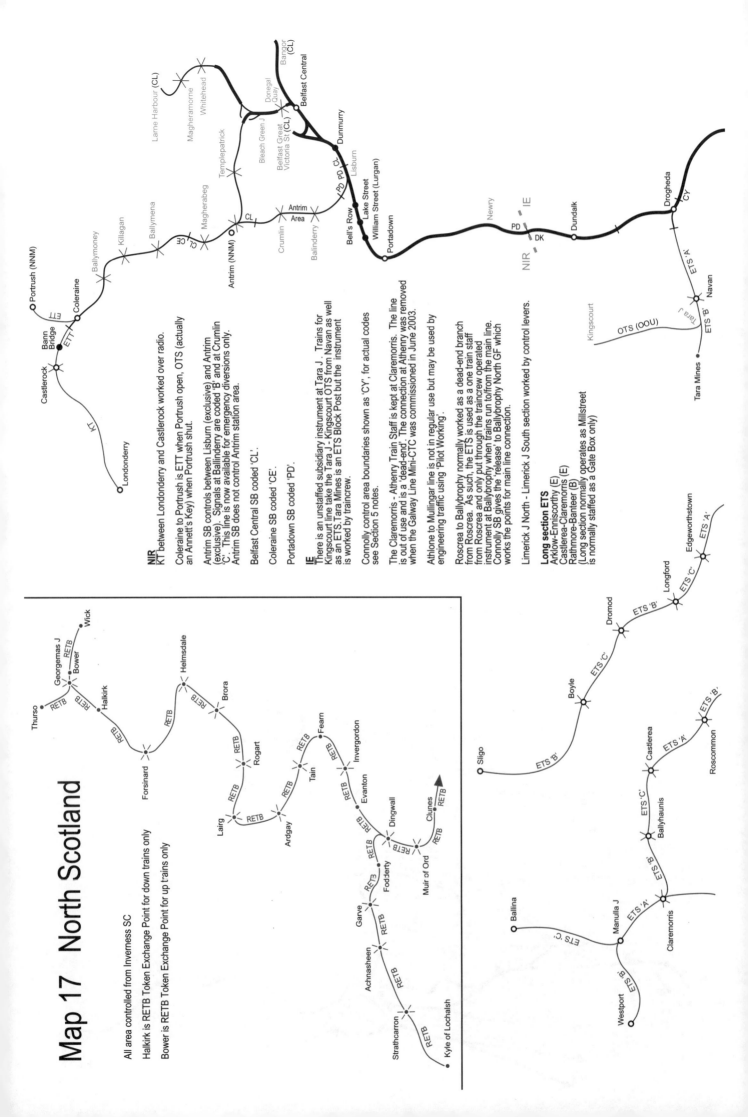

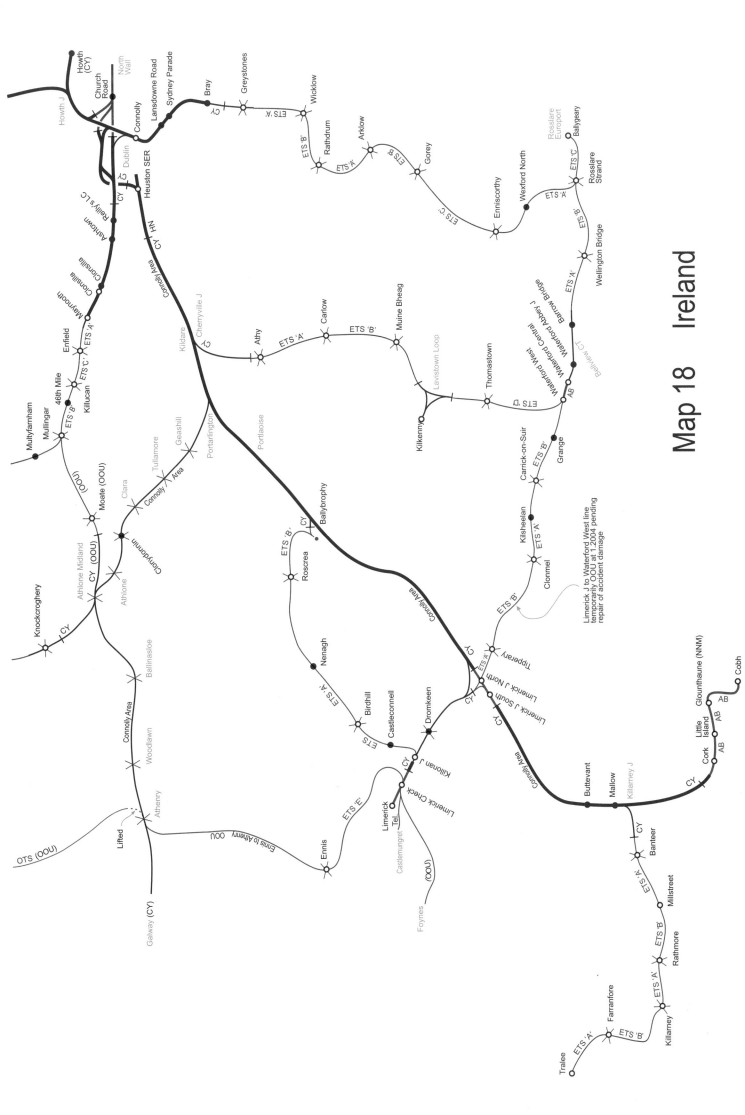

Map 18   Ireland

DIRECTORY SECTION THREE:
OTHER SYSTEMS IN GREAT BRITAIN

This section includes all those systems which are essentially separate from the main national railway system, and have full, or some element of, signalling provision. Only the briefest outline is given here of the signalling arrangements on the various systems and the reader is referred to other published material on these systems for full details.

Light Rail/Tram Systems:

CROYDON TRAMLINK

Trams on the 17½ mile, standard gauge system linking Wimbledon with New Addington, Elmers End and Beckenham Junction all via Croydon obtain power from overhead catenary (return is via running rails) at 750v DC. Visual signals (stop/proceed, automatically operated) are only used to guard junctions (including entry to single-line sections), road crossings and interlaced sections (of which there are two:- Mitcham station and west of Church Street in Croydon). Of the 50 pairs of points outside of the Therapia Lane depot, only nine are normally facing and therefore motored. These nine are fitted with indicators to allow drivers to check the computer-controlled route. The remainder are spring operated and drivers carry a lever to set them in an emergency. Blue section lights (similar to a SPAD, signal passed at danger signal) are being installed at the entry to single line sections which will illuminate if a tram incorrectly enters an already occupied section. A control room is situated at the Therapia Lane depot.

DOCKLANDS LIGHT RAILWAY

The 16¼ mile, standard gauge, 3rd rail 750v DC system operates a double-track network of lines radiating from Poplar/Canary Wharf in East London. There are no signals on the running lines of this system, which is operated by driverless trains with 'SELTRAC' 'moving block' train control, installed since 1994 in lieu of the original automatic train control equipment. The two depots at Poplar and Beckton have 2-aspect colour light signals (red/green) controlling internal movements and operated from NX panels. The system is supervised from the 'NCC' (New Control Centre) at Poplar depot where the Poplar NX panel is also situated. In normal circumstances, the Beckton NX panel is remotely controlled from a VDU screen at the NCC.

GLASGOW UNDERGROUND

The 6½ mile, 4 foot gauge system beneath Glasgow's city centre known as 'The Subway' is fully signalled with colour light signals. Train detection is through track circuits. The 'controlled area' covering the depot at Broomloan and the adjacent three stations is normally controlled by vital processor interlocking (VPI) and this is the only part of the system in which routes can be set. The 'automatic area' covers the rest of the system (12 stations) and is controlled by relay lockings at each station. The operator interface at Broomloan Depot control room comprises a system of VDU workstations and servers with the system mimic diagram displayed on rear projection screens. A telemetry system is used to bring status information and alarms back to the control room and transmit control signals in the opposite direction.

(Broomloan) Control Centre	1/9B	**		1980	VDUs	1996	-	E

MANCHESTER METROLINK

The 45½ mile, standard gauge system operates in two modes, 'Segregated Mode' with 2-position colour-light signals and TCB working away from the streets, and 'Street Running Mode' with stop/proceed traffic light signals and line of sight driving on the 'on road' sections. The whole system (except south of Timperley) is controlled from the Queens Road Operations and Management Centre. The signals on the plain line sections on the segregated areas are controlled via electronic interlockings. In the case of Cornbrook Junction, where the Eccles line leaves the Altrincham Line, the interlocking is a GRS Vital Processor Interlocking, whilst other points and junctions within the segregated areas are controlled via SSI located at Queens Road. Points and junctions 'on street' are locally controlled by the passage of trams via the on board Vehicle Recognition System, which also initiates requests for traffic light sequences. Point detection and locking are confirmed to the driver by fibre optic point position indicators. Key junctions at GMex and Piccadilly Undercroft although classified as 'Street Running' are SSI interlocked and controlled. The section between Timperley and Altrincham is owned by Network Rail and controlled by Deansgate Junction box (TCB Queens Road-Deansgate Junction), although normally working automatically, with the Deansgate Junction signalman only concerned with working the level crossings for the trams. There are connections between Metrolink and Network Rail at Altrincham and Manchester Victoria, but these are only usable under possession arrangements.

Queens Road OMC		-	-	1991	VDUs etc.	1991/9	-	SSI/E
(OMC re-equipped 1999)								
Hagside (RR)	4/47A	BR(LMR) N/S		1980	-	-	-	-

(Abolished 1991 when BR services ceased, re-opened as emergency Gate Box and Relay Room only when Metrolink services commenced).

MIDLAND METRO

The 12¾ mile, standard gauge system links Birmingham Snow Hill with Wolverhampton St George's using ex-GWR route plus a little over a mile of highway travel at the Wolverhampton end. The system is double track other than a short section on the approach to the

Birmingham, Snow Hill terminus. Signalling equipment is supplied by Ansaldo. The system is operated on the tramway 'Line of Sight' driving principle throughout. This is supplemented over the single line section by interlocking and tram signals to ensure that only one tram can be in the single line section at a time. All points on the main line and in the depot are automatically operated, except for three sets on the approach to the Wolverhampton terminus. Two of these are sprung to lie for the normal facing routes after being trailed through. The third is 'flip-flop' as it is normally only used in the trailing direction. Points are detected and tramway type point indicators are provided to confirm to drivers that the point blades are correctly set. Tram positions on the network are detected by track circuits and indicated on displays in the control room which is located in the depot at Wednesbury. Stop/Proceed tram signals are provided at road junctions and crossings linked to 'demand' and 'clear' tram detection loops in the track. Tramway control equipment for the junctions is linked to the highway traffic signal control equipment to ensure correct traffic operating sequences.

SOUTH YORKSHIRE SUPERTRAM
The 18 mile, standard gauge system comprises two routes operating across the city of Sheffield. Overall control of the system is aided by a simple signalling supervisory control and data acquisition (SCADA) computer system, with a video display in the Central Control room at Nunnery Sidings. The on-board computer equipment keeps Central Control aware of each tram's progress on the network. The whole system is worked on tramway 'driven on sight' principles, excepting that there are white light signals (automatically operated) which control the entry to single line sections (identical signals are used for road traffic purposes for the trams, at signalled road junctions). Computer equipment on board the tram, with vehicle identification loops between the rails, identifies the tram to special trackside detectors so as to give it priority through junctions. Centralised urban traffic control is the only overriding authority.

TYNE & WEAR METRO
The 45½ mile, standard gauge system north and south of the Tyne uses magnetic track circuits to operate the colour light signalling. The signals are generally 3-aspect in tunnels and 2-aspect on open line. A train identification and control system carries information from on-board transponders to track-level equipment which operates the points and station information systems. Control for the system is based at South Gosforth Control Centre (opened 1980). The Tyne and Wear Metro uses a train-stop system based on the Indusi signalling system used by German and Austrian national railways. The 8¾ mile section between Pelaw and Sunderland is signalled by Network Rail; it involves dual running with 'heavy rail' passenger/freight trains, and thus features additional train protection. The Sunderland-South Hylton section is also signalled by Network Rail, though used only by Metro trains.

Military Railway Network:

BICESTER MILITARY RAILWAY
The single line to Arncott is worked as OEIS using mobile telephones. The two boxes are still in place but only used as GFs for the changing of points. The link with Network Rail is unsignalled via exchange sidings.

Signal Boxes in Use

Graven Hill (Cabin A)	-	MoD	1979	Westinghouse A3	1979	12	T
Arncott (Cabin B)	-	MoD	1979	Westinghouse A3	1979	16	T

Isle of Man Operations:

ISLE OF MAN STEAM RAILWAY
Method of Working – Single line Douglas to Port Erin (15¼ miles, 3 foot gauge) with crossing places at Ballasalla (used daily during operating season) and Port Soderick, Santon, Castletown, and Colby (used as required). The single line working is effected by Radio with all arrivals and departures reported. The Staffs are:- Douglas – Ballasalla (divisible into two or three when Port Soderick and/or Santon loops in use), Ballasalla – Castletown, and Castletown – Port Erin (divisible into two when Colby loop in use). There are colour light signals at Douglas station but no visual signals at any other location on the line. Before the commencement of the 2004 operating season, all level crossings will be automated and operated by train treadles.

Signal Boxes in use

Douglas	1/23B	**	c1980	Panel	c1980	-	-

(Panel in SM's office works signals at Douglas)

Other Boxes on site – Douglas (see Section 7(3)).

MANX ELECTRIC RAILWAY / SNAEFELL MOUNTAIN RAILWAY
Method of Working – Double track (22 miles, 3 foot gauge), worked on tramway 'running on sight' principles. Any car stopping at an irregular place must be protected by flags placed in rear of it. All cars and staffed stations are in radio contact. In bad weather (in practice primarily on the Bungalow - Summit section) Radio 'Block' working is put into effect between Station Masters. When single line working is necessary, Staff & Ticket working is brought into use. There are three staff sections Douglas – Garwick – Dhoon Quarry – Ramsey, but there are several crossovers within each section and the single line working may be for any part of the section. There are no signals.

DIRECTORY SECTIONS FOUR AND FIVE: NORTHERN IRELAND RAILWAYS and IARNROD EIREANN BOXES

The Irish railways had a similar signalling history to the railways of Great Britain, except that (as noted in the introductory review) the poor financial situation of most of the Irish companies meant that the introduction of interlocking and block working was postponed to a later period on average. Hence there are very few 1870s and 1880s boxes, but a larger number of boxes built in the early 1890s, after the 1889 Act made interlocking compulsory. A large number of signal boxes were burnt in the civil war in the early 1920s and this required the building of many replacement boxes in the mid-'20s. However in cases where the burnt box was of brick-to-floor construction, a new top was generally built on the old brick base. In most such cases the old frame was also retained.

Another particular feature of the signal box scene in Ireland is that most of the remaining older mechanical boxes have been re-windowed in recent years, considerably altering their looks. In addition, most Irish signal boxes do not have external nameboards. Many signal boxes in Ireland were built to the standard designs of the British signalling contractors, with Railway Signal Co. boxes particularly common. However the major Irish companies all evolved signal box designs of their own latterly. The 1997 Edition of this Directory has illustrations of the principal types.

Again, most lever frames in Ireland were purchased from the British signalling contractors, with the Railway Signal Co. frames most common. The GS&W, however, in later years and the GS in succession, made their own frames in-house to a simple tappet design, referred to here as 'GS&W Tappet'. This frame shows affinity with the RSCo. Tappet design, possibly influenced by the GS&W's Signal Superintendent, J. Nicolson, who had worked with the Railway Signal Company.

As on BR, the number of boxes in Ireland reduced dramatically with line closures in the 1950s & '60s. However, there was little major signalling modernisation on the remaining lines of CIE (as it then was), until the first stage of the Connolly 'CTC' scheme on the Cork line was effected in 1976. [Although always referred to as 'CTC' in Ireland, the Connolly scheme is simply a TCB/MAS power box scheme on the same basis as contemporary BR schemes]. This has been extended subsequently to cover the whole line to Cork, the branches to Limerick and Galway, the DSER line as far as Greystones, and the GNRI line as far as Drogheda. Although originally effected with a panel, the whole Connolly control area is now on VDU operation. In consequence of the Connolly schemes, which have taken over almost all of the double lines on IE, there are now only four sections of Absolute Block working left on IE (all using Harper's blocks which were an established instrument with most Irish companies). CTC operation is accompanied by the Continuous Automatic Warning System (CAWS) providing in-cab signalling information (and ATP for DART units).

In contrast, traditional methods remain more entrenched on IE single line routes with the (Miniature) Electric Train Staff (ETS) in widespread use. Long-section working is provided for in three cases. (Large ETS instruments still exist on the Glounthaune to Midleton section of the Youghal branch, and at Roscrea, but are non-functional and are unlikely to ever be used again). A special feature of IE single line working is that both lines at crossing stations are usually reversibly signalled (a facility which is regularly used in practice). The GSR started this practice in the 1920s, after the Irish railways were freed from the attentions of the Railway Inspectorate in London, which had always opposed this arrangement.

Traditional methods of working are, however, set to diminish over the coming years. Following the replacement of mechanical signalling and ETS working on the Galway line west of Athlone in 2003, the other 'Mini-CTC' schemes for the Waterford, Tralee and Sligo lines are due to be completed in 2004. Further schemes are envisaged for the Westport and Rosslare lines, when these are completed. 'Mini-CTC' features SSI and colour-light signals, but without CAWS.

Due to concerns over the safe operation of ageing mechanical equipment, most traditional boxes have had the tappet locking of the frame and the ETS instruments refurbished. In some cases, total replacement of frames and ETS instruments has occurred with reconditioned similar equipment, and this process is continuing at the time of writing.

On Northern Ireland Railways (NIR), an even larger proportion of the boxes disappeared in the 1950s and '60s with line closures. Much of the remaining system has since been resignalled in the 1980s and '90s and mechanical signalling is now on the verge of extinction, being restricted to two boxes (Castlerock and the usually-switched-out Portrush). The rest of the system is controlled from panels in the station buildings at Portadown, Belfast Central, and Londonderry, plus panels in former mechanical boxes at Coleraine and Antrim. Absolute block working became extinct in 1996 but there are still two single line sections worked by Tyer's Tablet, and one by Key Token. In contrast to south of the border BR type AWS is used on NIR in colour-light areas.

SECTION FOUR: NORTHERN IRELAND RAILWAYS

Box Name	Quail Map	Box:- Type	Date	Frame/Equipment:- Design	Date	No. of Levers	Lock'g	Notes
Antrim (NNM)	6/19C	NIR	c1970	OCS panel (ML)	1978	-	E	1
Bann Bridge (B)	6/20A	Bridge Hut	1924	nk	1924	nk	nk	2
Belfast Central	6/18A	**	1976	NX panel/VDU etc	1988/2000	-	E	3
Bell's Row (G)	6/17D	NIR	1996	Switches	1996	-	E	
Castlerock	6/20A	NIR	c1970	RSCo Tappet 4"	2h c1970	10	T	
Coleraine	6/19F	NCC	c1923	NX panel (Whse)	1989	-	E	4
Dunmurry (G,E)	6/18A	NIR Flat roof	1981	OCS EC panel switches	1981	-	E	5
Lake Street (G)	6/17D	NIR Flat roof	1981	Switches	1996	-	E	
Londonderry	6/20B	**	1980	NX panel (Whse)	1980	-	E	6
Portadown	6/17D	**	(1970)	NX panel (Whse)	1996	-	E	6,7
Portrush (NNM)	6/19F	NCC	nk	RSCo Tappet 4"	nk	45	T	8
William Street (G) [Lurgan]	6/17D	NIR Flat roof	1981	Switches	1996	-	E	

Notes

1   OCS Panel 4/1/1978, controls Antrim-Lisburn line (both exclusive) with remote relay interlockings at Ballinderry and Crumlin. This line is not in regular use (last regular train 29/6/2003, but can be used for emergency working). The box also had an NX panel, but the area controlled by this was transferred to Belfast Central.
2   Released from Coleraine, interlocked with Tablet.
3   In 1994 the panel was extended to control the Larne line, formerly controlled by York Road, including remote interlockings at York Road, Bleach Green Junction, Carrickfergus, Whitehead, Magheramorne Loop and Larne. All interlockings relay locking. Control area further extended 2/11/2000 to control re-opened Bleach Green-Antrim section. This section features VDU, tracker ball and keyboard control. Control area again extended 18/6/2001 when area formerly controlled by Antrim NX panel transferred to control by Central.
4   In 1994 area of control extended to Ballymena, with remote interlockings (relay) at Killagan, Ballymena, and Ballymoney.
5   Remote interlocking normally controlled by Belfast Central. Panel works crossover, which is only used in emergency. Normally functions as a gate box only, with switches for signals.
6   In room in station building.
7   New panel BIU 13/10/1996 taking over Portadown station area, control area extended 17/11/1996 when Poyntzpass SB abolished (new remote interlockings, relay locking, at Poyntzpass and Newry, Newry SB abolished 2/9/1996). Control area further extended 24/11/1996 when Lisburn abolished and control of Lisburn interlocking taken over by Portadown (1984 interlocking, relay locking). Final extension 1 – 8/12/1996 when Lurgan area put on new panel (with new interlockings, relay locking, at Lake Street and Bell's Row). Lake Street and Bell's Row interlockings rebuilt after damage on 6/7/1997.
8   Only used when specials run, Coleraine – Portrush normally OTS, but ETT used when Portrush switched-in.

SECTION FIVE: IARNROD EIREANN

Box Name	Quail Map	Box:- Type	Date	Frame/Equipment:- Design	Date	No. of Levers	Lock'g	Notes
Arklow	6/15D	DWW	1893	McK&H u1886 Pat 5"	1893	16	R.T.	1
Ashtown (G)	6/13A	**	2000	Fortress Key Switches	2000	-	E	2,3
Athy	6/5B	GS&W Hip	c1923	GS&W Tappet	c1923	30	T	
Ballina	6/11F	CIE flat roof	1977	OCS Panel (CIE)	1977	-	E	
Ballygeary	6/8C	Portakabin	1997	Outside gf	1997	6	T	4
Ballyhaunis	6/11B	N/S +	nk	RSCo Tappet	nk	17	T	5,6
Banteer	6/8F	GS&W Hip +	c1923	GS&W Tappet	c1923	30	T	5
Barrow Bridge (B)	6/8A	Overhead	1906	u Knee (S&F)	1906	6+3	T	7
Birdhill	6/6C	GS&W Hip +	c1923	GS&W Tappet/OCS pnl	c1923/82	24	T/E	5,8
Boyle	6/14C	RSCo [MGW] +	1894	RSCo Tappet	1894	26	T	5
Bray (ECP,EBC)	6/15B	GS&W Hip	1927	ECP, EBC	1983	-	E	
Buttevant (G)	6/4C	CIE flat roof	1958	GS&W Tappet	1958	1R	-	9
Carlow	6/5C	GS&W Hip	1920s-	GS&W Tappet	1920s	32	T	10
Carrick-on-Suir	6/7C	GS&W Hip	1924-	GS&W Tappet recon.	2003	15	T	11
Castleconnell (G)	6/6C	GS&W Hip	c1924	None	-	-	-	12
Castlerea	6/11A	RSCo [MGW] +	1901	RSCo Tappet	1901	26	T	5
Church Road (NBP)	6/1	GS&W Hip	1920s	GS&W Tappet	1920s	46	T	13
Claremorris	6/11B	GS Hipped	1941	GS&W Tappet	1941	66	T	
Clonmel	6/7B	GS&W Hip	c1923-	GS&W Tappet	c1923	34R	T	14
Clonsilla (G)	6/13A	MGW Gabled	1924-	RSCo Tappet	1889	32	T	15
Clonsilla	6/13A	PR	2000	VDU etc.	2000	-	SSI	15
Clonydonnin (ECP)	6/9F	CIE flat roof	1974	ECP	1984	-	E	16
Cobh	6/5A	CIE flat roof	1959	RSCo-GNI/ OCS panel	1959/79	30	T/E	17
Connolly	6/1	PB	1976E	VDUs etc.	1999/2000	-	E/SSI	18
Cork	6/4D	GS&W Hip +	1932	u GS&W Tappet/pnl	1932/87	38R	T/E	5,19
Drogheda	6/16C	CIE flat roof	1978E	Whse ECP	1994	-	SSI	20
				VDU etc.	1997	-	E+SSI	

SECTION FIVE: IARNROD EIREANN

Box Name	Quail Map	Box:- Type	Date	Frame/Equipment:- Design	Date	No. of Levers	Lock'g	Notes
Dromkeen (G)	6/6E	Portakabin	c2003	nk	c2003	-	nk	
Dromod	6/14B	MGW Gabled	1924	N/S	1924	24	T	21
Dundalk	6/17B	**	(2002)	VDU etc. 2h	2002	-	SSI	22
Edgeworthstown	6/14A	MGW Gabled	1924	RSCo Tappet	1924	22	T	
Enfield	6/13C	CIE Hipped	c1950	GS&W Tappet	c1950	32	T	
Ennis	6/12B	RSCo [W&L] +	c1894	RSCo Tappet	1894	13	T	23
Enniscorthy	6/15E	DSE Gabled	1923	McK&H 1886 Pat 4"	1888	18	R.T	24
Farranfore	6/9D	RSCo [GS&W]+	1885	RSCo Tappet	u1885	36	T	5
46th Mile (G)	6/13D	GS&W Hip	1929	Outside gf	u1977	4	T	25
Foynes (OOU)	6/8C	**	nk	None	-	-	-	
Glounthaune (NNM)	6/4E	**	1931	GS&W Tappet	1931	20	T	26
Gorey	6/15E	DWW	1891	McK&H 1886 Pat 5"	1891	18	R.T	27
Grange (G)	6/7D	GS&W Hip	c1923	GS&W Tappet	c1923	3R	T	28
Greystones	6/15B	GS&W Hip +	1926	VDU etc.	1998	-	SSI	5,29
Heuston SER	6/2	N/S	2002	VDU etc.	2002	-	SSI	30
Howth (ECP)	6/16A	GNRI 3a	1892	McK&H 1886 Pat 4"/ECP	1892/1982	15	T/E	31
Kilkenny	6/5E	CIE	1979	OCS Panel	1979	-	E	32
Killarney	6/9B	S&F5 [GS&W]+	1880s	RSCo Tappet 4½"	nk	36	T	5
Killonan Junction	6/6C	RSCo [W&L] +	nk	GS&W Tappet/Panel	nk/1997	3R	T/E	33
Killucan	6/13C	MGW 'RSCo' +	1889	GS&W Tappet	nk	24	T	5,34
Kilsheelan (G)	6/7C	GS&W Hip	c1923-	RSCo Tappet	c1892	7R	T	35
Knockcroghery	6/10F	RSCo [MGW] +	1904	Alsthom Panel	2000	-	SSI	5
Lansdowne Road (EBC)	6/15A	DWW Hipped	u1871	EBC	1984	-	E	36
Limerick	6/6D	CIE N/S	u1974-	IFS Panel	1974	-	E	37
Limerick Check	6/6D	GS&W Gabled	1910	RSCo Tappet recon.	2003	50	T	38
Limerick Junction North	6/4A	CIE N/S	c1967-	GS&W Tappet/ECP	c1922/87	54	T/E	39
Limerick Junction South	6/4A	GS&W N/S	nk	GS&W Tappet	nk	45	T	40
Little Island	6/4E	GS&W Hip +	c1924	GS&W Tappet/OCS pnl	c1924/u75	3R	T/E	5,41
Longford	6/14A	RSCo [MGW] +	1893	RSCo Tappet	1893	30	T	5
Mallow (ECP)	6/4C	RSCo/GS&W	1889	ECP	1989	-	E	44
Manulla Junction	6/11C	Portakabin	1988	IFS Panel	1988	-	E	42
Maynooth	6/13B	**	2000	VDU etc.	2000	-	SSI	43
Millstreet	6/9A	GS&W Hip +	1920s	GS&W Tappet	1920s	18	T	5,60
Moate (OOU)	6/13E	RSCo [MGW] +	1890	RSCo Tappet	1890	24	T	5,45
Muine Bheag	6/5D	GS&W Hip	1920s	GS&W Tappet	1920s	18	T	
Mullingar	6/13D	MGW Gabled	1920	RSCo Tappet	1920	65	T	46
Multyfarnham (G)	6/13F	MGW Gabled	1923-	McK&H 1886 Pat 4" 2h	u1924	30	R.T	47
Navan	6/20C	GNRI 3a +	c1892	McK&H 1886 Pat 4"	c1892	25	R.T	5
Nenagh (NBP)	6/6B	GS&W Hip	c1923	u GS&W Tappet	nk	3R	T	48
Rathdrum	6/15C	DWW	1888	McK&H u1886 Pat 4"	1888	13	R.T	
Rathmore	6/9A	CIE Hipped	nk	GS&W Tappet	nk	24	T	
Reilly's LC (G)	6/13A	Container	1991	Fortress Key Switches	1991	-	E	3
Roscommon	6/10F	MGW 'RSCo'	1921	RSCo Tappet	u1929	34	T	34,49
Roscrea	6/6A	RSCo/GS&W	nk	RSCo Tappet	nk	24	T	
Rosslare Strand	6/8B	RSCo/GS&W	1910	RSCo Tap 4½"/IFS pnl	1910/nk	26	T/E	50
Sligo	6/14E	MGW Gabled +	1923-	RSCo Tappet	1885	28	T	5,51
Sydney Parade (EBC)	6/15A	DWW Hipped	u1871	EBC	1984	-	E	52
Thomastown	6/5E	GS&W Hip	1920s	RSCo Tappet	1920s	17	T	
Tipperary	6/7A	RSCo [W&L]	1892	RSCo Tappet	1892	21	T	5,53
Tralee	6/9D	GS flat roof	1935	GS&W Tappet	1935	50	T	
Waterford Abbey Junction (NBP,G)	6/7D	GS&W Hip	c1923	GS&W Tappet	c1923	6R	T	54
Waterford Central	6/7D	GS&W Hip	1923-	GS&W Tappet/VDU etc.	1923/95	64	T/SSI	55
Waterford West	6/7D	GS&W Hip	1923	GS&W Tappet	1923	48	T	
Wellington Bridge	6/8A	GS&W Hip	1923-	RSCo Tappet 4½"	1906	20	T	5,56
Westport	6/11D	RSCo [MGW] +	c1896	RSCo Tappet	c1896	30	T	57
Wexford (North) (NBP)	6/15F	McK&H 3 [DWW]	1894	McK&H nk	1894	3R	T	58
Wicklow	6/15C	DWW	1884	GS&W Tappet	1927	22	T	59

SECTION FIVE: IARNROD EIREANN

Notes

1 Also one switch for signal.

2 In new station building, built 2000, replacing a similar arrangement with a smaller 1991 structure, which was demolished.

3 Fortress Keys are normally kept in the gates. When a train is due the gateman removes the keys and inserts them in switches in the building, which clears the signals.

4 SB (GS&W Hip, 1936) destroyed by fire night of 22 – 23/12/1996. Portakabin for Signalman's accommodation and ETS, and outdoor 6-lever GF moved from Waterford, provided 15/4/1997 to replace cabin.

5 Box re-windowed in 1980s/1990s.

6 Box existed by 1891; box as it is latterly is rebuilt around original timber box.

7 Bridge released by Waterford Central.

8 Panel (29/8/1982) controls Kilmastulla Sidings.

9 One lever only of frame remains, for gate locks.

10 New top on old brick base of unknown design.

11 New top on 1892 RSCo base. New 15-lever frame made up of reconditioned parts from Athenry frame installed 11/2003 (not yet connected up).

12 Box used only as accommodation for crossing keeper. Signals worked off gates.

13 Computer terminal for interface with Connolly.

14 New top c1923 on old brick base of unknown design. Frame reduced 55 to 34 c1985. Frame being replaced 12/2003 by 28-lever new frame made up of reconditioned parts from Athenry.

15 Old cabin has a new top on 1889 RSCo base. Frame extended 26 to 32 c1930. Now only 2 levers in use for gates control. Gate wheel operated gates. Former panel (17/2/1991) still in cabin but no longer functional. Westinghouse SSI with VDU, tracker ball and keyboard control, provided in new Interlocking building opposite old cabin at Clonsilla, 4/12/2000, in connection with new signalling and doubling of Clonsilla - Maynooth section. Old cabin functions as gatebox to new SSI. It had been intended that this arrangement would be temporary, and the old cabin and gates would be replaced by full barriers and CCTV, but this plan has not been carried through to date.

16 Box was a BP 1974 - 1984.

17 Panel (26/8/1979) controls Marino Point, but points have been disconnected since closure of the factory.

18 CONNOLLY — Building constructed 1976 for Main Line CTC original section (Inchicore - Ballybrophy), with panel. The later sections of the Main Line CTC were VDU console from the start, and the original section was subsequently converted to VDU console, vice panel. The MAIN LINE CONTROL ROOM (which is the 1976 room) now has a VDU console, with keyboard and tracker ball control , which was BIU on 19/3/2000, replacing an earlier system. This was extended in 2003 to cover the Galway line 'Mini-CTC' scheme, which was commissioned on 8/6/2003 to control new SSI signalling from Ballinasloe to Galway. This was initially controlled by VDU, keyboard and tracker ball from the Athlone ECP and interlocking building, but control subsequently passed to Connolly, the Athlone installation remaining as an ECP only. The Main Line Control Room also has a console for CCTV control of some level crossings in its area.

The CTC building was extended to house the SUBURBAN CONTROL ROOM which opened 3/2/1984 with VDU console, but the present VDU console comprises largely new equipment BIU in 1999. This replaced a previous VDU installation of 15/5/1994. The Suburban Control Room also has a console for CCTV control of level crossings in its area.

The Main Line CTC has remote interlockings at the following locations (Relay locking), most of which have local Emergency Control Panels. These panels are located in the interlocking building itself except where noted otherwise.

Hazelhatch	Code CY	(No ECP)
Sallins	Code CY	"
Newbridge	Code CY	"
Kildare	Code CY	"
Cherryville Junction	Code CY	"
Portarlington Junction	Code CY	"
Portlaoise	Code CY	"
Geashill	Code CY	"
Ballybrophy	Code BY	Plus ECP
Lisduff	Code LF	Plus ECP
Thurles	Code TS	Plus ECP
Limerick Junction	Code LJ	Plus ECP, in North SB
Rathluirc	Code RC	Plus ECP (not now in SB)
Mallow	Code MW	Plus ECP, located in old SB
Rathpeacon	Code RP	Plus ECP
Tullamore	Code TE	Plus ECP
Clara	Code CA	Plus ECP
Clonydonnin	Code CN	Plus ECP, located in old SB
Athlone [at Athlone Midland]	Code AE	Plus ECP
Dromkeen	Code DN	Plus ECP (not now in SB)
Killonan	Code KN	Plus ECP, located in SB

As stated above, the Athlone interlocking also has a VDU/SSI interlocking for the Ballinasloe-Galway section (Code GL), and acts as an Emergency Control point for that section.

The Suburban CTC has remote interlockings at the following locations (Relay locking):

Howth	Code HT	Plus ECP, located in old SB
Howth Junction	Code HJ	Plus ECP
Killester	Code KR	Plus ECP
Connolly	Code CY	Plus ECP (located in Connolly building itself)
Pearse	Code PE	Plus ECP
Booterstown	Code BN	Plus ECP, located in Merrion gate box
Dun Laoghaire	Code DL	Plus ECP
Dalkey	Code DK	Plus ECP
Bray	Code BR	Plus ECP, located in old SB

Also there are the SSI interlockings for 'North Dublin' (Malahide to Drogheda) (ND) located at Malahide and Drogheda with the ECP located in Drogheda box.

[Note – those ECPs located in former SBs are given their own entries in the Directory.]

19   Frame reduced from 110 to 38 (former 73 - 110 remain). Panel controls line towards Kilbarry.

20   Box operating floor extended 1993. A new SSI interlocking, covering the mainline part of Drogheda station and the line towards Dundalk, took over from part of the 1978 Drogheda interlocking on 17/3/1997. This SSI installation is controlled by keyboard, tracker ball and VDU. Part of the 1978 relay interlocking remains, covering the Navan branch area of Drogheda station, and out to Platin cement works. This section is also controlled by the VDU etc. controlling the station SSI, via a programmable logic controller. The cabin also has an 'A' pattern ETS for the section Drogheda for Platin to Navan. The 1994 ECP is for the SSI for the 'North Dublin' area, and is located in the operating room. 'North Dublin' has SSI interlockings at Drogheda and Malahide.

21   Frame is of a design otherwise unknown, and not attributable. However box has RSCo - supplied parts.

22   Keyboard, tracker ball and VDU controlling new SSI signalling provided 1996 in Dundalk North box. Equipment moved to room in station buildings 25/9/2002 and Dundalk North box subsequently demolished.

23   Upper half of box largely rebuilt c1970s.

24   Box new after old box burnt, old frame retained.

25   Abolished as BP 1977.

26   Bay in station building. Station renamed Glounthaune and box also, although the box diagram still bears the name 'Cobh Junction'.

27   Box structure built by Thompson Bros. of Wexford (makers plate).

28   Full 18 - lever frame still in situ downstairs. Box abolished as BP 19/10/1980.

29   Keyboard, tracker ball and VDU controlling new signalling provided 1/11/1998, replacing frame.

30   SSI with VDU, tracker ball and keyboard control, provided in new interlocking building near Islandbridge Junction, commissioned 18/3/2002 allowing closure of Inchicore, area extended 1/9/2002 allowing closure of old Heuston box (which was subsequently demolished).

31   Abolished as BP 4/2/1984. Frame can work crossover at platform end, but this has not occurred for some years.

32   Panel altered 1995 for Lavistown loop.

33   Box closed 1931, reopened 1949. Much altered, also rewindowed 1980s. Works as a BP during the day when the branch is open for traffic, and as a Gate Box only at times when the branch is closed. The Panel also acts as ECP for Connolly. Main line signalling controlled by Connolly when Killonan Junction is not switched in as a BP.

34   Box built by MGW to near RSCo design.

35   New top on c1892 RSCo base. Abolished as BP 1/4/1984, and frame reduced from 16 to 7.

36   Regularly used on match days when traffic over the LC is very heavy.

37   Box is re-build of Brick-to-floor RSCo box, with new upper blockwork and windows, and all over rendering. Panel was originally NX, but converted to IFS owing to unreliability in NX mode.

38   New frame made up of reconditioned parts from Castletown and Balla, and spare levers removed from Sligo and Limerick Check itself, installed to replace original 50 lever RSCo Tappet frame of 1910.

39   Box is rebuild of former GS&W Hip Timber box.

40   GS&W (Non-Standard – same design as Cherryville Junction) box.

41   Panel controls North Esk sidings and main line signalling. Remaining levers for LC control.

42   Portakabin also serves as station building.

43   Westinghouse SSI in new interlocking building. VDU, tracker ball and keyboard control, provided in new Station building, 4/12/2000, in connection with new signalling and doubling of Clonsilla-Maynooth section. ETS instrument for Enfield section moved to this room also.

44   Formerly 'Mallow South'.

45   Line OOU except still available for engineer's traffic by 'Pilot Working'.

46   'Mullingar No.1' per nameboard, frequently 'Mullingar East' in official documents. Many replacement windows.

47   New top on 1891 RSCo base. Box abolished as BP 17/11/1985.

48   Box abolished as BP 8/10/1989. Subsidiary Miniature ETS (METS) instrument in box.

49   Frame may be 1921 frame extended c1929, or replacement frame c1929.

50   Box top is 1906, re-erected on new base 1910, re-positioned due to lengthening of loop. Frame may also have moved from old box. Panel is for release for Wexford North.

51   New top 1923 on 1885 RSCo base, old frame retained. Further building alterations c1980s.

52   Frame, RSCo Tappet 10 levers, remains in box, out of use.

53   Frame was 15 levers originally, 6 added u1907 at 4½" pitch.

54   Box abolished as BP 14/5/1995, frame reduced 26 to 6. Now acts as Gate Box and GF only. Works points for New Ross branch (which is now closed).

55   Box (gantried) built 1906 as RSCo/GS&W type, rebuilt 1923, after burning, with hipped roof and new windows. VDU, tracker ball and keyboard control for SSI of 14/5/1995 for Belview and Barrow Bridge releases, when Abbey Junction abolished as BP.

56   New top on 1906 RSCo/GS&W type base, after burning 1922.

57   New roof and re-windowed c1970s.

58   Ground Frame status, released from Rosslare Strand. Subsiduary METS instrument in box.

59   Rebuilt roof.

60   Millstreet normally acts as Gate Box only, but it is staffed by a signalman when required to function as an ETS Block Post.

Waterford Central (2003) – This gantry box above the running lines at Waterford station has had a chequered history. Built in 1906 as a RSCo/GS&W (Eire) type, it was rebuilt in 1923, after burning, with hipped roof and new windows. The box was being repainted at the time the picture was taken.

DIRECTORY SECTION SIX: HERITAGE RAILWAYS

In this section there is a separate entry for each Heritage Railway detailing the methods of working and signal boxes, with a few other notes where appropriate. The details of the working boxes are in the same format as in Sections 1 - 5.

- All standard gauge lines and other lines of greater than miniature gauge are included here (except for a few which have no functional signal boxes). The length of the Heritage Railway's operational line is given for all but demonstration lines; the gauge of all non-standard gauge lines is also provided. Locations which are essentially preservation sites with no significant running line are included only if they have functional signal box(es). Miniature railways with a significant length of purposeful route are included but those of the woodland/park/garden type are excluded. Inclusion/exclusion is necessarily subjective in some cases. Any ex-BR boxes existing at those preservation sites or miniature railway sites not included in Section 6, will be found listed (under their former BR location name) in Section 7. However small new-built sheds acting as 'signal boxes' on miniature railways are not included in this Directory at all.

- For each Heritage Railway listed here in Section 6, there are separate listings of (1) Boxes in use, and (2) summary of other boxes on site. Included in the 'Boxes in use' are certain boxes which are structurally complete on their new site and being prepared for opening, but not yet in use ('NIU') as at 1.1.2004. For full details of the 'other boxes on site' see Section 7.

- Boxes on Heritage Railways are, variously, ex-BR boxes on their original site re-opened by the Heritage Railway after some years of disuse since abolition by BR; second-hand ex-BR boxes moved to the line from elsewhere; or wholly new structures erected by the Heritage Railway either to a pre-grouping box design or to a new design.

- Boxes which have been dismantled for removal to the line, and have not yet been re-erected, and are therefore not recognisable to a visitor as structures, are usually enclosed within brackets. These dismantled boxes are not included in Section 7. Experience has shown that many of them are never actually re-erected! On occasions, stored frames are listed.

- Quail map references are given. Where the reference is in italics, the location is identified but the box is not.

- The status note (NBP) is not used in Section 6, as many boxes on these lines are of 'odd' status by main-line standards; the notes on Methods of Working explain the status of boxes when appropriate.

AVON VALLEY RAILWAY
Method of Working – Single line from Bitton northwards to Oldland Common (1 mile) and eastwards for 70 ch, with potential for further eastward extension to Countryside Halt (1¼ miles). Normally One Train Staff working. When two engines are in use a 'Responsible Officer' is appointed. No signals in use.
Signal Boxes in use – Nil.
Other Boxes on site – (Boxes dismantled - Skipton Station North with frame parts in store at Bitton).

BALA LAKE RAILWAY
Method of Working – Single line Llanuwchllyn to Bala (1' 11½" gauge, 4½ miles), with crossing place at Llangywair. One Train Staff Llanuwchylln to Bala when one train working; One Train Staff Llanuwchllyn to Llangywair and One Train Staff Llangywair to Bala (exchanged between engine crews at Llangywair) when two trains working. At Bala, the points are released by key on the Staff. Semaphore signals are in use at Llanuwchllyn and exist at Llangywair but are out of use.
Signal Boxes in use –

Llanuwchllyn	4/24H	GW 5	1894*	GW DT	1894	21	DT

      (* Abolished by BR 1965, re-opened by B.L.R. 1973).

Other Boxes on site – A 1980s purpose-built box with a 2h 4-lever Stevens Knee (Dutton) frame exists at Llangywair but is out of use. (Boxes dismantled - Sealand (RSCo) and 20-lever RSCo Tappet frame in store).

BATTLEFIELD LINE
Method of Working – Single line Shackerstone to Shenton (4¾ miles). One Train Staff operation. There is only a Ground Frame at Shenton. Semaphore signals are in use at Shackerstone and Shenton.
Signal Boxes in use –

Shackerstone	4/34E	New ('Mid 1') 2h*	1980s	McK&H 1873 Pat 2h	1980s	16R	HCS

    (*Box is made up from 'Mid 1' style hut from Measham Wharf, moved here 1978, on new base. Frame 2h ex Uttoxeter North, reduced).

Other boxes on site – Market Bosworth.

BIRMINGHAM RAILWAY MUSEUM, TYSELEY
Method of Working - Preservation site line only.
Signal Boxes in use –

Tyseley Warwick Road	4/15B	GW 28b 2h	1980s	GW VT 3 2h	1980s	47	T

    (Box and frame 2h ex Holesmouth Junction. Box structure 1941 there, re-build around original frame after bomb damage destroyed most of original box structure; frame 1910s there).

BLUEBELL RAILWAY

Method of Working – Single line Sheffield Park to Kingscote with crossing place at Horsted Keynes (9 miles). Large Electric Train Staff (BIU 1972) Sheffield Park to Horsted Keynes, and Key Token (BIU 1996) Horsted Keynes to Kingscote. Kingscote box is switched in only when two-train working is in operation. Full semaphore signalling at all three stations.

Signal Boxes in use or to be BIU –

Horsted Keynes	5/35D	LBSC1	1882	S&F Rocker 5"	1882	40	T

(Formerly 'Horsted Keynes South'. Abolished by BR, re-opened by Bluebell Railway).

Kingscote	5/35D	S&F5[LBSC] 2h	NIU	S&F Rocker 5" 2h	NIU	43	T

(Box top and frame 2h ex Upper Goods Brighton, 1882 there. Box top placed on new base 1996. Box will only come into use when extension to East Grinstead is fully operational).

Kingscote (Temporary)	5/35D	Shed	1996	Stevens Knee 2h	1996	11	T

(Frame 2h ex Southerham Junction G.F.) (This box will be closed when the permanent Kingscote box opens).

Sheffield Park	5/35D	See note	1935/62	Westinghouse gf	1935	19	T

(SR platform frame, opened 1935: closed by BR 1955 and OOU until re-opened by Bluebell Railway in 1960. In 1962 box structure was placed around the frame by the Bluebell Railway).

BODMIN STEAM RAILWAY

Method of Working – Single line Bodmin Parkway to Bodmin General (3½ miles); Bodmin General to Boscarne Junction (2½ miles). One Train Staff operation for entire line. No signals in use although installation work is in progress at Bodmin General. Connection with Network Rail at Bodmin Parkway is via Exchange Siding.

Signal Boxes in use or to be BIU –

Bodmin General	3/9A	GW 3	NIU	nk	NIU	nk	-

(Box has been built in style of the original GWR Type 3 structure using old foundations).

BO'NESS & KINNEIL RAILWAY

Method of Working – Single line in two sections: One Train Staff Bo'ness to Birkhill (3½ miles), One Train Staff Birkhill to Manuel (1¼ miles).

Signal Boxes in use –

Bo'ness	1/12	Cal S4 2h	1999	Stevens/Cal 2h	1999	24	T

(Box and frame 2h ex Garnqueen South Junction, box 1899 there, frame date nk).

BOWES RAILWAY

Method of Working – Single line Springwell Yard to Wrekenton (1¼ miles). One Train Staff operation. Springwell Yard has ground signals.

Signal Boxes in use –

Springwell Yard Frame	2/49A	Shed	nk	McK&H gf 2h	nk	9	T

(Frame 2h ex St. Anthony's, Newcastle).

BRECON MOUNTAIN RAILWAY

Method of Working – Single line Pant to Dol-y-Gaer (1' 11¾" gauge, 3 miles). One Train Staff operation. The GFs (8) on the line are released by key attached to Staff. No signalling on the line.

Signal Boxes in use – Nil.

Other Boxes on site – Pontsticill Junction ('Replica GW box' used as holiday accommodation).

BUCKINGHAMSHIRE RAILWAY CENTRE, QUAINTON ROAD

Method of Working – Preservation site lines only. The Centre consists of wholly separate up and down yards either side of the Network Rail line. The majority of passenger trains run in the up yard, which has no functional signalling. The down yard has been re-laid to double track with a run-round facility. The signal box is in the down yard and it is planned that it will work points and signals in 2005. Some passenger train working in the down yard has commenced.

Signal Boxes in use or to be BIU –

Quainton Road	3/32E	Mid 4c 2h	NIU	uMid. Tappet	NIU	40	T

(Box 2h ex Harlington, 1913 there; re-erected here 1980s).

BURE VALLEY RAILWAY

Method of Working – Single line Aylsham to Wroxham (15" gauge, 9 miles) with crossing places at Brampton, Little Hautbois, and Coltishall. Working is controlled by the controller at Aylsham who maintains a mimic diagram on a computer screen to show the sections which are occupied or which trains have been given permission to enter. Radio control of all movements: drivers ask permission for line clear to section/s. Unworked weighted points at loops. Stop boards at approach and exit of loops. In event of radio failure, One Train in Section (OTIS) token working can be introduced with controller giving instructions. Also One Train On Line (OTOL) train staff working with no controller.

Signal Boxes in use – Aylsham Control Office (in new structure resembling a signal box built 2001).

CALEDONIAN RAILWAY (BRECHIN)
Method of Working – Single line Brechin to Bridge of Dun (4 miles). One Train Staff operation.
Signal Boxes in use – Nil.

CHINNOR & PRINCES RISBOROUGH RAILWAY
Method of Working – Single line Chinnor to Thame Junction (3 miles). One Train Staff operation. Permission has been given by Network Rail to use the Watlington Bay platform at Princes Risborough and Princes Risborough North box. It is planned to renovate the latter to its 1950s state but for display purposes only.
Signal Boxes in use – Nil.
Other Boxes on site – Princes Risborough North. (Boxes dismantled – Gerrards Cross).

CHOLSEY & WALLINGFORD RAILWAY
Method of Working – Single line Cholsey to Wallingford (2½ miles). One Train Staff operation.
Signal Boxes in use – Nil.

CHURNET VALLEY RAILWAY
Method of Working – Single line Leek Brook Junction to Kingsley & Froghall (5½ miles); One Train Staff operation. Run-round loops at Leek Brook Junction and Kingsley & Froghall are worked by GFs released by the Train Staff.
Signal Boxes in use or to be BIU –

Cheddleton Shunt Frame	4/25B	NS 2 2h	1980s	McK&H 1873 Pat.2h	1980s	15	HCS

(Box top 2h ex Elton Crossing, nk date there, on new base. Frame made up from parts ex Elton Crossing and parts ex Ford Green).

Consall	-	NS 2 2h	NIU	McK&H 1873 Pat.2h	NIU	15	HCS

(Former Clifton Station box, nk date there, on new brick base to be BIU 2004. Frame is largely ex Leigh with parts ex Ford Green).

Other Boxes on site – Leek Brook Junction.

COLNE VALLEY RAILWAY
Method of Working – Single line Drawell to Nunnery Junction via Hedingham (½ mile), with crossing place at Hedingham. Train Staff & Ticket Drawell GF – Hedingham. Tokenless Block Hedingham-Nunnery Junction. (Key Token will be BIU for Drawell-Hedingham early in 2004). Drawell GF is a 5-lever open frame but it is planned to build a new signal box here, using McK&H frame ex Honington Junction.
Signal Boxes in use –

Hedingham	-	GE 7 2h	1984	McK&H u1886 Pat 5" 2h	1984	20	R.T

(Box top 2h ex Cressing, 1891 there, on new base, frame also 2h ex Cressing, 1891 there. New locking supplied by Westinghouse 1982).

Nunnery Junction	-	GE 1 2h	1987	S&F Rocker 5" 2h	1987	25	R.T

(Box 2h ex Wrabness, 1875 there, on new base: frame also 2h ex Wrabness, nk date there, new locking by CVR 1993).

CORRIS RAILWAY / RHEILFFORDD CORRIS
Method of Working – Single line Corris to Maespoeth Junction (2' 3" gauge; ¾ mile). Worked by Train Staff and Ticket (with paper tickets) and block working messages communicated by telephone. At the ends of the line a Point Key unlocks the relevant GF; if the station is manned, then Key held by the Blockman, if not, then held by the driver.
Signal Boxes in use or to be BIU –

Maespoeth Junction	-	Corris (new)	2002	-	-	-	-

(Currently used as base for the line's Controller on operating days).

DARTMOOR RAILWAY
Method of Working – Single line from Dartmoor Railway's property boundary with Network Rail close by the site of Coleford Junction to Meldon Station (15¾ miles). The line is operated in two sections. One Train Staff working Crediton Signal Box (Network Rail) to Okehampton Station (18 miles) with Staff fitted with an Annett's Key to release Okehampton GF; and One Train Staff working Okehampton Station to Meldon Station (2 miles) with Staff fitted with an Annett's Key that releases GFs at Okehampton, Meldon Quarry and Meldon Station. Signals are reflectorised 'Stop' and 'Distant' boards.
Signal Boxes in use – Nil.
Other Boxes on site – Okehampton.

DEAN FOREST RAILWAY
Method of Working – Single line Lydney Junction to Parkend (4¼ miles). Lydney Junction – Norchard is Key Token; Norchard – Parkend is Train Staff and Ticket. Full signalling at Lydney Junction and Norchard.
Signal Boxes in use or to be BIU –

Lydney Junction	3/20D	BR(LMR) 15 2h	1996	LMR Standard 2h	1996	35	T

(Box and frame 2h ex Heysham Harbour, 1970 there).

Norchard	3/20D	GW 28b 2h	1996	GW Stud 2h	1998	13	Stud

(Box and frame 2h ex (Gloucester) Mileage Yard GF date nk. Box and frame re-erected here in 1996; part of frame BIU 1998).

Parkend	3/20D	GW 28b 2h	NIU	-	-	-	-

(Box 2h ex Maesmawr (c1930 there) re-erected here 2003. No frame yet installed).

Other Boxes on site – Barnwood Sidings, Barton GF, Bowley's Crossing, Pirton Crossing, Walnut Tree Junction.

DERWENT VALLEY LIGHT RAILWAY

Method of Working – Preservation site line only. One Train Staff operation.

Signal Boxes in use –

| Murton | 2/19A | NE S4 2h | 1993 | McK&H 16 2h | 1993 | 8 | T |

(Box and frame 2h ex Muston Crossing, 1908 there).

DOWNPATRICK RAILWAY MUSEUM

Method of Working – Single lines Downpatrick Station – Home Junction – Inch Abbey Station (North Line) (2 miles) and Home Junction – Ballyduggan (South Line) (approx. 1 mile). One Train Staff operation with three sections – Blue Staff for Downpatrick – Home Junction; Red Staff for Home Junction – Inch Abbey; Green Staff for Home Junction – Ballyduggan. No signalling on line although installation of point rodding and signal wires linked to Downpatrick box will commence in 2004.

Signal Boxes in use or to be BIU –

| Downpatrick | 6/20F | B&NC 2h | NIU | RSCo Tappet 4" 2h | NIU | 40 | T |

(Box 2h ex Kingsbog Junction, 1906 there, rebuilt at Downpatrick 1990; frame originally ex Magherafelt NCC, then at Bangor BCDR).

EAST ANGLIAN RAILWAY MUSEUM (CHAPPEL & WAKES COLNE)

Method of Working – Preservation site line only. One Train Staff working, under control of Chappel North box. Chappel South functions as a GF released by the Staff.

Signal Boxes in use –

| Chappel North | 2/5E | GE 3 2h | 1986 | McK&H 1873 Pat 5" 2h | 1986 | 27 | R.T |

(Box and frame 2h ex Mistley, 1882 there. Locking new 1986).

| Chappel South | 2/5E | GN Hut 2h | 1986 | Stevens(Stevens) 2h | 1986 | 14 | T |

(Box 2h ex Fotherby, 1886 there, was 'Chappel North' in 1970s and then moved to Chappel South. Frame 2h ex Beckton Gasworks Railway, part (remainder is on Moors Valley Railway)).

Other Boxes on site – Chappel & Wakes Colne.

EAST KENT RAILWAY

Method of Working – Single line Shepherdswell to Eythorne (1¾ miles); extension to Wigmore Lane (¼ mile) due to open in 2004. One Train Staff working. Shepherdswell box works the points and basic operating signals. Selling box has been re-erected at the end of the platform at Eythorne but is not yet operational. Eythorne Sidings operated by GF released by Annett's Key on Staff.

Signal Boxes in use or to be BIU –

| Eythorne | 5/13 | S&F 5 [LCD] | NIU | - | - | - | - |

(Box 2h ex Selling, 1870s there; 6-lever gf (not Selling) planned to be installed in box).

| Shepherdswell | 5/13 | Hut | 1995 | Westinghouse gf 2h | 1995 | 4 | T |

Other Boxes on site – Barham.

EAST LANCASHIRE RAILWAY

Method of Working – Single line Hopwood to Rawtenstall via Bury Bolton Street (12 miles) with crossing places at Bury and Ramsbottom. Hopwood GF is ELR interface with Network Rail. Hopwood GF to Bury worked by One Train Staff; Bury to Ramsbottom worked by Miniature Electric Train Staff (will become Track Circuit Block by Direction Levers when Bury South box is commissioned in 2004); Ramsbottom to Rawtenstall worked by Key Token. Until Bury South box is commissioned, points at Bury operated by GF and Staff machines located in trackside cabinets.

Signal Boxes in use or to be BIU –

| Bury South | 4/30B | LYR (RSCo) | 1910* | LMR Standard 2h | NIU | 65 | T |

(*Abolished by BR 1980, still OOU at present. Frame is formed of 50 levers from Wigan S&T store plus 15 levers ex-Hadfield).

| Ramsbottom Station | 4/30B | LMS 11c | 1938* | REC | 1938 | 40 | T |

(*Abolished by BR 1980, re-opened by ELR 1990).

| Rawtenstall West (G) | 4/30B | BR(LMR) 15 | 1957* | REC | 1957 | 20 | T |

(*Abolished by BR 1980. Used by ELR only as a shelter for gateman who works gates and gives hand/lamp signals (re-opened 1991 in this role). Frame OOU).

| Townsend Fold (G) | 4/30B | BR(LMR) 15 | 1959* | LMR Standard | 1959 | 10 | T |

(*Abolished by BR 1980, Re-opened by ELR 1991).

Other Boxes on site – Crumpsall.

(Frames in store – Burn Naze (REC, 40 levers); Hadfield (LMR Std, 30 levers); Ditton Jn No. 2 (LMR Std, 60 levers)).

EAST SOMERSET RAILWAY

Method of Working – Single line Cranmore to Mendip Vale (1¾ miles). One Train Staff operation. Points worked by traincrew, GFs released by Staff. No signalling.

Signal Boxes in use –

| Cranmore West | 3/12A | Dutton Hut 2h | 1980s | nk 2h | 1980s | nk | T |

(Box 2h ex Cossington, Bridgwater Railway, 1890 there. Frame 2h ex nk location. Functions as gf only).

Other Boxes on site – Cranmore (it is planned to restore this as a working box in due course).

EMBSAY STEAM RAILWAY

Method of Working – Single line Bow Bridge to Bolton Abbey (4½ miles). One Train Staff for each section Bow Bridge – Embsay, Embsay – Stoneacre, Stoneacre – Bolton Abbey. Run-round loop at Bolton Abbey controlled by GF released by key on Staff.

Signal Boxes in use –

Box	Ref	Type	Date	Frame	Date	Levers	Work
Bolton Abbey	-	Mid 3a 2h	NIU	Westinghouse pf 2h	NIU	21	-
(Box 2h ex Guiseley, 1906 there; frame is ex Stratford (London Underground), date nk).							
Embsay Station	4/34F	Mid 4a	1923*	Midland Tappet	1923	20	T
(*Abolished by BR 1968, re-opened 1970s).							
Stoneacre	4/34F	New	1997	L&Y 2h	1997	16	T
(Box is of own design; origin of frame nk).							

Other Boxes on site – Finghall Lane.

FAIRBOURNE RAILWAY

Method of Working – Single line Fairbourne - Porth Penrhyn (12¼" gauge) with intermediate crossing loop near Gorsa (Golf Halt). Worked by Divisible Train Staffs (the two halves of the Staff acting as 'Staff' and 'Ticket') Fairbourne – Loop, Loop – Porth Penrhyn. Two trains can proceed through each section together, the second train follows 'on sight'. Drivers exchange Staffs at the Loop, which is unstaffed. When only one train operation, both halves of Staff are joined. There is full signalling at Fairbourne but the SB and signals are only used on special occasions. The Loop and Porth Penrhyn are unsignalled.

Signal Boxes in use –

Box	Ref	Type	Date	Frame	Date	Levers	Work
Fairbourne	4/20B	New	c1988	Switches	c1988	-	-

Other Boxes on site – One signal box remains from the Reseau Guerdelan CdeFer Touristique, Brittany, at Porth Penrhyn (shown in Quail), brought over c1986 but now disused (second box from the same source has been destroyed by vandals).

FAWLEY HILL RAILWAY

Method of Working – Single line on private estate close to Henley-on-Thames. Normally One Train Staff working. Signalmen at Shobnall Maltings and Bourne Again Junction control the line by block bells and indicator instruments.

Signal Boxes in use –

Box	Ref	Type	Date	Frame	Date	Levers	Work
Bourne Again Junction	-	MS&L Hut* 2h	1990s	Midland nk 2h	1990s	12	nk
(*Ex Upwell Street Wharf Sheffield Shunters' Hut).							
Shobnall Maltings	-	Midland 3a 2h	1980s	Midland Tumbler 2h	1980s	8	Tum
(Originally Swadlincote East (1905). Sold to Bass for Shobnall Maltings, opened there 1956, closed c1968).							

Other Boxes on site – Invergordon North, Inverness Stn Frame, Star Lane (Wokingham), and Windmill Lane (Cheshunt).

FFESTINIOG RAILWAY / RHEILFFORDD FFESTINIOG

Method of Working – Single line Porthmadog to Blaenau Ffestiniog (1' 11½" gauge, 13½ miles) with crossing places at Minffordd, Rhiwgoch, and Tan-y-Bwlch (Tan-y-Grisiau crossing loop to be commissioned in 2004). Minffordd and Tan-y-Bwlch are 'automated' loops with colour light signals and automatic points, and are not staffed for signalling purposes. Line worked by Electric Train Staff, 'M' type (configuration F) Porthmadog – Minffordd, Large ETS Minffordd – Rhiwgoch, Large ETS Rhiwgoch – Tan-y-Bwlch, and 'S' type ETS (configuration A) Tan-y-Bwlch – Blaenau Ffestiniog (Glan-y-Pwll). Rhiwgoch is only opened on peak service days and when switched out there is long section ETS ('M' type, configuration E) working Minffordd – Tan-y-Bwlch. The ETS instruments are worked by traincrew under the supervision of a Controller at Porthmadog. Intermediate instruments exist at Boston Lodge and Dduallt to enable trains to be shut in. A new box has been completed at Tan-y-Grisiau (not yet in use). This was to have incorporated a mechanical frame, but the points here are now to be 'Train Operated Trailable' with 'Points Set' indicators. The box will house the token instruments (which will be operated by the train crew) and telephone and is expected to open in 2004. Also a panel will be installed at Blaenau Ffestiniog station and signalling to enable the second platform here to be brought into use.

Signal Boxes in use or to be BIU –

Box	Ref	Type	Date	Frame	Date	Levers	Work
Rhiwgoch	4/24J	Shed	c1968	LNW gf	-	9+ switches	T/E
(Abolished 1989 but remained in situ and re-commissioned).							
Tan-y-Bwlch	4/24J	New	-	-	-	-	-
(Box completed c1970 but never opened; now used as battery and relay room for automatic signalling. A Westinghouse A2 frame (ex Surbiton) intended for the box lies disused outside).							
Tan-y-Grisiau	4/24J	New	NIU	-	-	-	-
(Box completed. To be BIU in connection with installation of additional crossing loop here).							

FOXFIELD STEAM RAILWAY

Method of Working – Single Line Blythe Bridge to Foxfield Colliery (2¾ miles). Three sections: Blythe Bridge (Caverswall Road) – Dilhorne Park (passenger line) operated by Train Staff & Ticket; Dilhorne Park – Foxfield Colliery (non-passenger); Blythe Bridge Exchange Sidings – Blythe Bridge (Caverswall Road) (non-passenger). Blythe Bridge (Caverswall Road) station is fully signalled with mix of semaphore and colour light signals.

Signal Boxes in use –

| Blythe Bridge (Caverswall Road) | 4/25A | NS 2 2h | | 1980s | LMR Standard 2h | 1980s | 20R | T |

(Box 2h ex Hockley Crossing, top on new base; frame 2h u ex 40 lever Stoke Area Emergency Frame).

GARTELL LIGHT RAILWAY

Method of Working – Single line Common Lane to Park Lane via Pinesway Junction (¾ mile), with crossing loop at Pinesway Junction. Interlocking Block Instruments Common Lane – Pinesway Junction, One Train Staff Pinesway Junction – Park Lane. Plans exist to extend northwards from Pinesway Junction to Common Lane Crossing, thence to Templecombe.

Signal Boxes in use –

| Common Lane | 5/36D | New | | c1990 | Stevens(Stevens) recon. | c1990 | 18 | T |
| Pinesway Junction | 5/36D | LSW N/S 2h | 1994 | McK&H 16 2h | 1994 | 30 | T |

(Box 2h ex Wyke, with extra section added; frame 2h ex Beckton Gasworks).

GLOUCESTERSHIRE WARWICKSHIRE RAILWAY

Method of Working – Single line Toddington to Cheltenham Racecourse via Winchcombe and Gotherington (9¼ miles), with Winchcombe as only operational crossing place. Tyer's Tablet working Toddington – Winchcombe; One Train Short Section Staff Winchcombe – Cheltenham Racecourse. (One Train Long Section Staff Toddington – Cheltenham Racecourse when Winchcombe switched out). Ground frame at the run-round loop at Cheltenham Racecourse is released by a key on the Staff. It is planned to complete a signal box at Cheltenham Racecourse in 2005 when Tablet working Winchcombe – Cheltenham Racecourse will be introduced. Toddington and Winchcombe are fully signalled.

Signal Boxes in use –

| Toddington | 3/32F | GW 7b | 1905* | GW HT 3 5¼" 2h | 1984 | 29R | T |

*Abolished by BR 1976, re-opened 1984. (Frame 2h ex Earlswood Lakes).

| Winchcombe | 3/32F | GW 7a 2h | 1987 | GW VT 5 2h | 1987 | 37R | T |

(Box 2h ex Hall Green; frame ex Honeybourne West Loop).

Other Boxes on site – Brize Norton & Brampton GF, California Crossing, Honeybourne North Loop; also a GWCo or RSCo box of unknown origin.

(Boxes dismantled – Stratford on Avon East; Frames in store – Claydon Crossing (GW Stud, 21 levers); Hall Green (GW HT3 5¼", 30 levers); Whiteball Siding (GW VT3, 27 levers)).

GREAT CENTRAL RAILWAY

Method of Working – Loughborough to Leicester North (8 miles). Double line Loughborough to Rothley (Up line to Rothley; Down line to Loughborough) worked on Absolute Block system Loughborough-Quorn & Woodhouse-Rothley (Quorn & Woodhouse can be switched out leaving AB Loughborough-Rothley). Single line Rothley to Leicester North worked by One Train Staff. Loughborough, Quorn & Woodhouse and Rothley are fully signalled.

Signal Boxes in use or to be BIU –

| Loughborough North | 4/17D | MS&L 4 | 1896* | RSCo – LNER Std 2h | 1981 | 50 | T |

(*Abolished by BR , re-opened by GCR 1981) (Frame 2h ex Ruddington).

| Quorn & Woodhouse | 4/17D | MS&L 3 2h | 2004 | RSCo Tappet 2h | 2004 | 29 | T |

(Box and frame 2h ex Market Rasen, 1890 there; re-erected at Quorn with frame 1987).

| Rothley | 4/17D | GC N/S 2h | 1990 | GC (S&F) 2h | 1992 | 20 | T |

(Box and frame 2h ex Blind Lane, 1905 there. Re-erected here 1986; manned from 1990 no equipment; points and signals operational 1992).

| Swithland | *4/17D* | GC5 2h | NIU | GW HT 3 2h | NIU | 55 | T |

(Box and frame 2h ex Aylesbury South, 1908 there, re-erected at Swithland 1993).

Other Boxes on site – Wrexham Exchange.

GREAT CENTRAL RAILWAY (NORTH)

Method of Working – Single line Hotchley Hill to 'Nottingham Heritage Centre' (4½ miles) worked by One Train Staff. The Hotchley Hill – Loughborough North Junction line (5½ miles) is in use by main line freight trains from the Midland Main Line's Up Slow Junction to East Leake Plaster Works Sidings at Hotchley Hill. However, the GCR(N) is responsible for track-work on this latter section up to a point just short of the MML junction and do run trains over this line when permission has been obtained from Leicester PB by extending the One Train Staff operation.

Signal Boxes in use or to be BIU –

| Asher Lane (G) | - | [Military Rly] | c1942 | LMR Standard 6" 2h | c1996 | 9R | T |

(Box closed with line, but subsequently re-opened c1996; frame ex Nottingham Goods Yard North; now functions as Gate Box only).

| Ruddington Fields | - | GC 5 2h | NIU | GC(RSCo)2h | NIU | 84 | T |

(Box and frame 2h ex Neasden South, 1906 there, re-erected on new base).

| Ruddington North Junction | - | New | 2003 | gf | 2003 | 3 | T |

Other Boxes on site – Hotchley Hill.

GREAT WESTERN SOCIETY, DIDCOT

Method of Working – Preservation site only, OEIS working over passenger single lines.

Signal Boxes in use – Signal boxes are not necessarily opened on all operating days. Both boxes are still known by their previous site names.

Frome Mineral Junction	3/3E	GW 2+ 2h	1990s	GW Stud 2h	1990s	18	Stud

(Box 2h ex Frome North, formerly known as Frome Mineral Junction, 1875 there. Frame 2h ex Stoneycombe Sidings).

Radstock North	3/3E	GW 27c 2h	1985	GW DT 5¼ " 2h	1985	24	DT

(Box and frame 2h ex Radstock North, box 1904 re-build and frame 1898 there; also has small 2-lever frame for wickets).

GWILI RAILWAY

Method of Working – Single line Bronwydd Arms to Danycoed (2¼ miles). One Train Staff operation.

Signal Boxes in use –

Bronwydd Arms	3/25D	GW 3 2h	c1986	GW Stud 2h	c1986	21	Stud

(Box and frame 2h ex Llandebie, 1884 box / 1906 frame). (Also has small 2-lever frame for wickets).

Other Boxes on site – Crundale Crossing (at Llwyfan Cerrig, 'information display'), Ffairfach (intended for future use at Carmarthen using ex Caedu frame currently in store).

ISLE OF WIGHT STEAM RAILWAY

Method of Working – Single line Wootton to Smallbrook Junction (4¾ miles) with crossing place at Havenstreet. One Train Staff working Wootton to Havenstreet. This 'Staff' is a Key Token and is passed through the KT Instrument at Havenstreet in order to release the starting signal towards Wootton. One Train Staff working Havenstreet to Smallbrook Junction. This 'Staff' is a Tablet and is passed through the Tyer's Tablet Instrument at Havenstreet in order to release the starting signal towards Smallbrook Junction. The frame at Wootton and ground frame at Smallbrook Junction are released by the Key Token/Tablet.

Signal Boxes in use –

Havenstreet	5/35C	SR BO/SB	1926*	Stev. Knee (RSCo)	1926	16	T

(*Abolished by BR 1966, re-opened c1974).

Smallbrook GF	5/35C	Hut 2h	c1990	gf 2h	-	2	T

(Box 2h believed ex Dean Crossing [Whitwell], moved here from previous private garden site at Newport and placed over existing open gf).

Wootton	5/35C	RSCo [FYN] 2h	1983	S&F 1888 Dx 2h	1983	8R	Dx

(Box 2h ex Newport FYN, 1913. Frame 2h ex Shanklin (part)).

KEIGHLEY & WORTH VALLEY RAILWAY

Method of Working – Single line Keighley to Oxenhope (4¾ miles); crossing place, Damems Junction. Three methods of working:- (1) One Train Staff for whole line, in custody of Responsible Officer based at Howarth, Damens Junction box switched out. (2) When Damems Junction box is open, NSKT Damems Junction-Keighley and NSKT Damems Junction – Oxenhope. Subsidiary instruments with locking-in facilities at Keighley, Ingrow, Oakworth, Haworth, and Oxenhope. Traincrew are not normally required to put the token through the instruments at Keighley or Oxenhope. (3) During peak services a Signalman is appointed at Keighley and operates the (open) GF and signals there, collects the token from the traincrew and puts it through the instrument.
[A further crossing loop south of the station at Haworth has been installed and will be commissioned when signalling is complete].

Signal Boxes in use or to be BIU –

Damems Crossing (G)	2/54F	Mid Hut 2h	c1970	Midland Tumbler 2h	c1970	5	Tum

(Box and u frame 2h ex Earby Crossing, 1923 there).

Damems Junction	2/54F	Mid 3a 2h	1973	Midland Timbler 2h	1973	16	Tum

(Box and frame 2h ex Frizinghall, 1907 there).

Haworth	2/54F	Mid 2b 2h	NIU	Mid Tum Wks Rlk 2h	NIU	16	R.T

(Box and frame 2h ex Esholt Junction, box 1899 there, frame 1979 there ex Moorthorpe Station (part). This box was previously re-erected at Keighley in the 1980s before being moved again to Haworth Loop).

Keighley West	2/54F	Mid 4a 2h	NIU	Mid Tum Wks Rlk 2h	NIU	20	R.T

(Box and frame 2h ex Shipley Bingley Junction, box 1907 there, frame 1979 there ex Moorthorpe Station (part)).

There is also an open frame at Oakworth level crossing.

Other Boxes on site – Keighley Station Junction, Rushton.

KEITH & DUFFTOWN RAILWAY

Method of Working – Single line Dufftown to Keith Town (11 miles). One Train Staff operation.

Signal Boxes in use – Nil.

Other Boxes on site – Spey Bay.

KENT & EAST SUSSEX RAILWAY

Method of Working – Single line Tenterden Town to Bodiam (10 miles), with crossing places at Rolvenden, Wittersham Road and Northiam. Operation is by Tyer's No.6 Tablet (modified operation) Tenterden Town – Rolvenden; Key Token Rolvenden – Wittersham Road and Wittersham Road – Northiam; and One Train Staff Northiam – Bodiam. Long Section One Train Staff working Rolvenden – Northiam when Wittersham Road closed. Northiam can be operated as a crossing-place by traincrew when SB is unstaffed. Full signalling with semaphores at Northiam, Rolvenden, Tenterden Town, and Wittersham Road.

Signal Boxes in use –

Northiam		5/13A New	2000	Dutton 1893 Pat. 2h	1997	22	T

(Box modelled on Wadhurst; frame ex Wadhurst).

Rolvenden		5/13A New	1989	Stevens recon.	1989	30	T

(Box is 'modelled' on S&F Type 12 design. Frame made up from parts including ex Gipsy Hill , Westgate-on-Sea & Mitcham Junction).

Tenterden Town		5/13A S&F 12a [SE] 2h	1976	S&F 1888 Dx 2h	1976	23	T

(Box top and frame 2h ex Chilham, 1893 there).

Wittersham Road		5/13A S&F 5 2h	1982	SEC NP 2h	1982	20	T

(Box top 2h ex Deal Junction, 1881 there, on new base. Frame ex Cliffe, 1934 there).

Other Boxes on site – Nil (Frames in store – Robertsbridge 'A' and Herne Bay).

KIRKLEES LIGHT RAILWAY

Method of Working – Single line Clayton West to Shelley (15" gauge, 3¼ miles) with crossing place at Skelmanthorpe. If one train working, then Staff carried for both Clayton West – Skelmanthorpe and Skelmanthorpe-Shelley sections. If two trains, first proceeds from Clayton West with ticket and Skelmanthorpe – Shelley Staff, second follows with Clayton West – Skelmanthorpe Staff and exchanges Staff with returning train at Skelmanthorpe loop (final train returning to Clayton West is given permission by telephone to enter Skelmanthorpe – Clayton West section).
Signal Boxes in use – Nil.

LAKESIDE & HAVERTHWAITE RAILWAY

Method of Working – Single line Lakeside to Haverthwaite (3 miles). One Train Staff operation.
Signal Boxes in use –

Haverthwaite		4/31D Furness 2	1891*	RSCo 1877 Pat.	1891	18	R.T

(*Abolished by BR, re-opened by L&HR).

Lakeside		4/31D Furness 4	1913*	RSCo Tappet	1913	42	T

(*Abolished by BR 1967, re-opened by L&HR).

LAUNCESTON STEAM RAILWAY

Method of Working – Single line Launceston to Newmills (60cm gauge, 2½ miles) with crossing place at Hunts Crossing (currently OOU; planned re-instatement 2004). Line divided into two sections with Annett's Keys for each: Launceston –Hunts Crossing and Hunts Crossing – Newmills. Annett's Keys combined when only one train working. Keys release ground frames for running round at ends of line; for Hunts Crossing loop (when operational); and to provide access to workshops line at Kemps Jn.
Signal Boxes in use – Nil.

LAVENDER LINE

Method of Working – Single line northwards from Isfield Station (1 mile). One Train working.
Signal Boxes in use – Nil.
Other Boxes on site – Isfield.

LEADHILLS & WANLOCKHEAD RAILWAY

Method of Working – Single line Leadhills to Glengonnar (60cm gauge, ½ mile). Planned extension to Wanlockhead (½ mile). One Train Staff operation.
Signal Boxes in use

Leadhills		1/10F New	1996	S&F 1888 Dx 2h	1996	17	R.T

(Frame 2h ex Arrochar & Tarbet, 1894 there).

LLANGOLLEN RAILWAY

Method of Working – Single line Llangollen to Carrog (8 miles) with crossing places at Llangollen Goods Junction, Deeside, and Glyndyfrdwy. Key Token Llangollen Station – Llangollen Goods Junction, Llangollen Goods Junction – Deeside, Deeside – Glyndyfrdwy. One Train Staff Glyndyfrdwy – Carrog. Deeside and Llangollen Goods Jn can be switched out with Long Section One Train Staff Llangollen Station – Glyndyfrdwy. Full signalling at all locations with boxes (at Deeside the signals are LED 'colour lights').
Signal Boxes in use or to be BIU –

Carrog	-	GW 7a	NIU	GW VT 2h	NIU	21	T

(Replica of original Carrog box on same site) (Frame 2h ex Green Lane Crossing, Chester, 1925 there).

Deeside		4/17B New	1995	CLC 2h	1995	16	T

(Box is 'CLC' top on 'Dutton' base. Frame 2h ex Northwich Central (part)).

Glyndyfrdwy	-	GW 27c 2h	1992	GW Stud 2h	1992	21	Stud

(Box ex Leaton, 1904 there. Frame 2h ex Golds Hill, 1909 there).

Llangollen Goods Junction		4/17B GW 8a	1990	GW VT 3 2h	1990	25R	T

(Box built on original site, of bricks from the original Llangollen Goods Junction box, and timber parts from Green Lane Crossing, Chester. Frame 2h ex Ruabon Middle, 1919 there).

Llangollen Station		4/17B GW 7a	1898*	Dutton Combination 2h	1991	17	R.T

(*Abolished by BR 1967, re-opened by L.R. 1991). (Frame 2h ex Borth, 1891 there).

Other Boxes on site – Barmouth South, Weston Rhyn.

LYNTON & BARNSTAPLE RAILWAY

Method of Working – Single line Woody Bay in direction of Parracombe (60cm gauge; approx. ½ mile). One Train Staff (actually a Key Token). Three GFs at Woody Bay all released by keys on Token.

Signal Boxes in use – Nil.

Other Boxes on site – Woody Bay.

MANGAPPS FARM

Method of Working – Preservation site line only.

Signal Boxes in use –

'Berney Arms'	2/54E	GE Hut 2h	1990s	gf 2h	1990s	4	T

(Box 2h ex Berney Arms, 1885 there).

Other Boxes on site – Billericay GF, Haddiscoe, Spelbrook.

MID-HANTS RAILWAY

Method of Working – Single line Alresford to Alton (10 miles) with crossing places at Ropley and Medstead & Four Marks. Medstead & Four Marks – Alresford fitted with AWS 1996. Key Token Alresford – Ropley – Medstead & Four Marks, Train Staff & Ticket Medstead & Four Marks – Alton (the Staff is actually a Key Token). A train can be locked in at Alton. All three functional boxes are always open when passenger trains run. GF 'A' commissioned at Alton 2002 to control connection to Network Rail and Platform 2 (current release by Train Staff Key but will be from Alton box when commissioned). Meon Loop GF and Station GF (both Alton) released by Train Staff Key.

Signal Boxes in use or to be BIU –

Alresford	5/24D	LSW 1	c1875*	Stevens(Dutton)	1893	18	T

(*Abolished by BR 1973, re-opened by MHR, frame extended from original 16 levers and reconditioned with many new parts 1995).

Alton	5/24D	LSW 1 2h	NIU	-	-	-	-

(Box top 2h ex Bentley North; was on platform at Alton as shed for many years. Switch panel to be installed to control station area to mp51).

Medstead & Four Marks	5/24D	LSW 1 2h	1980s	Stevens recon.	1980s	21	T

(Box 2h ex Wilton c1871 there, on new base. Frame (largely ex Bentley) eventually to be replaced by a Westinghouse 2h ex Brockenhurst 'A').

Ropley	5/24D	LSW Hut 2h	c1983	Stev Knee(RSCo) recon.	c1983	15	T

(Box 2h ex Dean G.F. Frame outside hut under new timber shed 1997).

Ropley	5/24D	LSW 1 2h	NIU	-	-	-	-

(Box top 2h ex Netley. Partly-installed Stevens frame (2h ex Barnstaple Junction) in the box. When BIU this will replace existing box).

MIDLAND RAILWAY CENTRE

Method of Working – Single line Hammersmith to Riddings (3½ miles) with crossing place at Swanwick Junction. When no signal boxes are open, whole line is worked with One Train Staff (actually a single Tablet). When Hammersmith box only is open, ditto. When Swanwick Junction box is open also, Tablet working is in use Hammersmith to Swanwick Junction, with One Train Staff Swanwick Junction to Riddings. Butterley box is not a Block Post.

Signal Boxes in use –

Butterley GF	4/5	Mid 2b 2h	c1984	Mid Tum 2h	c1984	16	Tum

(Box and frame 2h ex Ais Gill, 1900 there).

Hammersmith	4/5	Mid 3b 2h	1989	Mid Tum 2h	1989	32	Tum

(Box and frame 2h ex Kilby Bridge, 1900 there).

Swanwick Junction	4/5	Mid 4c 2h	1990	Mid Tap 2h	1990	44	T

(Box and frame 2h ex Kettering Station, 1913 there).

Other Boxes on site – Desford Colliery Sidings, Linby Colliery Sidings, Linby Station.

MID NORFOLK RAILWAY

Method of Working – Single line Dereham to Wymondham (11½ miles) (connection to Network Rail at Wymondham South Junction). One Train Staff operation; GFs at Dereham released by Annett's Key. The separate short restored section at County School is currently OOU.

Signal Boxes in use or to be BIU –

Dereham Central	2/13B	GE 7 2h	NIU	McK&H 4" 2h	NIU	44R	T

(Box top and frame 2h ex Stratford Southern, 1895 there, new brick base on previous Dereham Central foundations).

Yaxham	2/13B	GE 2	c1882	-	-	-	-

(Box now privately owned but used by MNR as accommodation for crossing keeper).

Other Boxes on site – Great Bentley, Laundry Lane Crossing.

NENE VALLEY RAILWAY

Method of Working – Single line Yarwell Mill to Peterborough via Wansford (7¼ miles) with crossing places at Wansford and Orton Mere. One Train Staff Yarwell Mill – Wansford. Train Staff & Ticket Wansford – Orton Mere. One Train Staff Orton Mere – Peterborough. When Orton Mere box is shut, trains carry the Staffs for both sections Wansford – Orton Mere – Peterborough.

Signal Boxes in use or to be BIU –

Orton Mere	-	Mid 1 2h	c1977	Mid nk 2h	c1977	12R	Nk

(Box 2h ex Maxey Crossing, 1900 there. Frame 2h ex Nene Junction).

Peterborough Wharf	-	GE 2 2h	NIU	EOD 2h	NIU	40	T

(Box 2h ex Welland Bridge, 1882 there. Frame 2h ex Grassmoor Junction).

Wansford	-	LNW 5	1907*	LNW Tap	1907	40R	T

(*Abolished by BR 1971, re-opened c1974).

NORTHAMPTON & LAMPORT RAILWAY

Method of Working – Single line either side of Pitsford & Brampton station (1¼ miles). Train Staff & Ticket for 29 chains between Pitsford Sidings and Pitsford & Brampton boxes and One Train Staff north from there.

Signal Boxes in use –

Pitsford & Brampton	-	LNW 4 2h	1997	LNW Tap 2h	1997	20	T

(Box top 2h ex Little Bowden Crossing, 1879 there. Frame is some parts ex North Pole Junction (1922 there) and some ex Willesden New Station box. The frame from Little Bowden Crossing box itself is in store).

Pitsford Sidings	-	LNW 4 2h	1997	LNW Tum 2h	1997	12	B&S

(Box and frame 2h ex Wolverton Works, 1903 there).

Other Boxes on site – Harringworth (plus frame), Lamport, Spratton Crossing.

NORTH NORFOLK RAILWAY

Method of Working – Single line Sheringham to Holt (5¼ miles), with crossing place at Weybourne. When Weybourne box is switched out, Long Section One Train Staff for whole line. When Weybourne box is switched in, Tyer's Tablet (No.6) Sheringham West to Weybourne, and One Train Staff Weybourne to Holt. When Holt box is commissioned, Tyer's Tablet will be introduced for Weybourne to Holt section and Holt GF (switch panel, released by key on Staff and housed in ex M&GN Hut) will be abolished. Sheringham and Weybourne stations are fully signalled.

Signal Boxes in use or to be BIU –

Holt	2/54B	Mid 3a 2h	NIU	REC 2h	NIU	25	T

(Box top 2h ex Upper Portland Sidings, 1905 there, on new 'M&GN style' concrete block locking room; frame ex Steeton Station).

Sheringham West	2/54B	GE 7 2h	1985	Dutton 1893 Pat. 2h	1985	31	R.T

(Box top 2h ex Wensum Junction, on new base. Frame 2h ex Leyton).

Weybourne	2/54B	M&GN 1 2h	1989	S&F Rocker 5" 2h	1989	30	R.T

(Box 2h ex Holt, c1913 there, on foundations of original Weybourne box. Frame also 2h ex Holt, c1913 there, originally made 1882).

Other Boxes on site – Sheringham East.

NORTH YORKSHIRE MOORS RAILWAY

Method of Working – Single line Grosmont to Pickering (17¾ miles), with crossing places at Goathland and Levisham. New Bridge box controls Pickering station (track circuited). Tyer's No.6 Tablet Grosmont Crossing – Goathland, Train Staff & Ticket Goathland – Levisham, TS&T Levisham – New Bridge (Staffs are Annett's Keys, with brass 'Tickets'). Long Section TS&T Goathland – New Bridge when Levisham switched out (Staff is a Key Token with brass 'Tickets'). All stations are fully signalled.

Signal Boxes in use –

Goathland	2/51D	NE S1b	1876*	McK&H 16 recon.	1972	21	T

(*Abolished by BR, re-opened 1972).

Grosmont Crossing	2/51D	NE S1a	1996	McK&H 17 2h	1996	52	T

(New box, built from bricks from Whitby and Eskdale Mines. Frame 2h ex Horden).

Levisham	2/51D	NE S1b	1876*	McK&H 17 recon.	1975	25	T

(*Abolished by BR, re-opened 1975).

New Bridge	2/51D	NE S1a	1876*	McK&H 16 recon.	1978	25	T

(*Abolished by BR, re-opened 1978).

PAIGNTON & DARTMOUTH STEAM RAILWAY

Method of Working – Single line Paignton to Kingswear (6¾ miles), with crossing place at Churston. Whole line controlled from panel at Britannia Crossing. All signals are colour-light. The link with Network Rail at Paignton is operated by a GF.

Signal Boxes in use –

Britannia Crossing	3/7C	New	1998	NX Panel	1998	-	E
Churston	3/7C	New	1979	-	-	-	-

(Former signal box, relay room only since 1991).

PEAK RAIL

Method of Working – Single line Matlock to Rowsley South (4½ miles). One Train Staff working. At Matlock there are ground frames. Darley Dale box not yet in use. Church Lane Crossing box is already in use as a gate box for engineer's trains only.

Signal Boxes in use or to be BIU –

Church Lane Crossing	-	Mid 2a 2h	c1995	REC 2h	c1995	15R	T

(Box 2h ex Gorsey Bank, 1890 there, repaired with some parts from Marple Station box: frame 2h ex Marple Wharf Junction).

Darley Dale	-	Mid 2b 2h	NIU	LMR Std 6" 2h	NIU	29	T

(Box 2h ex Bamford (1893), repaired using parts from Glendon North Junction box. Frame 2h ex Glendon North Junction, 1960 there).

PONTYPOOL & BLAENAVON RAILWAY

Method of Working – Single line Furnace Sidings to Whistle Inn (½ mile). One Train Staff operation. GF at north end of Furnace Sidings released by Annett's Key on Staff.

Signal Boxes in use – Nil.

RAVENGLASS & ESKDALE RAILWAY

Method of Working – Single line Ravenglass to Dalegarth (15" gauge, 7 miles) with crossing loops at Miteside, Irton Road, and Fisherground. The signal box at Ravenglass controls directly the station area. The remainder of the line including the crossings at the loops is controlled by Train Order given by radio from the Ravenglass signalman.

Signal Boxes in use –

Ravenglass	4/34G	R&ER	1969	REC 2h	1969	30	T

(Frame 2h ex Brigham).

RIBBLE STEAM RAILWAY

Method of Working – Single line Preston Strand Road to Preston Riverside (approximately 2 miles). One Train Staff operation. Three GFs awaiting commissioning.

Signal Boxes in use –

Riversway Control Centre	4/27C	New	nk	Switch panel	nk	-	E

Other Boxes on site – (Boxes dismantled – Ainsdale, plus frame).

ROMNEY, HYTHE & DYMCHURCH RAILWAY

Method of Working – Hythe to Dungeness (15" gauge; 13¾ miles). Double line Hythe to New Romney, with 'Radio Block' Hythe – Dymchurch – New Romney. Single line New Romney – Dungeness, with crossing place at Romney Sands, worked by Train Staff & Ticket New Romney – Romney Sands and Romney Sands – Dungeness. Romney Sands is normally unstaffed for signalling purposes, the traincrew exchanging Staffs themselves. Full signalling, with mainly semaphore signals, at Hythe and New Romney, and with colour-lights at Dymchurch.

Signal Boxes in use –

Dymchurch	5/18E	**	-	Panel	nk	-	E
	(BP in station office. Also Annett's Key to release crossover gf).						
Hythe	5/18E	RH&DR	1927	Greenly Knee	1927	16	T
New Romney	5/18E	RH&DR	1927	Greenly (Foot release)	1927	24	-

SEVERN VALLEY RAILWAY

Method of Working – Kidderminster to Bridgnorth (14¼ miles). Single line Kidderminster to Bewdley South, worked by Acceptance lever (TCB). Double line Bewdley South to Bewdley North, worked Absolute Block. Also at Bewdley: direction lever working on back platform line; telephone working for two through sidings. Single line Bewdley North – Arley – Highley – Hampton Loade – Bridgnorth, all four sections worked by Key Token. Arley and Hampton Loade can switch out with Long Section Key Token working Bewdley North – Highley/Highley – Bridgnorth. Arley, Highley and Hampton Loade all have crossing loops but Highley cannot cross two passenger trains. Telephone working Kidderminster Junction box (Network Rail) – Kidderminster Station box. All stations are fully signalled.

Signal Boxes in use –

Arley	4/20B	LNW 4 2h	1976	GW VT 3 2h	1976	30	T
	(Box 2h ex Yorton, 1882 there: frame 2h ex Kidderminster Station).						
Bewdley North	4/20B	McK&H 3 [GW]	1878*	GW HT 3 5¼"	1908	37	T
	(*Abolished by BR 1970, re-opened 1974).						
Bewdley South	4/20B	McK&H 3 [GW]	1878*	GW VT 3	nk	34	T
	(*Abolished by BR 1970, re-opened 1974).						
Bridgnorth	4/20B	GW 28b 2h	1970	GW VT 3 2h	1970	30	T
	(Box top 2h ex Pensnett South, 1925 there, on base of 1923 Bridgnorth box: frame 2h ex Windmill End Junction).						
Hampton Loade	4/20B	McK&H 3 [GW]	1883/1973	GW VT 5 2h	1973	16	T
	(*Abolished by BR 1963, re-opened 1973. Much of the present structure was new in 1973. Frame 2h ex Ledbury North End).						
Highley	4/20B	McK&H 3 [GW]	1883*	McK&H 1873 Pat 5"	1883	14	R.T
	(*Abolished by BR 1970, re-opened 1974. Frame now VT 5 locking).						
Kidderminster Station	4/20B	GW 7	1987	GW VT 5 2h	1987	62	T
	(New box built by SVR. Frame 2h ex Acton Yard, 1959 there, extended with parts ex Stourport-on-Severn and Acton West).						

SNOWDON MOUNTAIN RAILWAY

Method of Working – Single line Llanberis to Summit (80cm gauge, 4½ miles) , with crossing loops at Hebron, Halfway, and Clogwyn. Hebron and Halfway have automatic points actuated by treadles. Clogwyn points are operated by a pointsman with an outside lever frame. Points at Llanberis and Summit are hand operated. A 'Train Order' system of working is used, with all movements authorized by the Traffic Controller at Llanberis using radio.

Signal Boxes in use –

Clogwyn	4/24F	SMR Hut	nk	Stev. Knee(RSCo)	u1897	2R	T
Llanberis	4/24F	**	nk	-	-	-	-

SOUTH DEVON RAILWAY

Method of Working – Single line Buckfastleigh to Totnes (Littlehempston) (7 miles), with crossing place at Bishops Bridge box (immediately west of Staverton station). Key Token Buckfastleigh South – Bishops Bridge, One Train Staff Bishops Bridge – Totnes (Littlehempston). When Bishops Bridge is switched out, Long Section One Train Staff for whole line. With the long section Staff in use, Buckfastleigh South can be switched out and worked as a GF by traincrew. Full signalling at Buckfastleigh and Bishops Bridge/Staverton , but there is only an open GF at Totnes (Littlehempston). It is planned to rebuild Cradley Heath box to replace this GF. The connection with Network Rail at Totnes is controlled by Exeter PSB.

Signal Boxes in use –

Bishops Bridge	3/7C	GW 27c 2h	1996	GW Stud 2h	1996	37	R.T

(Box 2h ex Athelney, 1906 there. Frame also 2h ex Athelney, now VT5 locking).

Buckfastleigh South	3/7C	New	1989	GW VT5 2h	1989	25	T

(Box modelled on GWR practice but no specific design; incorporates windows ex Bathampton SB. Built 1984 and in partial use, with train crew operation of some functions, prior to full opening in 1989. Frame 2h ex Ufton Crossing).

Staverton Crossing GF (G)	3/7C	GW 21	1911*	GW Stud	1911	12	Stud

(*Abolished by BR 1958. Hut removed to garden c1962, returned 1967; frame had remained in situ. Re-opened late 1960s).

Other boxes on site – Buckfastleigh, Cradley Heath.

SOUTH TYNEDALE RAILWAY

Method of Working – Single line Alston to Kirkhaugh (2' gauge; 2¼ miles). One Train Staff operation.

Signal Boxes in use –

Alston	2/46D	NE S5 2h	1991	McK&H 16 2h	1991	21R	T

(Box 2h ex Ainderby, 1915 there. Frame 2h ex Leeming Bar).

Other Boxes on site – Grosmont.

SPA VALLEY RAILWAY

Method of Working – Single line Tunbridge Wells West to Groombridge (3 miles); One Train Staff operation. Groombridge to Eridge (2 miles) is out of use.

Signal Boxes in use or to be BIU –

Tunbridge Wells West	5/14B	Mid 1 Hut 2h	NIU	Westinghouse A2 2h	nk	21	T

(Box 2h ex Buckden, 1880s; was formerly at Knebworth Park, then Bygone Village, Fleggburgh. Frame 2h ex Crabtree Crossing).

Other Boxes on site – Eridge.

STRATHSPEY RAILWAY

Method of Working – Single line Aviemore Speyside to Broomhill (9½ miles), crossing place at Boat of Garten only if one train is non-passenger. Train Staff & Ticket Aviemore Speyside to Boat of Garten (a Key Token system is planned to be installed during 2004). One Train Staff Boat of Garten to Broomhill. Aviemore Speyside box functions only as a GF worked by traincrew, released by the Staff (as is GF at Aviemore Main Line). GF at Broomhill released by Staff. Boat of Garten South is fully signalled .

Signal Boxes in use or to be BIU –

Aviemore Speyside	1/19D	McK&H 3/High 2h	c1990	McK&H C&T 2h	c1990	21R	T

(Box 2h ex Garve West, 1893 there; frame 2h ex Wick).

Boat of Garten North	1/19D	McK&H3/Highland	NIU*	nk	NIU	20	T

(*u1885 box abolished by BR 1965; original 40-lever McK&H frame in store. Frame ex Carr Bridge, 1968 there and fitted here in 1993).

Boat of Garten South	1/19D	Highland	1922*	McK&H C&T (Whse)	1922	30	T

(*Box abolished by BR 1965; re-opened 1970s; now a Listed Building).

Other Boxes on site – Strome Ferry West (in use as storeroom at Aviemore Speyside Station).

SWANAGE RAILWAY

Method of Working – Single line Swanage to Norden (5¾ miles), with crossing loop at Harmans Cross. Key Token Swanage – Harmans Cross and One Train Staff Harmans Cross – Norden. Long Section One Train Staff Swanage – Norden when Harmans Cross switched out. Corfe Castle box to be BIU shortly and working will then be: Key Token Swanage – Harmans Cross and Harmans Cross – Corfe Castle; One Train Staff Corfe Castle – Norden. Long Section Tablet Swanage – Corfe Castle when Harmans Cross switched out.

Signal Boxes in use or to be BIU –

Corfe Castle	5/35E	**	NIU*	Stevens (RSCo)	NIU	12	T

(*'Box' established with frame in room in station building 1956, abolished by BR 1972 but has remained in situ with frame).

Harmans Cross	5/35E	New	1997	Stevens (Stev.) 2h	1997	22	T

(Box is Swanage Railway own build to an LSWR-based style. Frame 2h ex Gunnersbury, 1898 there).

Swanage	5/35E	New	2003	Westinghouse A2 2h	2003	40	T

(Box is Swanage Railway own build to an SR style. Frame 2h ex Brockenhurst, 1935 there).

Other Boxes on site – Wool East GF (temporary waiting shelter, Harman's Cross).

SWANSEA VALE RAILWAY

Method of Working – Single line Six Pit to Cwm Crossing (¾ mile), with non-passenger extension to Upper Bank (¾ mile). One Train Staff operation.

Signal Boxes in use or to be BIU –

Upper Bank	3/24A McK&H 3/TV [SHT] 2h	NIU	-	-	-	-

(Top, 2h ex Kings Dock Jn, 1908 there, re-erected on new base. Frame ex Kings Dock Jn, GW VT5, 1955, 100 levers, is still in store).

Other Boxes on site – Luffenham Junction.

SWINDON & CRICKLADE RAILWAY

Method of Working – Single line Blunsdon to Hayes Knoll (½ mile). One Train Staff operation (introduction of Key Token working is planned). Blunsdon box functions to work points only.

Signal Boxes in use or to be BIU –

Blunsdon	3/32B LMS 11c 2h	c1990	REC 2h	c1990	26	T

(Box and frame 2h ex Claydon L&NE Junction).

Hayes Knoll	3/32B GW 24c 2h	2000	GW VT5 2h	2000	30	T

(Box 2h ex Rowley Regis, 1887 there. Frame 2h ex Totnes (part), 1943 there).

TALYLLYN RAILWAY

Method of Working – Single line Tywyn Wharf to Nant Gwernol (2' 3" gauge, 7¼ miles) with crossing places at Tywyn Pendre, Brynglas, Quarry Siding, and Abergynolwyn. Key Token Wharf – Pendre, Pendre – Brynglas, Brynglas – Quarry Siding, Quarry Siding – Abergynolwyn, with train working centrally controlled from Tywyn Wharf Control Office by telephone. Train Staff & Ticket (divisible Staff with metal tickets and Annett's Key welded on) Abergynolwyn – Nant Gwernol. The boxes at Pendre, Brynglas, Quarry Siding, and Abergynolwyn are only opened when trains are crossing there. There are semaphores at Abergynolwyn and colour light signals at Wharf. At Nant Gwernol there is only an open ground frame (no signals).

Signal Boxes in use –

Abergynolwyn	4/24E TR	1976	LMR Standard 2h	1976	14	T

(Frame 2h ex Bold Colliery Sidings, part).

Brynglas	4/24E TR Hut	1968	REC 2h	1968	5	T

(Frame 2h ex Swadlincote G.F.).

Pendre	4/24E TR	1974	LMR Standard 2h	1973	15	T

(Frame ex Miles Platting S&T Stores; BIU 1973 as open gf, cabin then built around it and installation fully commissioned 1974).

Quarry Siding	*4/24E* TR Hut	1970	GW Stud 2h	1969	7	Stud

(Frame 2h ex Watlington; BIU 1969 as open gf, cabin created for 1970 season).

Wharf	*4/24E* **	Nk	IFS panel	nk	-	E

(In Control Office, also Key Token instrument. Panel works signals, points worked from 4-lever open gf).

TANFIELD RAILWAY

Method of Working – Single line East Tanfield to Sunniside (2½ miles) with crossing place at Andrews House station (controlled by Marley Hill SB adjacent to station). Short branch to Marley Hill (non passenger). One Train Staff operation, East Tanfield – Andrews House; Andrews House – Sunniside.

Signal Boxes in use –

Marley Hill	2/47D NE N/S	1989	McK&H nk 2h	1989	15	T

(Box is entirely new but built as replica of original box on original foundations. Frame 2h ex Howdon-on-Tyne).

TEIFI VALLEY RAILWAY

Method of Working – Single line Llandyfriog to Henllan (1' 11½" gauge, 1 mile). One Train Staff operation.

Signal Boxes in use – Nil.

Other Boxes on site – Rhiwderin.

TELFORD STEAM RAILWAY

Method of Working – Single line Horsehay & Dawley – Heath Hill (½ mile) . One Train Staff operation. Staff is a 'Mark 2 Clamp Lock' which releases/controls yard points at Horsehay & Dawley.

Signal Boxes in use – Nil.

VALE OF RHEIDOL LIGHT RAILWAY

Method of Working – Single line Aberystwyth – Devil's Bridge (60cm gauge, 11¾ miles) with crossing places at Capel Bangor and Aberffrwd. Telephone dispatch from Control Office at Aberystwyth combined with One Train Staff operation for each of three sections: Section A – Aberystwyth to Capel Bangor; Section B – Capel Bangor to Aberffrwd, Section C – Aberffrwd to Devil's Bridge. Semaphore home signals at Aberystwyth, Capel Bangor and Aberffrwd. Open GFs (LNW pattern), operated by train crews and controlling facing points and protecting signals, at Aberystwyth, Capel Bangor (2), Aberffrwd (2) and Devil's Bridge.

Signal Boxes in use – Nil.

WEARDALE RAILWAY

Method of Working – Single line Wolsingham to Stanhope (5¼ miles), leased from Network Rail. One Train Staff operation. Key on Staff releases the GF for run-round loops at Stanhope and Wolsingham. The Bishop Auckland – Wolsingham and Stanhope – Eastgate sections are OOU.

Signal Boxes in use – Nil.

WELLS AND WALSINGHAM LIGHT RAILWAY

Method of Working – Single line Wells to Walsingham (10¼" gauge, 4 miles). One Train Staff operation.
Signal Boxes in use – Nil.
Other Boxes on site – Swainsthorpe (gift shop at Wells station).

WELSH HIGHLAND RAILWAY (Caernarfon) / RHEILFFORD ERYRI

Method of Working – Single line Caernarfon to Rhyd Ddu (1' 11½" gauge, 13 miles). Crossing places at Dinas and Waunfawr (both loops have Train Operated Trailable Points with 'Points Set' indicators). Caernarfon – Dinas and Waunfawr – Rhyd Ddu worked by One Train Staff. Dinas – Waunfawr worked by Train Staff which can be divided to act as Train Staff & Ticket. Points at Caernarfon and to access the sidings at Dinas are worked from 2-lever GFs locked by the Staff. All Train Staff working is controlled from the Ffestiniog Railway Control Office at Porthmadog Harbour station by telephone.
Signal Boxes in use – Nil.

WELSH HIGHLAND RAILWAY (Porthmadog) / RHEILFFORD UCHELDIR CYMRU

Method of Working – Porthmadog to Pen-y-Mount (1' 11½" gauge, ¾ mile). One Train Staff operation controlled from Ffestiniog Railway Control Office at Porthmadog Harbour station by telephone.
Signal Boxes in use – Nil.

WELSHPOOL & LLANFAIR LIGHT RAILWAY

Method of Working – Single line Llanfair Caereinion to Welshpool (2' 6" gauge, 8 miles) with crossing places at Cyfronydd, Castle Caereinion, and Sylfaen. Worked by Train Staff & Ticket for each section, referred to as 'Divisible Staff', as on many days, when use of one or more of the loops is not necessary, the Staffs are screwed together to form a single Staff for two or more sections. The box at Llanfair Caereinion is always open when passenger trains run and the signalman there acts as line controller supervising the single line block working which is conducted by radio. However a Blockman is always present at any loop that is in use for crossing trains. Welshpool box is switched out except on a few peak service days.
Signal Boxes in use –

Llanfair Caereinion		4/24D	Dutton	2002	Dutton D.T. 2h	1967	u17	T
	(Box is new structure in 'Dutton' style, replacing 1967 box (frame not moved). Frame 2h ex Llanbrynmair).							
Welshpool		4/24D	W&L	1981	LNW Tappet 2h	1981	18	T
	(Frame 2h ex Groeslon).							

Other Boxes on site – Castle Caereinion.

WENSLEYDALE RAILWAY

Method of Working – Single line Castle Hills to Redmire (22 miles), leased from Network Rail. One Train Staff operation. No crossing places on line. Run-round loop at Castle Hills operated by 2 GFs released by Annett's Key on Staff; Redmire loop operated by GFs. When a train from the national rail system is to run onto the line, the WR Line Controller takes the Staff by road to Castle Hills and makes telephone contact with York PSB.
Signal Boxes in use – Bedale (Network Rail box but staffed by Wensleydale Railway; see Section 1).

WEST SOMERSET RAILWAY

Method of Working – Single line Minehead to Norton Fitzwarren Junction (22¾ miles), with crossing places at Blue Anchor, Williton, Crowcombe Heathfield, and Bishops Lydeard. Key Token Minehead to Blue Anchor (blue). Train Staff & Ticket Blue Anchor to Crowcombe Heathfield (red); Crowcombe Heathfield to Bishops Lydeard (blue). One Train Staff Bishops Lydeard to Norton Fitzwarren (yellow). Long Section Staff Williton to Bishops Lydeard (brown) when Crowcombe is switched out.
Signal Boxes in use or to be BIU–

Bishops Lydeard		3/6C	GW 7d	1906*	GW VT5 2h	1998	33	T
	(*Abolished by BR 1970, re-opened by WSR 1998. Frame 2h ex Westbury South (part)(1953 there)).							
Blue Anchor		3/6C	GW7b	1904*	GW Stud	1904	17	Stud
	(*Abolished by BR 1971, re-opened by WSR).							
Crowcombe Heathfield		3/6C	GW 27c 2h	1996	GW VT5 2h	1996	29	T
	(Box top 2h ex Ebbw Vale Sidings South, 1905 there, on new base; frame 2h ex Frome North, 2h 1970 there ex Marsh Junction).							
Minehead		3/6C	GW 31 2h	1990	GW VT5 2h	1990	27	T
	(Box 2h ex Dunster, 2h 1934 there, abolished by BR 1971: frame 2h ex Westbury South (part) (1953 there)).							
Williton		3/6C	B&E	1875*	GW VT5	1937	25	T
	(*Abolished by BR 1971, re-opened by WSR).							

Other Boxes on site – Burnham-on-Sea, Washford.

DIRECTORY SECTION 7:
OTHER PRESERVED AND DISUSED BOXES

Boxes in signalling use (or shortly to come into signalling use) on the heritage railways <u>are</u> listed here in Section Seven, but without full details being given; a cross-reference is provided to Section Six where full details will be found under the relevant railway's entry. There are separate tabulations here for:

(1)   Former BR boxes. (As in Directory Section One, a few boxes are also included here with other former ownerships, if on lines which effectively formed branches off the main national railway system).

(2)   Former London Underground boxes. (Excluding boxes built by the GER and GNR on lines now owned by LUL - these are in (1)).

(3)   Other systems in Great Britain.

(4&5)   Ireland (all boxes in Ireland are included in this one tabulation).

The boxes listed here in Section Seven naturally have many different present-day functions (or no use), but the majority of them come under the following categories

- Boxes abolished in recent years but not yet demolished. Many of these are derelict.
- Boxes abolished but with new uses, still in Network Rail (etc.) ownership, on functional railway lines, as offices, messrooms, etc.
- Boxes on Heritage Railways but not in, or intended for, active signalling use.
- Boxes preserved, with frame and other signalling equipment, by signalling enthusiasts, at other locations (either original or moved).
- Boxes still on their original site on lifted lines, used by the present day owners of the station houses or other railway land as garages, sheds, greenhouses, etc.
- Boxes moved to new locations and used as offices, sheds, etc. in private or business premises.

The tabulations here are arranged in much the same way as in Sections 1 – 5, but a 'Present State' column is added (where there is not room to describe the present state briefly, it is referred to in a footnote), and the 'Locking' column is omitted for space reasons (where frames have been re-locked with tappet locking, this is noted 'R.T' in the 'Frame Design' column). Absence of an entry here would normally indicate that the box is 'empty and unused'. <u>M</u> after the box name indicates that the box has been moved from its original location to a new site as noted in the footnotes. (A large proportion of the preserved boxes in England and Wales have actually been moved to new sites; but there are few cases of this in Ireland).

Quail references are given for those boxes situated on functional lines included in Quail. As in Sections 1 – 5, an entry in italics indicates that the box itself is not shown by Quail, which is more commonly the case here in Section Seven as Quail does not generally show disused boxes; these references will nevertheless help some users in identifying the location. (Many of the boxes that <u>are</u> in Quail are only in because they were still functional at the time of the Quail edition). Some of the boxes listed here are in very obscure out-of-the-way locations and have not, as a result, been 'seen' for several years; it is therefore possible that a few in fact have been demolished without this fact having become known to us. Correspondingly, every year sees the 'discovery' of a few more boxes still extant at obscure locations on our large mileage of long-closed and lifted railways, plus more boxes which were moved years back to new sites on non-railway premises and have been forgotten by 'railway' people. There is therefore no possibility of Section Seven ever being fully comprehensive as Sections 1 – 5 are. Advice of future 'discoveries' is of course welcomed.

Pinesway Junction (2000) – The LSW non-standard box, ex-Wyke, controls the fully signalled junction on the Gartell narrow gauge railway near Templecombe in Somerset. This is one of many signal box structures that have found a new home on heritage and other railways and gardens since the 1960s.

SECTION 7(1): OTHER PRESERVED AND DISUSED BOXES: EX BR BOXES

Box Name	Quail Map	Box:- Type	Date	Frame:- Design	Date	No. of Levers	Present State	Notes
Aberbeeg Junction	3/28A	GW 5	1892	GW HT3 5 1/4"	1914	65	Derelict	
Aberdour L	1/13	NB 2*	1890	-	-	-	P.Way (good)	
Ableton Lane Crossing M	-	GW 29	nk	GW gf	nk	3		
Acton Lane SF	5/1A	BR(LMR) 15	1964	LMR Standard	1964	30		
Adelphi Street	-	Mersey	u1888	RSCo Tappet	u1888	5	Derelict	1
Ainderby M (see Alston, South Tynedale Railway)								
Airdrie	1/8L	BR(ScR) 16	1960	-	-	-	Boarded up	
Ais Gill M (see Butterley GF, Midland Railway Centre) L								
Aldwarke Junction	2/33A	BR(ER) 18 PB	1965	-	-	-	Bricked up	
All Hallows Colliery Middle SF M	-	M&C	nk	-	-	-	Boarded up	139
Alness North M	-	McK&H3/High.	1891	-	-	-	Garden shed	4
Alness South M	-	McK&H3/High.	1891	-	-	-	Garden shed	4
Alresford (see Mid Hants Railway)								
Anchor Pit Junction M	-	L&Y	1901	-	-	-	Derelict	5
Appleby (Lincs) L	2/34C	RSCo[MS&L]	1885	RSCo Tappet	1885	23		112
Ardgay South M	-	Dutton 1/High+	1890	-	-	-	Privately pres'd	
Ardlui	1/21A	NB 6a	1894	-	-	-	Waiting Room	
Arisaig L	1/22B	RSCo/WHE	1901	Stev GOP (RSCo)	1901	15		
Armathwaite	4/34C	Mid 2b	1899	Mid Tumbler	1899	16	Restored	6
Arrochar & Tarbet M	1/21A	NB 6a	1894	-	-	-	Waiting Room	7
Asher Lane (see Great Central Railway (North))								
Ashford	5/11b	BR(SR) 18 PB	1962	-	-	-	(good)	
Athelney M (see Bishops Bridge, South Devon Railway)								
Attadale M	-	McK&H3/High	1893	-	-	-	Shelter	9
Aughton Road M	-	Mid 4d	1928	REC	1928	14R		10
Auldbar Road	-	Cal N1	c1876	-	-	-	Store	
Axe Gates	5/34A	SR Hut	1949	-	-	-		
Axminster Gates	5/34A	LSW Hut	nk	-	-	-		
Aylesbury South M (see Swithland, Great Central Railway)								
Aysgarth	-	NE S1A	1878	McK&H 16 2h	c2000	16	Preserved	170
Balham	5/4	BR(SR) 15	1952	-	-	-	(poor)	
Bamford M (see Darley Dale, Peak Rail)								
Banavie Swing Bridge M	-	RSCo/WHE	1901	-	-	-		13
Barham M	-	SE	1887	-	-	-	Museum	14
Barmouth South M	-	Dutton 1 [Cam]	1890	GW VT3	1924	27	Llangollen Rly	15
Barnes	5/1A	BR(SR) 17	1959	OCS panel	1985	-		
Barnstaple Town	-	LSW 4	1898	-	-	-	Restored	
Barnwood Sidings M	-	Mid 4c	nk	-	-	-	Dean Forest Rly	12
Barry Dock Basin	-	Barry 1	nk	nk	nk	nk	Boarded up	16
Barry Island M	-	McK&H 3 2h	1929	-	-	-		54
Barton GF M	-	GW 21	nk	-	-	-	Dean Forest Rly	17
Barton Junction M	-	RSCo[MS&L]	1885	-	-	-	-	18
Baschurch M L	-	McK&H 3 [GW]	1880	GW Stud	1911	25	(good)	174
Belah	-	NE C2a	nk	-	-	-	Derelict	
Bells Bank Foot	-	NEC 2b	1901	-	-	-	Derelict	
Bendor	-	NE N/S	1887	-	-	-	Store (good)	
Bentley North (see Alton, Mid Hants Railway)								
Bere Alston	3/8D	LSW 3b	1890E	-	-	-		20
Berney Arms M (see Mangapps Farm)								
Betchworth	5/24B	SR BO Extn	1934	-	-	-		
Betteshanger Colliery	5/9A	SR 11a	1923	SEC NP	1923	16		207
Bewdley North (see Severn Valley Railway)								
Bewdley South (see Severn Valley Railway)								
Biggar	-	Cal S4	1906	-	-	-		167
Billericay GF M	-	LNER Hut	1937	-	-	-	Mangapps Farm	204
Birkdale	4/41B	L&Y Hipped	1905	L&Y	1905	24		22
Bishops Lydeard (see West Somerset Railway)								
Bishops Stortford L	2/11B	LNER 11b	1931	RSCo-LNER Standard	1931	45R		127
Blackpool South M	-	BR(LMR) 15	1965	-	-	-		24
Blind Lane M (see Rothley, Great Central Railway)								
Blue Anchor (see West Somerset Railway)								
Boat of Garten North (see Strathspey Railway)								
Boat of Garten South (see Strathspey Railway)								
Bodmin Road	3/9A	GW 3+	1887	-	-	-	Café	
Bogside	-	NB 2b	1890	-	-	-	Timber yard office	
Bolsover Coalite GF	2/30A	BR Hut	nk	gf	nk	2	Derelict	

SECTION 7(1): OTHER PRESERVED AND DISUSED BOXES: EX BR BOXES

Box Name		Quail Map	Box:- Type	Date	Frame:- Design	Date	No. of Levers	Present State	Notes
Bootle Junction		4/41A	Portakabin	1986	-	-	-	Derelict	
Borough Market Junction M		-	SE	nk	Whse 'K' pf	1928	35		25
Botany Bay M		-	GN 3	1901	GN 4"	1901	12		26
Botley		5/28B	LSW 1+	1873	-	-	-		
Bournemouth Central	L	5/31A	SR 11c*	1928	Westinghouse A2	1928	60		147
Bourton-on-the-Water M		-	GWCo[B&CD]	1881	-	-	-		28
Bowes M		-	NE C1	nk	-	-	-	Preserved	142
Bowley's Crossing M		-	Mid 1 (Hut)	1877	-	-	-	Dean Forest Rly	30
Brading	L	5/35C	IOW	1882	Stevens (Stevens)	1882	30	Boarded up	212
Brampton Junction		2/46A	NE N1	c1874	-	-	-	Derelict	
Bratton Fleming M		-	L&B Hut	1898	-	-	-		217
Brent		3/7c*	GW 25+	1893	-	-	-	P.Way	31
Bridgefoot M		-	LNW 4/5	1913	-	-	-		32
Bridge of Orchy		1/21D	NB 6a	1894	S&F 1888 Dx R.T	1894	16		
Brimsdown		2/10B	GE 7*	1944-	McK&H 4"	u1902	37R	Derelict	
Bristol Old Station	L	3/5B	Mid/GW N/S	nk	-	-	-		57
Brize Norton & Brampton GF M		-	GW 29	nk	Stud	nk	5	Glos. Warks. Rly	33
Broomielaw		-	NE C2a	1897	Stevens (Stevens)	1897	u17	Derelict	
Broom West		-	LMS 13	1942	-	-	-	Derelict	
Broxbourne		2/11A	BR(ER) 18 PB	1960	NX panel	1960	-	S&T office	
Bruern Crossing M		-	GW 28b	c1934	-	-	-		34
Bryn-y-Gwynon Crossing		3/23A	GW 2+	1870s	-	-	-	Boarded up	
Buckden M (see Tunbridge Wells West, Spa Valley Railway)									
Buckfastleigh		3/7C	GW 7d	1906	GW Stud	1906	27	South Devon Rly	36
Buckland Crossing		-	LCD Hut	nk	LCD	nk	7		
Burghclere		-	GW 13	1942	-	-	-	Derelict	
Burgh-le-Marsh		-	GN 1	c1890	-	-	-	Tea shop	37
Burnham-on-Sea M		-	S&DJ Hut	nk	-	-	-	W. Somerset Rly	38
Burnley Central M		-	L&Y	1900	nk	nk	nk	Preserved	39
Burrelton		-	Cal N1	c1876	-	-	-	Derelict	40
Bursnip Road		-	(Colliery)	nk	-	-	-	Craft shop	29
Burton Agnes	L	2/39B	NE S1b	1875	-	-	-	Boarded up	
Bury South (see East Lancashire Railway)									
California Crossing M		-	Mid 4d	1920	Mid Tappet	1920	12	Glos. Warks. Rly	43
Cannon Street		5/3D	BR(SR) 16*	1957	-	-	-	(good)	
Cardrona		-	NB B.O. Extn	c1890	-	-	-	Privately pres'd	
Carlisle No. 4A	L	4/29C	LNW N/S	1880	-	-	-		215
Carlisle Down Tower		4/29D	BR(LMR) C/T	1963	-	-	-	Derelict	
Carlisle Up Departure		4/29C	BR(LMR) Hut	1985	-	-	-		
Carlisle Up Tower		4/29D	BR(LMR) C/T	1963	-	-	-	Derelict	
Carnforth Station Jn (Old Box)	L	4/28B	Furness N/S	nk	-	-	-		235
Carr Bridge	L	1/19D	BR(ScR) N/S	1957	-	-	-		46
Carr Bridge South		1/19D	McK&H3/High	c1892	-	-	-	P.Way	
Carterhouse Junction		4/38A	LNW 4	1896	LNW Tumbler	1896	30	Boarded up	
Carville		-	NE N2+	1900	-	-	-		96
Castle Caereinion		4/24D	Tyer Hut [W&L]	1907	-	-	-	W&LLR	
Castleford Gates		2/42A	NE S1*	1870sE	McK&H16 recon.	1927	32		214
Castleford Station	L	2/42A	NE S1*	1882E	McK&H16	1914	40		
Cefn Junction		3/23B	GW 7a	1898	-	-	-	Information centre	47
Chappel & Wakes Colne		2/5E	GE 7	1891	S&F 1888 Dx	1891	38	EARM	48
Cheadle Hulme		4/43B	LNW 4	1901	LNW Tumbler	1901	36		
Chelfham M		-	L&B Hut	1898	-	-	-		216
Chelmsford		2/5C	GE 7*	u1885	S&F 1888 Dx	1899	45	Abolished 1996	
Cheshunt Junction		2/11A	GE 8	1891	-	-	-	Boarded up	
Chilham M (see Tenterden Town, Kent & East Sussex Railway)									
Chilworth		5/24A	RSCo[SE]	nk	-	-	-	Music sch./shop	
Chingford		2/10B	GE 7	1920	-	-	-		
Chiswick		5/1A	SR 14	1944	-	-	-	Derelict	
Chorley No.3		4/48A	GW Co [L&Y]	1879	L&Y	1920	4		
Church Stretton		4/23B	LNW/GW Jt 1	c1872	LNW Tumbler	nk	25		236
Cilyrychen Crossing M		-	GW 28b	1912	GW No.6	1912	16		95
Clapham Junction B		5/2	(BR(SR) 15*	1952	-	-	-		
Clapham Junction C		5/2	LSW 4	nk	-	-	-	(poor)	
Claydon L&NE Junction M (see Blunsdon, Swindon & Cricklade Railway)									
Clayton West Junction M		-	L&Y+	1915	-	-	-	House	49
Cliburn		-	NE N/S	c1910	-	-	-	Restored/store	
Clifton Moor M		-	NE N/S	nk	-	-	-		171

SECTION 7(1): OTHER PRESERVED AND DISUSED BOXES: EX BR BOXES

Box Name		Quail Map	Box:- Type	Date	Frame:- Design	Date	No. of Levers	Present State	Notes
Clifton Station M (see Consall, Churnet Valley Railway)									
Coalville Crossing M		-	Mid 4a	1908	-	-	-		51
Cogload M		-	GW 27c	c1906	GW VT5 2h	1990s	nk		52
Cold Meece		-	LMS 13	1941	-	-	-	Derelict	
Cole Green M		-	GN 1+	nk	Mid Tumbler 2h	1970s	17	Preserved	53
Collingham		2/27E	Midland 3a	1901	-	-	-		
Coniston Station GF M		-	Furness 2	nk	Easterbrook 1872 2h	1970s	17	Preserved	55
Corfe Castle (see Swanage Railway)									
Corrour		1/21E	NB 6a	1894	-	-	-	Climbers' hut	
Cossington M (see Cranmore West, East Somerset Railway)									
Coton Hill North		4/22A	GW 7d+	c1912	-	-	-	Derelict	
Cottage Lane		2/27E	Midland 4d	1927	-	-	-		
Cottingham North M		-	NE S4	1906	McK&H 16	1906	21		56
Cove Siding		-	GW 3+	1884	-	-	-		
Cowbit		-	GN 1	1882	McK&H 1873 5"	1882	35		
Coxwold Gates		-	NE S5	nk	-	-	-	Store	
Cradley Heath M		-	GW 4c	1888	(GW VT 3	1915	36)	South Devon Rly	124
Cranmore		3/12A	GW 7b	1904	-	-	-	Art gallery/ESR	
Crawley	L	5/19B	S&F 5 [LBSC]	1877	S&F Rocker 5" R.T	1877	21		120
Cressing M (see Hedingham, Colne Valley Railway)									
Crewe 'A' M		-	LNW N/S	1907	LNW pf	1907	26		75
Crewe North Junction		4.13	LMS 13*	1940	Whse 'L' pf	1940	214		75
Crewe Sorting Sidings Middle Up		4/13	BR (LMR) 15	1961	-	-	-	(good)	
Crewe South Junction		4/13	LMS 13*	1940	-	-	-	Derelict	
Crewkerne		5/33D	BR(SR) 16*	1960	-	-	-	Boarded up	
Crianlarich Upper		1/21B	NB 6*	1894	-	-	-		
Cromer	L	2/8	M&GN N/S	c1920	RSCo Tappet 2h	c1954	35		45
Crossmichael		-	GSW 3	1891	-	-	-	(poor)	
Crowle		2/33B	BR(ER) 16a*	nk	-	-	-	P.Way	
Crumpsall M		-	GWCo[L&Y]	1880	(LMR Standard	1955	25)	East Lancs Rly	58
Crundale Crossing M		-	GW 3+	1885	-	-	-		59
Crundale Crossing M		-	GW 29	1916	-	-	-	Gwili Railway	60
Culworth Junction M		-	MS&L 4	c1897	GW VT5 2h	-	34	Preserved	220
Dainton M		-	BR(WR) 37a	1965	-	-	-		61
Dalanraoch		1/19B	BR(ScR) N/S	1966	-	-	-	Store	
Dalchonzie		-	Cal N/S	1901	-	-	-	(good)	
Dalcross M		-	nk	1882	-	-	-		62
Dalmally		1/21C	Cal N2	1896	-	-	-		
Dalnaspidal		1/19B	Highland	1901	-	-	-	P.Way	
Dartford		5/5	BR(SR) PB	1970	-	-	-		
Dawlish	L	3/7B	GW 27c	1918	-	-	-		
Deal Junction M (see Wittersham Road, Kent & East Sussex Railway)									
Dean M		-	LSW 1+	c1875	Stevens (u Stevens)	c1875	nk		63
Dean Crossing [Whitwell] M (see Smallbrook GF, Isle of Wight Steam Railway)									
Dean GF M (see Ropley, Mid Hants Railway)									
Derby 'A'		4/4B	BR(LMR) N/S	c1952	-	-	-	Railway office	64
Dereham North M		-	GE 2*	1880	-	-	-		65
Dersingham		-	GE 7	1891	-	-	-	Store	
Desford Colliery Sidings M		-	Mid 3a	1901	-	-	-	Midland Rly C'tre	66
Devonshire Bridge M		-	RSCo[Furness]	1883	-	-	-		67
Dingwall Level Crossing GF		1/22F	BR(ScR) N/S	1979	-	-	-		
Dodworth		2/36A	BR(ER) N/S	c1959	S&F 1888 Duplex 2h	c1959	22	Boarded up	
Douglas Bank East M		-	L&Y	1904	L&Y	1904	40		68
Dover Marine		5/13	SEC	1914	-	-	-		
Drumvaich Crossing		-	Cal N2	1892	-	-	-	Store (poor)	
Dumbarton		1/6B	BR(ScR) PB	1960	-	-	-	P.Way	
Dunham Hill No.2		-	LMS 13	c1942	-	-	-	Derelict	
Dunster M (see Minehead, West Somerset Railway)									
Eagle Crossing M		-	BR(LMR) 15	1970	LMR Standard	1970	35		133
Earby Crossing M (see Damems Crossing, Keighley & Worth Valley Railway)									
East Croydon		5/14C	BR(SR) 15*	1955	-	-	-	Railway offices	
East Finchley		5/39A	GN 1	1881	-	-	-	Store (boarded up)	
East Langton M		-	Mid 2b	1895	Midland Tumbler	1895	20		69
East Winch		-	GE 7	1886	-	-	-	Boarded up	
Ebbw Vale Sidings South M (see Crowcombe, West Somerset Railway)									
Effingham Junction		5/23A	LSW 3a	1885	-	-	-	Staff room	
Eggesford M		-	BR(WR) 37a 2h	1969	-	-	-		70

SECTION 7(1): OTHER PRESERVED AND DISUSED BOXES: EX BR BOXES

Box Name		Quail Map	Box:- Type	Date	Frame:- Design	Date	No. of Levers	Present State	Notes
Elgin Centre		1/18A	GNS 2a	1888	-	-	-		
Elsham	L	2/34C	RSCo [MS&L]	1885	RSCo Tappet	1885	22		112
Elton Crossing M (see Cheddleton Shunt Frame, Churnet Valley Railway)									
Embsay Station (see Embsay Steam Railway) L									
Enfield Town		2/10B	GE 7	1905	Westinghouse 17A	1959	25		
Eridge		5/14B	S&F 5 [LBSC]	1880	S&F Rocker 5" R.T	1880	32	Spa Valley Rly	72
Esholt Junction M (see Haworth, Keighley & Worth Valley Railway)									
Euston		4/1	BR(LMR) PB	1965	-	-	-	Railway offices	
Evanton North M		-	McK&H3/High	c1891	-	-	-		73
Exeter Central 'B'		5/34C	SR 11c	1925	-	-	-	Railway store	
Exeter West M		-	GW 27c	1913	GW VT 5	1959	131		75
Exminster		3/7B	GW 28b	1924E	GW VT 5	1941	80	(fair)	76
Eye M		-	GE Hut	1892	-	-	-		19
Factory Junction		5/2	BR(SR) 15*	1953	-	-	-		
Falmer		5/16	SR BO Extn	1930	Knee (nk)	1951	22	Preserved	218
Falstone		-	NB 5	1893	-	-	-		77
Faversham Creek Branch GF M		-	LCD Hut	nk	Stevens (Stevens) 2h	nk	10	Privately pres'd	223
Fencote		-	GW 7	1897	GW Stud 2h	1990s	23	Preserved	221
Ffairfach M		-	GW 31	1935	-	-	-	Gwili Railway	78
Finghall Lane M		-	NE Hut	nk	-	-	-		79
Forden		4/23C	Dutton 3 [Cam]	1897	-	-	-	Private store	
Forest Hill		5/4	BR(SR) 15	1950	-	-	-	Derelict	
Forsinard North		1/20D	Dutton 1/High	1894	-	-	-	P.Way	
Fossway Crossing		4/18	LNW 3	1875	-	-	-		
Fotherby M (see Chappel South, East Anglian Railway Museum)									
French Drove		-	GN1	1882	-	-	-	Store	81
Frizinghall M (see Damems Junction, Keighley & Worth Valley Railway)									
Frome North M (see 'Frome Mineral Junction', GWS Didcot)									
Frongoch		-	McK&H 3 [GW]+	1882	-	-	-	Greenhouse	83
Garden Street	L	2/32A	MS&L 2	1881	MS&L Iron Brack.	1881	19		212
Garelochhead		1/21A	NB 6a	1894	-	-	-	Boarded up	
Garnqueen South Junction M (see Bo'ness, Bo'ness & Kinneil Railway)									
Garve East M		-	McK&H 3/High	1893	-	-	-		85
Garve West M (see Aviemore Speyside, Strathspey Railway)									
Georgeham Gates		-	LSW 3b	1889	-	-	-	Store	87
Gillingham IECC		5/8A	PB	-	-	-	-	Archive store	149
Gisburn		4/33B	S&F 9 [L&Y]	1879	-	-	-	Summerhouse	
Glaisdale		2/51B	NE S1a	1902	-	-	-	Derelict	
Glamis		-	Cal N1	c1876	-	-	-	(fair)	74
Glanamman Crossing		3/31C	GW 7b	c1901	-	-	-	Inhabited	
Glencruitten		1/21C	Cal Box-House	1903	-	-	-	Holiday cottage	
Glenfinnan		1/22B	RSCo/WHE	1901	Stev.GOP(RSCo)	1901	15	Garage	89
Goathland (see North Yorkshire Moors Railway)									
Goldsborough		-	LNER N/S	1942	-	-	-	Garage	
Gomshall & Shere		5/24A	SR 14	1941	-	-	-	P.Way	
Goostrey No.2		4/34B	BR(LMR) 15	1954	-	-	-	Derelict	
Gorsey Bank M (see Church Lane Crossing, Peak Rail)									
Great Bentley M		-	GE 7	u1889	-	-	-	Mid Norfolk Rly	224
Great Missenden	L	3/18E	Met 1	1892	Met	nk	30		
Grosmont M		-	NE N/S	1904	-	-	-	Sth Tynedale Rly	90
Guestwick		-	M&GN 1	nk	-	-	-	Summerhouse	
Guiseley M (see Bolton Abbey, Embsay Steam Railway)									
Gunthorpe Gates		-	M&GN 1	nk	-	-	-	Station owners	
Gwaun-y-Bara M		-	McK&H 3 [BM]	nk	-	-	-		92
Hackney Downs	L	2/10B	BR(ER) 18 PB	1960	-	-	-	Railway office	
Haddiscoe Junction M		-	GE 7	1904	-	-	-	Mangapps Farm	93
Halesworth M		-	GE 2*	1881	S&F Rocker 5" R.T	1881	35		94
Hall Green M (see Winchcombe, Gloucestershire Warwickshire Railway)									
Haltwhistle	L	2/46C	NE N/S	nk	McK&H 17 recon.	1927	61R		229
Hampton Loade (see Severn Valley Railway)									
Harker		-	LNER 12	1938	-	-	-	Garage	
Harlington M (see Quainton Road, Buckinghamshire Railway Centre)									
Harlow Mill		2/11A	BR(ER) 18 PB	1960	-	-	-	S&T store	
Harringay Up Siding M		-	GN Hut	u1893	GN gf	nk	5		97
Harringworth M		4/3A	Midland 4c	c1928	REC	c1928	25	N'n & L'port Rly	
Hartford Junction		4/26A	LNW 5	1925	-	-	-	Derelict	41
Hartington		-	LNW 4/5	1899	LNW Tumbler	1899	20	Tourist office	27

SECTION 7(1): OTHER PRESERVED AND DISUSED BOXES: EX BR BOXES

Box Name		Quail Map	Box:- Type	Date	Frame:- Design	Date	No. of Levers	Present State	Notes
Hartlepool South Works		2/48A	BSC	1960	Whse A3	1960	44	Derelict	
Hassall Green M		-	NS 2	nk	McK&H 1873 5"	nk	21	(good)	98
Havenstreet (see Isle of Wight Steam Railway)									
Haverthwaite (see Lakeside & Haverthwaite Railway)									
Hawkhurst		-	McK&H 3 [SE]	1893	-	-	-	Bldr's yard office	
Heddon Mill		-	LSW 3b	1889	-	-	-	Conservatory	87
Helmsdale South	L	1/20C	Dutton 1/High	u1894	-	-	-	P.Way	
Helmshore M		-	S&F 8 [L&Y]+	1876	-	-	-		99
Helmsley		-	NE S4+	nk	-	-	-	Pigeon loft	
Herne Hill		5/4	BR(SR) 16*	1956	-	-	-	Railway use	
Hertford East	L	2/11A	GE 7/McK&H	1888	McK&H 1873 Pat5"	1888	45		
Heysham Harbour M (see Lydney Junction, Dean Forest Railway)									
Higham		-	Portakabin	1988	-	-	-	No use	
Highams Park	L	2/10B	LNER 11a	u1927	nk 4"	u1927	5		
High Barnet		5/39A	GN 1	1872	-	-	-	LUL store	
Highclere		-	GW 13	1942	-	-	-	Renovated	
High Ferry		2/26A	GN 1	1890	-	-	-	Boarded up	
Highley (see Severn Valley Railway)									
High Marnham		2/30B	BR(ER) 16a*	1959	RSCo-GNI	1959	nk	Derelict	
High Street Yard [Glasgow]		1/7L	NB 7	1908	-	-	-	Derelict	
Hindolvestone		-	M&GN 1	nk	-	-	-	Station owners	
Hockley Crossing M (see Blythe Bridge, Foxfield Steam Railway)									
Holesmouth Junction M (see Tyseley Warwick Road, Birmingham Railway Museum)									
Holme Hale		-	GE 7	1891	-	-	-	(good)	
Holt M (see Weybourne, North Norfolk Railway)									
Honeybourne North Loop M		-	GW 27c	1904	-	-	-	Glos. Warks. Rly	101
Honing East M		-	M&GN 1	1901	McK&H nk 4" 2h	c1970s	26		102
Honiton Incline		5/34A	LSW Hut	nk	-	-	-	Derelict	
Honiton Tunnel West M		-	LSW N/S	nk	-	-	-	Privately pres'd	223
Hoo Junction		5/7	BR(SR) 18 PB	1964	-	-	-	Yard office	
Horsemoor M		-	GE 7/Dutton	1899	-	-	-	Store	103
Horsted Keynes South (see Bluebell Railway) L									
Hotchley Hill		4/4A	LNER 15	nk	-	-	-	Great Central Rly	
Howden	L	2/38A	NE S1a	c1873	McK&H16	1905	15R		
"Hudson" [Crewe]		4/13	BR(LMR) 15	2h nk	LMR Standard	nk	20		104
Hyndland		1/7L	BR(ScR) PB	1960	NX Panel	1960	-		105
Immingham Empty Sidings M		-	GC 5	1912	-	-	-		106
Instow	L	-	LSW 1+	1870s	Stevens (Stevens)	1870s	16		107
Invergordon North M		-	Dutton 4 / High+	1890	-	-	-	Fawley Hill Rly	108
Inverness Station Frame M		-	McK&H / High	u1917	-	-	-	Fawley Hill Rly	
Inverugie M		-	GNS 2b	1894	-	-	-		110
Isfield		5/16A	S&F 5 [LBSC]	1877	S&F Rocker 5" R.T	(1877)	19	Lavender Line	111
Jackfield Sidings South GF M		-	GW 29	u1898	GW nk 2h	nk	8		3
Jumble Lane [Barnsley]		2/36A	GC N/S	nk	GC	nk	35	Boarded up	
Keighley Station Junction M	L	-	Mid 2a	1884	Mid Tappet	1934	32		80
Keresley Colliery		-	NCB	nk	-	-	-	Boarded up	
Kettering Station M (see Swanwick Junction, Midland Railway Centre)									
Kilby Bridge M (see Hammersmith, Midland Railway Centre) L									
Kinbrace M		-	Dutton 1/ High	1894	-	-	-		62
Kings Cross Freight Terminal Jn		2/14A	BR(ER) Hut	1975	-	-	-	Derelict	
King's Dock Junction M (see Upper Bank, Swansea Vale Railway)									
Kingswinford Junction South		4/20C	N/S	2003	gf	2003	14		161
Kinloss West		1/18D	Highland N/S	u1887	-	-	-		2
Kipling Cotes		-	NE S1a	nk	-	-	-	Restored	
Kippen	L	-	NB N/S	1893	-	-	-	Listed building	
Kirkbuddo		-	Cal N2	1892	-	-	-		114
Kirknewton		-	NE N/S	1887	-	-	-	Workshop (poor)	
Kirk Smeaton M		-	H&B 1	1900	-	-	-		115
Knockando	uL	-	GNS 3a	1899	nk	nk	nk	Distillery office	
Kyle of Lochalsh		1/22D	Dutton 3 / High	1897	-	-	-	P.Way	
Lakeside (see Lakeside & Haverthwaite Railway)									
Lamport		-	LNW 4+	1879	-	-	-		116
Langor Bridge		-	M&GN 1	1898	-	-	-	Under restorat'n	
Lansdown Junction		3/15D	GW 13	1942	-	-	-	(poor)	
Lartington West		-	NE C1	u1873	-	-	-	Derelict	
Laundry Lane Crossing M		-	GE Hut	u1903	nk 2h	nk	4	Mid Norfolk Rly	117
Leaton M (see Glyndyfrdwy, Llangollen Railway)									

SECTION 7(1): OTHER PRESERVED AND DISUSED BOXES: EX BR BOXES

Box Name		Quail Map	Box:- Type	Date	Frame:- Design	Date	No. of Levers	Present State	Notes
Leeds		2/37A	**	1967	-	-	-	Station office	
Leek Brook Junction		4/25B	McK&H 1 [NS]	c1872	McK&H 1873 5"	nk	40		118
Leigh M		-	NS 2	nk	-	-	-	Privately pres'd	50
Levisham (see North Yorkshire Moors Railway)									
Linby Colliery Sidings M		-	Mid 2b	1894	-	-	-	Midland Rly C'tre	8
Linby Station M		-	Mid 2b	1895E	Mid Tumbler	u1895	20	Midland Rly C'tre	42
Lincoln High Street Crossing		2/27A	Mid N/S	nk	-	-	-	Fastfood bar	
Lincoln Street [Nottingham] M		4/6D	Midland 4a	1916	-	-	-	Training centre	35
Liphook M		-	LSW 2	1878	Stevens (Dutton)	1895	20		119
Little Bowden Crossing M (see Pitsford & Brampton, Northampton & Lamport Railway)									
Little Bowden Junction M		-	Mid 2b	1897	-	-	-		121
Littleton Sidings SF		4/21B	LNW 4	1900	LNW Tumbler	1900	20	Boarded up	212
Liverpool Riverside M		-	RSCo [MDHB]	u1895	RSCo Tappet	1895	21R		205
Llandebie M (see Bronwydd Arms, Gwili Railway)									
Llandrindod Wells M	L	-	LNW 4	1876	LNW Tum R. VT 5	u1906	17R		123
Llangollen Station (see Llangollen Railway) L									
Llansantffraid Crossing M		-	Dutton 4 [Cam]	1893	Dutton 1893 Pat 2h	nk	8R		125
Llansantffraid Station M		-	Dutton 4 [Cam]	1893	-	-	-		151
Llanuwchllyn (see Bala Lake Railway)									
Llanwyrtd Wells M		-	LNW 5	1928	LNW Tappet	1928	nk		126
Llynvi Junction		3/27D	McK&H 1	nk	-	-	-	Boarded up	213
London Road [Manchester]		4/45D	BR(LMR) PB	1959	-	-	-	Railway offices	
Long Meg Sidings		4/34C	BR(LMR) 15	1955	-	-	-	Derelict	
Lords Bridge		-	LNW 4	1903	-	-	-		11
Loughborough North (see Great Central Railway)									
Louth North	L		GN 1	1890	S&F Rocker 5" R.T	2h 1920	c48	Derelict	128
Lowesby		-	GN 1	1882	-	-	-	Farm Shed (poor)	
Luffenham Junction M		-	Mid 4d	1924	REC	1924	10R	Swansea Vale Rly	129
Lymington Pier		5/30B	BR(SR) 16*	1956	-	-	-	No use	
Maentwrog Road		-	McK&H 3 [GW]	1882	-	-	-	Preserved/altered	
Maesmawr M (see Parkend, Dean Forest Railway)									
Maiden Newton		5/35A	GW 7d	1921	-	-	-	No use/derelict	
Mardock M		-	GE 7	1892	-	-	-		131
Market Bosworth		4/34C	LNW 4	1898	LNW Tumbler	1898	25	Battlefield Line	
Market Rasen M (see Quorn, Great Central Railway)									
Marsh Junction		3/5B	BR(WR) 17	1959	-	-	-	Railway offices	213
Maryhill Park Junction		1/7L	BR(ScR) N/S	1980s	-	-	-	Scrapyard office	91
Massingham		-	Mid 2a 2h	1920	-	-	-	(good)	
Maxey Crossing M (see Orton Mere, Nene Valley Railway)									
Melton GF M		-	NE Hut	nk	gf	nk	nk	At NRM	
Menheniot		3/9a*	GW 5	1892	-	-	-	Boarded up	
Mentmore Crossing M		-	LNW 4	nk	-	-	-	Whipsnade Rly	226
Midhurst M		-	LSW N/S	u1866	-	-	-		132
Mileage Yard GF [Gloucester] (see Norchard, Dean Forest Railway)									
Milford West Sidings		2/37B	Hut	1980	-	-	-		
Millerhill Down Tower		1/11a*	BR(ScR) C/T	1963	-	-	-	Disused	
Millerhill Up Tower		1/11a*	BR(ScR) C/T	1963	-	-	-	Disused	
Mistley M (see Chappel North, East Anglian Railway Museum) L									
Morton Crossing GF		-	Mid Hut	nk	REC	1929	10		
Mouldsworth Sidings GF M		-	CLC Hut	u1894	CLC	u1894	12		134
Mow Cop M		-	NS 2	nk	-	-	-	Pres'ved locally	
Muirhouse Junction		1/7R	BR(ScR) 16	1961	-	-	-	P.Way	
Murrow West		-	LNER 15+	1950	-	-	-	House	
Murthly (South)	L	1/19A	McK&H3/High 2h	1919	-	-	-		135
Muston Crossing M (see Murton, Derwent Valley Light Railway)									
Nairn East	L	1/18B	McK&H 3/High	1891	McK&H 1886 Pat. 5"	1891	13		
Nairn West	L	1/18B	McK&H 3/High	1891	McK&H C&T 5"	nk	19R		
Navenby		-	GN 1	1881	-	-	-	(poor)	
Neasden South M (see Ruddington Fields, Great Central Railway (North))									
Netley M (see Ropley, Mid Hants Railway)									
New Bridge (see North Yorkshire Moors Railway) L									
New Cross Gate GF 'C'		5/3A	BR(SR) Hut	c1975	-	-	-	Derelict	213
New Holland Pier		-	GC 5	nk	-	-	-		
Newport (FYN) M (see Wootton, Isle of Wight Steam Railway)									
Newton		1/7R	BR(ScR) PB	1960	-	-	-	S&T store	
Nigg M		-	nk	nk	-	-	-		140
Norham	L	-	NE N2*+	nk	McK&H 17 2h	c1979	20R	Privately pres'd	141

SECTION 7(1): OTHER PRESERVED AND DISUSED BOXES: EX BR BOXES

Box Name	Quail Map	Box:- Type	Date	Frame:- Design	Date	No. of Levers	Present State	Notes
North Dock [Llanelli]	-	uEOD [L&MM]	nk	-	-	-	Office	
North Side Staiths GF [Blyth]	-	Hut	1926	Stevens Knee	1926	6	Derelict	
North Weald	5/38B	GE 7	1888	S&F 1888 Dx R.T	1888	21		137
North Wootton	-	GE 7	1901	-	-	-	Scout store	
Nottingham 'A'	4/6A	Mid N/S	1904	-	-	-		64
Nottingham 'B'	4/6A	Mid N/S	1904	-	-	-		64
Okehampton	3/10C	SR 11c	1935	-	-	-	Dartmoor Rly	
Old North Road	-	LNW 5	1908	-	-	-	Restored (good)	
Old Oak Common	3/1B	BR(WR) PB	1962	-	-	-		44
Old Oak Common	3/1B	BR(WR) PB	1967	-	-	-		44
Onllwyn	3/24B	Dutton 3 [N&B]	1895	-	-	-	Derelict	
Orby Crossing M	-	GN 1	nk	-	-	-	Garden shed	143
Oswestry South	L -	Dutton 2 [Cam]	1892	-	-	-	Store	232
Otterington	-	LNER 12	1933	McK&H 17 2h	1991	20		144
Oxley South M	-	GW 25	1897	-	-	-	Privately pres'd	225
Oxwellmains	1/11C	BR(ScR) 16	1963	-	-	-	Yard office	
Painswick Road Crossing M	-	Mid 2b	1893	Mid Tumbler	u1893	12		145
Penistone	2/36a*	MS&L 2*	1888	McK&H 16 2h	c1953	29R	Boarded up	
Penmaenpool	-	GW 31	1936	-	-	-	Information centre	
Pensnett South M (see Bridgnorth, Severn Valley Railway)								
Perth Down Centre	L 1/15D	Cal N/S	1886	-	-	-		
Pilmoor	2/20	LNER 12	1933	-	-	-		237
Pilning GF Box M	-	GW Hut	nk	GW gf	nk	5		206
Pilton M	-	EOD [L&B]	1898	-	-	-		146
Pinhoe M	-	LSW 1	c1875	-	-	-	Bere Ferrers stn	
Pirton Crossing M	-	Mid 3a	1902	-	-	-	Dean Forest Rly	148
Pitcaple	1/17C	GNS 2a	1888	-	-	-	P.Way (poor)	
Pitsea	2/3B	BR(ER) 18 PB	1960	-	-	-	Abolished 1996	
Polmaise	-	Caledonian N3	1905	Stevens/Cal	1948	70		
Polsham M	-	S&DJ Hut	c1920	-	-	-	Garden Shed (poor)	
Pontypridd	L 3/29A	TV	1902	McK&H C&T 4"	1902	70R	Boarded up	
Postland	-	GN 1	1882	McK&H 1873 5"	1882	35	Derelict	
Princes Risborough North	L 3/19B	GW 7b	1905	GW VT 5	1958	57R		150
Princes Street Gardens	1/11a*	NB N/S	1895	-	-	-		
Queens Road East	L 5/2R	LSW 4	nk	-	-	-		
Radstock North M (see 'Radstock North', GWS Didcot)								
Ramsbottom Station (see East Lancashire Railway)								
Rannoch	1/21B	NB 6a	1894	S&F 1888 Dx R.T	1894	17		
Ravenglass	4/31C	Furness 1	c1874	-	-	-		152
Rawtenstall West (see East Lancashire Railway)								
Raydon Wood	-	GE 7	1891	-	-	-		153
Raynham Park	-	M&GN 1	c1900	-	-	-	Preserved	
Reedsmouth Junction	-	NB 7+	nk	-	-	-	House/altered	
Rhiwderin M	-	S&F 12b [B&M]	1884	-	-	-		154
Rhyl No.2	L 4/36B	LNW 4	1900	LNW Tumbler	1900	126	Boarded up	
Richborough Sidings	5/9A	BR(SR) 18	1962	SEC NP 2h	1962	18	Derelict	207
Robin Hoods Bay	-	NE S1b	u1885	-	-	-	Coal office	
Rogart South	1/20B	Dutton 1 / High	1894	-	-	-	P.Way	
Romsey M	-	LSW 1	c1875	Stevens (Stevens)	nk	23		155
Roseden	-	NE N/S	1887	-	-	-	Summerhouse	
Rowden Mill East GF	-	GW 29 Hut	nk	-	-	-	Preserved	
Rowley Regis M (see Hayes Knoll, Swindon & Cricklade Railway)								
Royal Albert Bridge	3/8C	GW 7d	1908	-	-	-	Railway office	
Roydon	L 2/11A	GE 1/S&F+	1876E	McK&H 4" 2h	1959	27		138
Rushbury	-	GW 6+	1892	-	-	-	Stn house store	
Rushton M	-	NS 2	nk	BP pf 2h	1980s	32		156
St Albans South	L 4/2A	Mid 2a	1892E	Mid Tumbler	1894	44	Being restored	
St Ann's Crossing [Faversham]	5/8B	LCD Hut	nk	-	-	-	Derelict	130
St Austell	3/9B	GW 7c	1906	-	-	-	Office	
St Fillans	-	Cal N/S	1901	-	-	-	Caravan site bldg	
St Germans	3/9A	**	1973	-	-	-	Boarded up	
St Mary's Church Road	-	McK&H 3 / TV	1892	-	-	-		
St Margarets	2/11A	GE 7	1887	McK&H 5"	1887	55		
St Olaves Swing Bridge Junc	-	LNER 11	1926	-	-	-	Inhabited	233
Sarnau M	-	GW 3	1885	GW DT	nk	14		157
Savernake High Level	3/11B	uGWCo [MSW]	1898	-	-	-	Derelict	158
Sculcoates Swing Bridge	2/38C	NE Bridge Box	1907	-	-	-		159

SECTION 7(1): OTHER PRESERVED AND DISUSED BOXES: EX BR BOXES

Box Name		Quail Map	Box:- Type	Date	Frame:- Design	Date	No. of Levers	Present State	Notes
Selling M (see Eythorne, East Kent Railway)									
Selside M	L	4/28B	Mid 4a	1907	Mid Tumbler	1907	8		185
Semley		5/33B	BR(SR) 16	1961	-	-	-		
Settle Station M		4/34A	Mid 2a	1891	Midland Tumbler	nk	20	Restored	122
Sevenoaks		5/6A	BR(SR) 18 PB	1962	-	-	-	(good)	
Shalford		5/24A	BR (SR) 16	1954	-	-	-		
Shankend		-	NB 7+	1916	-	-	-	Restored	234
Sheffield Park (see Bluebell Railway)									
Shenfield		2/5B	BR(ER) PB	1981	-	-	-	S&T office	
Sherborne		5/33C	BR(SR) 16	1960	-	-	-	Private office	
Sheringham East M		-	M&GN 1	1906	Mid Tumbler 2h	1906	14	North Norfolk Rly	160
Shipley Bingley Junction (see Keighley West, Keighley & Worth Valley Railway)									
Shortlands		5/4	BR(SR) 17	c1959	-	-	-		
Skidby M		-	H&B 1	1898	-	-	-		162
Slateford Junction		1/11A	BR(ScR) 16	1960	Stevens/Cal	1960	20+10		163
Sleights		-	NE S1b	c1876	-	-	-	Coal yard office	
Smeeth Road		-	GE 7	1886	RSCo Tappet	1886	16		
Snettisham M		-	GE 2	1880	McK&H nk 5" 2h	c1987	15		164
Soham M		-	GE 2	1878	S&F Dx 2h	1944	10R	Privately pres'd	165
Southampton Central		5/29	SR N/S	1935	-	-	-	Empty	
South Croydon		5/14C	BR(SR) 15	1955	-	-	-		
Southend Central		2/3C	BR(ER) 18 PB	1960	-	-	-	Staff rooms	
Spath Crossing M		-	NS 2	nk	-	-	-		166
Spean Bridge		1/21E	LNER 15	1949	-	-	-	Greenhouse	
Spekes Wood Crossing M		-	GW Hut	nk	-	-	-	Privately pres'd	223
Spelbrook M		-	GE 7	1898	McK&H 4"	1898	24	Mangapps Farm	
Spey Bay M		-	GNoS 2	1884	-	-	-	Preserved	136
Spratton Crossing M		-	LNW 4 2h	1879	LNW Tumbler	1879	9R	N'n & L'port Rly	82
Sprotborough M		-	S&F 12b	1893	-	-	-		168
Stamford M		-	Mid 2b	1893	-	-	-		169
Stanton Gate		4/7A	BR(LMR) 15	1969	LMR Standard	1969	50	Derelict	
Staplehurst		5/10C	BR(SR) 18*	1962	Stevens (Stev.) 2h	1962	18	Abolished 1993	
Star Lane [Wokingham] M		-	Hut	nk	-	-	-	Fawley Hill Rly	
Staverton Crossing GF (see South Devon Railway)									
Stixwould		-	GN 1+	1876	-	-	-	Summerhouse	
Stoke Canon	L	3/7A	S&F 4 [B&E]	1874	GW Stud	1912	17		
Stokesley M		-	NE S5	nk	-	-	-		171
Stoneham Sidings		-	SR Hut	1943	-	-	-	Derelict	
Stoneycombe Sidings		3/7C	GW 5*	1894	-	-	-	Boarded up	
Stow Bardolph M		-	GE 2	c1881	Stev(Stev) 5 1/8"	c1881	17		172
Strata Florida M		-	S&F 12b [M&M]	1895	-	-	-		173
Stratford		2/2B	LNER 15*	1949	-	-	-	Railway offices	
Stratford Southern M (see Dereham Central, Mid Norfolk Railway)									
Strome Ferry East M		-	McK&H 3 / High	1893	-	-	-		175
Strome Ferry West M		-	Dutton 3/High	1897	-	-	-	Strathspey Rly	86
Surbiton		5/21B	BR(SR) 19 PB	1970	-	-	-		
Sutton Bridge Swing Bridge		-	Mid Bridge Box	1897	-	-	3		176
Swadlincote East M (see Shobnall Maltings, Fawley Hill Railway)									
Swainsthorpe M		-	GE 7*	1885	-	-	-		177
Talerddig M		-	uMcK&H1+ [Cam]	1870s	GW VT 5 2h	nk	18		222
Taynuilt M		-	Cal N3	1921	-	-	-		178
Temple Meads Goods Yard M		-	GW N/S	1902	-	-	-		179
Theddingworth		-	BR(LMR) N/S	nk-	-	-	-		180
The Mound		-	Dutton 4 / High	c1894	-	-	-	Privately pres'd	231
Thrapston M		-	Mid 2a	1892	-	-	-		21
Tilbury Riverside		2/4B	BR(ER) 18 PB	1961	-	-	-	Damaged by fire	
Tinsley West Junction M		-	GC 5	1923	-	-	-		181
Tintern	L	-	McK&H 3 [GW]	1876	-	-	-	Craft studio	
Tisbury Gates		5/33B	LSW Hut	1892	-	-	-		
Toddington (see Gloucestershire Warwickshire Railway)									
Tollerton		2/20A	BR(NER) PB	1961	-	-	-	Boarded up	227
Topsham	L	3/18B	LSW 1+	1870s	-	-	-	Office	
Torquay South	L	3/7C	GW N/S	c1876	-	-	-	Office	
Torre	L	3/7C	GW 7d	1921	GW VT 3	1921	42		182
Totnes		3/7C	GW 7d	1923E	-	-	-	Café	
Toton Centre		4/7A	BR(LMR) 14	1949	-	-	-	Shell only	
Totteridge		5/39A	LNER N/S	1926	-	-	-	Under stairs	

SECTION 7(1): OTHER PRESERVED AND DISUSED BOXES: EX BR BOXES

Box Name	Quail Map	Box:- Type	Date	Frame:- Design	Date	No. of Levers	Present State	Notes
Townsend Fold (see East Lancashire Railway)								
Tramway Crossing M	-	S&F 12b [GN]	1888	RSCo Tappet 2h	1980s	9R		183
Trewerry & Trerice M		GW 29	-	-	-	-		184
Tulloch	1/21E	NB 6a	1894	S&F 1888 Dx R.T	1894	15		230
Tutbury GF M	-	NS Hut	nk	-	-	-		186
Tyndrum Upper	1/21B	NB 6a	1894	S&F 1888 Dx R.T	1894	15		
Tyne Yard	2/21B	BR(NER) PB	1963	-	-	-	(poor)	
Uckfield L	5/14A	S&F 5 [LBSC]	1882	S&F Rocker 5" R.T	1882	22		187
Uckfield Shunting M	-	LBSC 2c	1900	-	-	-	Bird hide	
Umberleigh M	-	LSW 3b	1890	-	-	-		188
Upper Goods [Brighton] M (see Kingscote, Bluebell Railway)								
Upper Portland Sidings M (see Holt, North Norfolk Railway)								
Vickers Gun Range Sidings M	-	Furness N/S	1897	-	-	-		190
Victoria Central	5/2L	SR N/S+	1939	-	-	-	Offices/altered	
Wall	-	NB 5	1893	-	-	-	Restored (good)	
Walnut Tree Junction M L	-	TV	1910s	GW VT5	c1951	79	Dean Forest Rly	
Walsall P.Way Sidings Frame M	-	LNW 4	nk	LNW Tumbler	nk	10		191
Wansford (see Nene Valley Railway) L								
Wapping Goods	-	LMS 13	nk	-	-	-		219
Warcop	4/34B	NE C2a	nk	-	-	-	Eden Valley Rly	228
Ware	2/11A	BR(ER) 18	1960	Westinghouse 17A	1960	20	Boarded up	
Wark	-	NB 5	1893	-	-	-	Unused (fair)	
Warmley L	-	Mid 4d	1918	Mid Tappet	1918	16	Preserved	192
Waterhouses M	-	NS 2	1905	-	-	-	Preserved	109
Warthill	-	NE S1a	nk	-	-	-	Garage/store	
Warthill Road	-	NE S5	nk	-	-	-		100
Washford	-	GW N/S	nk	Stevens (EOD) 2h	c1982	16R	W. Somerset Rly	193
Watton-at-Stone M	-	GN Hut	1921	GN gf	nk	6		194
Waverley West	1/11L	LNER 13	1936	-	-	-		
Welland Bridge M (see Peterborough, Nene Valley Railway)								
Wellow	-	S&DJ 2	1892	-	-	-	Play house	
Wellowgate M	-	MS&L 2	1881	MS&L Iron Brack.	1881	30		195
Wembley Stadium	-	LNW Hut	1913	-	-	-	Derelict	
Wensum Junction M (see Sheringham West, North Norfolk Railway)								
Weston Rhyn M	-	GW N/S	1924-	(GW VT 3	1924	47)	Llangollen Rly	196
Weston-super-mare L	3/6A	B&E	u1866	-	-	-		
West Ruislip	3/19A	GW 7b	1905	GW DT	1905	47	P.Way	
Weymouth	5/31D	BR(SR) 16	1957	-	-	-	Derelict	
Whitwood	2/42A	NE S1b	1890	McK&H 16	1906	50		
Willesden Brent Sidings	4/8A	LNW 4	1878	-	-	-	Boarded up	
Williton (see West Somerset Railway) L								
Wilton M (see Medstead, Mid Hants Railway)								
Wimbledon 'A'	5/21A	SR 13	1948	Whse A2 recon.	1948	112		105
Winchester	5/27C	BR(SR) 16	1960	-	-	-		
Windmill Lane [Cheshunt] M	-	GE Hut	nk	-	-	-	Fawley Hill Rly	
Wing Crossing M	-	LNW 4	1893	-	-	-	Whipsnade Rly	226
Wingland M	-	Mid 2a	1891E	-	-	-		197
Witham [Essex]	2/5C	BR(ER) 18 PB	1961	-	-	-	Railway office	
Withyham M	-	S&F 1 [LBSC]	1877	S&F Rocker R.T	1877	12		198
Witton-le-Wear	2/47A	NE Hut	nk	Outside gf	nk	7	Derelict	
Woking L	5/23	SR 13*	1937	Westinghouse pf	1937	131		
Wolferton L	-	GE 5*	1884	McK&H nk 4"	u1899	41		199
Wolverton Works M (see Pitsford Sidings, Northampton & Lamport Railway)								
Woodside Park	5/39A	GN 1	1872	-	-	-	Store	
Woodside Park	5/39A	GN 3	1906	-	-	-	Store/Boarded up	
Woody Bay	-	L&B Hut	1898	-	-	-		113
Wool East GF M	-	LSW Hut	1918	-	-	-	Swanage Railway	88
Wooller Haugh Crossing	-	NE N/S	1887	-	-	-	Garden house	
Woolston	5/29	LSW 4	1901	-	-	-	Empty	
Wootton Bassett Incline	3/4B	GW 15	1952	-	-	-		
Worksop East L	2/31A	MS&L 2	c1880	McK&H	1975	20		
Worksop West	2/31A	MS&L 1	1874	GC(McK&H)	c1928	28		
Worstead	2/8	GE 7	u1891	-	-	-	Garage (poor)	
Wrabness M (see Nunnery Junction, Colne Valley Railway)								
Wrexham Exchange M	-	GC 5	1912	(GC(RSCo)	1912	28)	Great Central Rly	71
Wroxham	2/8	GE 7	1900	McK&H 4"	1900	50		189
Wye	5/11B	S&F 12a [SE]	1893	S&F 1888 Dx R.T	1893	24		

SECTION 7(1): OTHER PRESERVED AND DISUSED BOXES: EX BR BOXES

Box Name	Quail Map	Box:- Type	Date	Frame:- Design	Date	No. of Levers	Present State	Notes
Wyke M (see Pinesway Junction, Gartell Light Railway)								
Yalding M	-	S&F 12a [SE]	1894	-	-	-	At Horsebridge	
Yaxham (see Mid Norfolk Railway)								
York Platform	uL 2/19	NE N/S	1907	-	-	-		23
Yorton M (see Arley, Severn Valley Railway)								

BOXES OF UNKNOWN ORIGIN

Box Name	Quail Map	Box:- Type	Date	Frame:- Design	Date	No. of Levers	Present State	Notes
At Bletchington M	-	McK&H 3	-	-	-	-		210
At Burgh-le-Marsh M	-	Composite	-	uRSCo Tappet 2h	nk	nk		201
At Friog M	4/24A	Dutton 1 [Cam]	-	-	-	-		211
At Garston M	-	LNW 5	-	-	-	-		138
At Muir of Ord M	1/18C	McK&H 3 / High	-	-	-	-		202
At New Beckenham M	5/4	SE Hut	-	-	-	-		200
At Tain M	-	McK&H 3 / High	-	-	-	-		203
At Toddington M	-	GWCo or RSCo	-	-	-	-		209
At Westward Ho! M	-	(Timber, Hipped)	-	-	-	-		208

Notes

1   All levers removed but rest of frame remains. Tunnel box, in recess.
2   Moved 1904. Boarded.
3   At Harpenden Railway Museum since 1988; frame ex Avonmouth.
4   Moved to private address nearby.
5   On farm near original site.
6   Restored 1991/2; owned by Network Rail but maintained by Friends of Settle & Carlisle Line (FoS&CL). No public access.
7   Moved a few yards only.
8   At Swanwick station, used as station office. (Frame has been dismantled).
9   Re-erected at Strathcarron, as shelter.
10   Moved to Brookside Garden Centre, Poynton (on A52).
11   Part of station area now used as radioastronomy centre.
12   At Norchard, Dean Forest Railway, for eventual use at Tufts Junction.
13   Was removed for preservation but present location of box and frame not known.
14   At Shepherdswell EKR (top half only). Box has been repainted but no frame.
15   Re-erected at Glyndyfrdwy (Llangollen Railway); intended as training facility.
16   Situated at Basin Swing Bridge. Has frame but is inaccessible.
17   Formerly BO at Bulmers, Hereford. Now at Norchard, Dean Forest Railway.
18   In garden at Barrow on Humber, good condition. Said locally to be this box.
19   Originally in garden at Eye, then went to Bressingham Steam Museum. Still there, but now owned by Mid Norfolk Railway.
20   Used by station house owners. Box extended u1927.
21   Moved 1989 from original site to unknown location, present state unknown.
22   Box in situ with frame awaiting possible refurbishment/preservation.
23   Cafeteria upstairs, W H Smith bookstall downstairs.
24   Sports pavilion, exact site not known.
25   Top only, with frame - at NRM.
26   Top only, with frame - at private address, Worksop.
27   Frame still functional and interlocked, available for visitors to work, but not connected to anything.
28   Garage at private house at Bourton-on-the-Water (top only). Good condition.
29   See p.242 of 'The Signal Box'. Became derelict but now fully restored as craft shop.
30   At Norchard, Dean Forest Railway. No signalling use.
31   Type 25 box bricked up in 1937.
32   Top only in use as garage at private house in Greysouthern. Very decayed.
33   At Toddington. Controls part of miniature railway. Frame is outside box. Formerly at Ashchurch in 1970s.
34   Moved to nearby garden, good condition.
35   Now located behind Leicester PSB and used for training purposes.
36   Closed for signalling purposes. Good condition. Arrangements can be made to visit.
37   Restored station site.
38   At Washford since 1989; was at Toddington to 1988. Previously at Ashchurch and Yieldingtree Museum.
39   Moved with frame to Brewood Hall, Staffs for private preservation.
40   Buried up to floor level.
41   LNW Tappet 54-lever frame of 1925 removed; possibly now with Ffestiniog Railway.
42   Top, on new brick base. Used as demonstration box at Swanwick ('Brands Siding'). Open to the public.
43   At Toddington. Controls part of miniature railway (incl 2-lever WR frame). Formerly at Ashchurch 1970s.
44   No use, but cannot be demolished owing to asbestos.
45   In conservation area; possible conversion to a museum.
46   Part of station buildings.

47   Box preserved and used as information centre, some public access. Frame to Lower Swansea Valley Railway.

48   Fully equipped box preserved by East Anglian Railway Museum and open to visitors. No signalling use.

49   Box moved short distance. Re-erected but considerably altered for domestic use on new brick base. Frame dismantled.

50   Location of preserved box top nk; McK&H 1873 Pat 5" frame at Churnet Valley Railway largely in Consall box.

51   Moved to Snibston NCB Museum site. Re-erected, but permission needed to gain access to box.

52   Moved to private owner, Coleford Museum. Frame to WSR. 2h frame installed ex Shelwick Junction.

53   Present location unknown. To Stapleford (1955); then Knebworth Park (1980s).

54   Went from operational use to ownership of Vale of Glamorgan Railway. Present situation nk.

55   In use at Holywath, Hext Miniature Railway (private). Frame ex Woodland.

56   Re-erected 1995 at Hull Transport Museum. Reduced frame of 16 levers levers latterly but 21 levers restored.

57   Box is part of a listed train shed structure.

58   Top only at Bury ELR, awaiting re-erection at Green Lane Crossing, Heywood.

59   Top only, preserved at Garden Centre nearby.

60   Refreshment kiosk and information display at Llwyfan Cerrig, Gwili Railway.

61   Sailing Club clubhouse at Westbury.

62   Top only, in garden near station.

63   Private owner, near Wareham.

64   Part of island paltform buildings.

65   Architect's office at Mattishall.

66   Used as S&T store at Hammersmith.

67   In park, Barrow in Furness.

68   Box shortened. Preserved at Wigan Pier Leisure Centre.

69   Now at Rushden station.

70   At Wembworthy Outward Bound Centre (moved there 1989).

71   Top only, at Great Central Railway, awaiting re-use. Frame in store.

72   Sold to Spa Valley Railway, remains in situ, boarded up, no use.

73   Top, in garden near station. (Was 'Novah North' until 1937).

74   Owned by Caledonian Railway (Brechin) and temporarily still in situ at Glamis.

75   At Crewe Heritage Centre. Open to public at certain times.

76   Restored by birdwatching group. Box now subject of preservation group project to move it to Swindon.

77   Station and box now used by Forestry Commission.

78   Top, now at Gwili Railway for eventual use at Carmarthen. Previously at Cadoxton, Vale of Neath Railway.

79   Office at Holywell, Embsay Railway. Frame was sold to private purchaser elsewhere.

80   Moved 200 yards north. Owned by Network Rail but looked after by K&WVR (no access).

81   Frame removed, sold to private purchaser elsewhere.

82   Reconstructed at Pitsford & Brampton station, to be moved back to Spratton Crossing and re-erected there on new brick base.

83   Box largely rebuilt as GW Type 8c.

84   Frame removed to Moors Valley Railway, not yet in use.

85   In farm yard south of Garve station.

86   On platform at Aviemore Speyside station, used as a storeroom.

87   Situated north of Braunton, at level crossing.

88   Temporary waiting shelter at Harmans Cross, Swanage Railway.

89   Frame had been removed but now restored by station owner. Station museum open at certain times.

90   Now at Slaggyford, partly dismantled.

91   Box built but never BIU.

92   Top only in garden of crossing house at Graig-yr-Rhacca.

93   At Mangapps Farm, to be joined with S&F Rocker frame ex Edmonton Junction. Box has been reduced in length; was formerly on display at Science Museum, London who have retained the McK&H 4", 1904 frame.

94   Preserved at Halesworth Middle School.

95   Formerly at Gwili Railway; now at the Oldtown Miniature Railway and has been fully restored.

96   Altered c1980 (top of box removed and former locking room converted to operating floor).

97   Present location unknown. Formerly at Knebworth Park ('Molewood Sidings').

98   Now at Hadlow Road, preserved station on Wirral Way linear walk.

99   Much altered structurally. In private garden, locally.

100   Preserved in garden immediately north of original site (half-mile east of Warthill).

101   Box (top), S&T store at Toddington. GW Stud frame, 21 levers, is loose inside box (2h, ex nk). No signalling use.

102   Box controls miniature railway at Barton House, Wroxham (limited public access). Frame ex Lowestoft North.

103   At Murrow in builders yard (poor condition). Frame (Dutton 1893 Pat. 25 levers) also here but dismantled.

104   Crewe S&T Training School box.

105   S&T training box.

106   Farm building near Roxton, poor condition.

107   Owned by Devon CC; looked after by Bideford & Instow Railway Group. Limited public opening.

108   Top only, moved to Fawley Hill Railway.

109   At Amerton Farm Railway.

110   Now a summerhouse at a farm near Longside.

111   Lavender Line. Frame was removed but now restored back in box. Possibility of eventual restoration to signalling use.

112   Boxes replaced by Portakabin structures pending decision about future of these Listed Buildings.

113   Restored by Lynton & Barnstaple Railway Association. Frame (9-levers from Stevens Knee, ex Halwill Jn 'A' GF) to be installed in box.

114   Box extended at front and altered.

115   Top only, shed in farmyard at Upton.

116   Rebuilt flat roof. Top in use as BO at Pitsford & Brampton, Northampton & Lamport Rly. Many parts of frame in store.

117   Was at East Anglian Transport Museum, now at Mid Norfolk Railway, Dereham. Frame 2h ex unknown location.

118   Last manned 1989, boarded up and stairs removed. Now in care of Churnet Valley Railway.

119   At Hollycombe Steam Park.

120   Restored by Crawley SB Preservation Society in its original location and in very good condition.

121   At Coventry Steam Centre. Frame possibly also there.

122   Box (closed 1984) now re-sited nearer station, some public access. Network Rail owned but maintained by FoS&CL.

123   VT 5 locking added below original locking. Moved to new position on station platform.

124   Top at Buckfastleigh, South Devon Railway; will be erected at Totnes (Littlehempston) as 'Ashburton Junction'.

125   At private address, Shrewsbury. Formerly at Myddlewood Railway.

126   Preserved by private owner at Porthyrhyd.

127   Temporary use as an office for WAGN train company personnel.

128   Box bought in derelict condition by GN&ELR in 1992 and to be restored.

129   Top only, at Pentiecwyth, Swansea Vale Railway.

130   Retained until c1990 as hut for LC. Crossing now closed, box remains but derelict.

131   Shed in orchard at Helham Green.

132   In garden at Easebourne. Much altered; identity uncertain.

133   Box dismantled and re-erected on private premises in Nottinghamshire.

134   Controls miniature railway in private garden at Bath Road, Littlewick Green, Maidenhead.

135   Box 2h ex Inverness Station 1898. Was to have gone to Kingdom of Fife Railway.

136   At Dufftown station yard, Keith & Dufftown Railway.

137   Line closed 1994. Box now in care of Epping Railway Ltd but is in derelict condition.

138   Box has been extended at both ends and at front.

139   Hypothesised that this is the structure in the corner of a field by the main road in Mealsgate.

140   Store, in private garden.

141   Fully equipped preserved box. Frame 2h ex Christon Bank.

142   Has been restored by the Eden Valley Railway Trust at Warcop.

143   At private address in Vicar's Cross area of Chester. Box shortened; no frame.

144   Fully equipped preserved box. Frame 2h ex Grosmont.

145   Previously at Bitton, Avon Valley Railway. Present location nk.

146   Lynton & Barnstaple Railway box. Now located at Landkey.

147   Basically still the 1928 frame but incorporates some parts from Weymouth's Westinghouse A3.

148   At Tufts Junction, Dean Forest Railway.

149   Built 1994 but not opened; current use is for storing archive material.

150   Owned by Network Rail. Leased to Chinnor & Princes Risborough Railway; plan is to restore to 126 levers with parts ex Silk Mill Crossing.

151   At Oswestry, Cambrian Railways Society; occasional use as refreshment hut.

152   Owned by Ravenglass & Eskdale Railway. Currently not in use but in process of being restored.

153   Being restored at Bressingham and likely to be joined by McK&H frame ex Oakington.

154   At Teifi Valley Railway. Frame (S&F Rocker 1884, 11 levers) now with Gwili Railway.

155   Now at Romsey Infants School and restored to working condition. Open to public first Sunday of each month.

156   Owned by Bahamas Locomotive Society. Was at Dinting, now at Ingrow. Frame 2h ex GC box, possibly Guide Bridge North.

157   Top only at Scolton Manor Museum, Dyfed.

158   Box is 2h ex Wolfhall Junction 1882; privately owned, condition is poor.

159   Taken over by Hull Corporation after line closed, in use to control footpath swing bridge (aka 'Wilmington Bridge').

160   Fully equipped box, moved to station platform, no use, open to visitors.

161   New box built to replace GWR box which has been fire damaged beyond repair. Built 2003 but not yet commissioned.

162   In private garden at Raywell and used as a shed.

163   Signalling training school. Also has panels.

164   Used as plant hire firm's office. Frame 14 levers ex Welland Bridge + 1 ex French Drove + gate wheel ex Magdalen Road.

165   Box moved to Whipsnade after closure, then Colne Valley Railway. Now privately preserved at Prickwillow.

166   In garden at Etwall.

167   Still on original station platform; now surrounded by industrial site.

168   In private garden at Sprotborough.

169   Moved a few feet only after abolition. Store Office for R. Humm & Co. bookshop.

170   Frame 2h ex Long Lane, 1905 there.

171   Moved a few yards only.

172   At Sedgeford station.

173   Box top sold after abolition to private owner but now back at Strata Florida in station cottage garden.

174   At Cambrian Railways Society, Oswestry.

175   Top only, in garden near Plockton station.

176   Bridge still in use for road traffic.

177   Gift shop at Wells station, Wells & Walsingham Railway.

178   Moved a short distance. Waiting room.

179   Last known location, Carnforth. Continued existence uncertain.

180   New top on 1878 LNW 4 base. Studio.

181   Top only, at South Yorks Railway, Meadowhall.

182   Let to preservationist group. Fully equipped box. Access by invitation only.

183   Bought by local farmer after abolition. Sold 1985 and moved to Legbourne Road station (private railway museum) and re-erected on new base. Frame is 2h ex part of Claxby & Usselby.

184   In back garden on south side of railway east of St Austell station.

185   Box remains in situ at site of Steamtown Carnforth (re-erected there 1970s).

186   Intended for Shackerstone but never went there, now in private ownership elsewhere.

187   Box repaired since abolition.

188   At Landkey, Lynton & Barnstaple Railway.

189   A trust has been formed to preserve box; likelihood that structure will have to be moved back from running lines.

190   Dismantled 1992 and removed for private preservation near Ulverston, present state unknown. Frame at NRM.

191   Preserved in garden at Penkridge.

192   Also has small 2-lever frame for wickets.

193   Fully equipped box, open to visitors. Frame is 2h ex Woolston (part).

194   Was at Knebworth Park ('Nup End Junction'), present location unknown.

195   Moved to NRM, in Great Hall.

196   Box, top only, on ground at Carrog awaiting re-use at Corwen. Frame not in the box.

197   Shed, in orchard, north of Sutton Bridge.

198   Privately preserved in garden at Woodmancote, Henfield.

199   Fully equipped preserved box, not open to the public.

200   SE pre-interlocking period signalman's hut. On down platform.

201   Largely a GC box of unknown origin. Windows from Thonock Siding. Frame 2h ex Spilsby Road Crossing.

202   On station platform as waiting room.

203   Shelter in park near Tain station.

204   At Mangapps Farm. Also frame, dismantled.

205   Previously at Southport Railway Centre; subsequently reported at Liverpool Albert Dock; present location nk.

206   In private garden near original site.

207   Box unusable but not formally abolished by Network Rail.

208   Origins of this box remain unknown. Has been for many years in back garden of house at Westward Ho! Has been alleged to be a Bideford, Westward Ho! & Appledore Railway box but no proof.

209   Allegedly ex Bourton on the Water area, but no likely source evident.

210   Box top at Smith's Haulage, Bletchington, now a storeroom. Possibly the first Bletchington box (abol. 1914).

211   In garden, allegedly ex Barmouth Junction South.

212   Not certain that frame is still in box.

213   Not seen for many years, may not now exist.

214   Box extended 1900.

215   Part of station building on island platform, at first floor level. Used by S&T.

216   On station platform, moved a few yards only. Awaiting restoration.

217   Private owner in locality; box said to have been dismantled and stored after storm damage.

218   When BO became 'SB' in 1930 there was a full-size frame, present knee frame installed 1951 when B.O. extended.

219   Totally buried by infilling of cutting with refuse.

220   In garden at Sulgrave Court. Certain timberwork from other GC boxes incorporated. Frame 2h ex Fosse Road, 1950 there.

221   Frame 2h ex Gerrards Cross (part), 1905 there, converted VT 1923. Box restored in working condition.

222   Recreated in brick in garden of house between Llanbrynmair and Talerddig; contains original frame.

223   Preserved, private owner Stoke-sub-Hamdon. Faversham GF has frame ex Axminster Gates. Honiton Tunnel West was in situ c1898-c1930; previously erected in a garden in Honiton.

224   Originally preserved in garden at Clacton. Now with Mid Norfolk Railway at Dereham.

225   Box top privately preserved in garden at Tettenhall, Wolverhampton and used as a greenhouse.

226   Staff accommodation linked to Great Whipsnade Railway; no operating use.

227   Derelict, but not yet demolished due to asbestos content.

228   Restored and partially equipped by Eden Valley Railway Trust.

229   Restored by Network Rail 2002; frame situation nk. Possibility that this will become station's operational box again.

230   Contains water supply equipment for hostel in station building. Most of frame intact.

231   Remains on original base but turned around to face garden rather than running lines.

232   Grade 2 listed building at Cambrian Railways Society, Oswestry.

233   Instruction from owner - 'visitors not welcome'!

234   Rebuilt 2002/3 as a summerhouse; although altered, is recognisable.

235   Used as a store. Situated at north end of Furness platforms (south of later Station Junction SB).

236   Closed in practice, but not formally abolished.

237   Contains hot axle box equipment icw York IECC.

SECTION 7(2): OTHER PRESERVED AND DISUSED BOXES; EX LONDON UNDERGROUND BOXES

Box Name	Quail Map	Box:- Type	Box:- Date	Frame:- Design	Frame:- Date	No. of Levers	Present State	Notes
Acton Town	5/43B	UER	1932	-	-	-	Offices	-
Aldersgate	5/44B	Met 4	1932	-	-	-	-	-
Arnos Grove	5/46B	UER	1932	-	-	-	-	-
Baker Street (Met)	5/43B	Met 4	1924	-	-	-	-	-
Bank (Central)	5/37C	CLR	1900	-	-	-	-	1
Boston Manor	5/43B	S&F 5 (Met D)	1883	-	-	-	-	-
Bow Road	5/45A	LT	1946	-	-	-	-	-
Canal Junction	5/45C	LT	1950	-	-	-	-	-
Chesham	5/41C	Met 1	1889	Met	u1889	25	-	-
Chorleywood	5/41C	Met 1	1889	-	-	-	P.Way	-
Covent Garden	5/46A	UER	1906	-	-	-	-	1
Debden	5/38B	LT	1949	-	-	-	-	-
Ealing Common	5/43B	LT	nk	-	-	-	-	2
Edgware	5/39A	UER+	1924	-	-	-	Office	3
Epping	5/38B	LT	1949	-	-	-	Preserved	4
Farringdon	5/44B	Met 4	1932E	-	-	-	-	-
Finchley Road	5/43A	LT	1937	-	-	-	Office	-
Golders Green	5/39A	UER+	1907	-	-	-	Office	3
Grange Hill (Subsid.)	5/38A	LT	1948	-	-	-	-	-
Hainault	5/38A	LT	1948	Westinghouse N pf	1948	83	-	4
High Street Kensington	5/44B	LT	u1936	-	-	-	-	-
Holborn (Picc)	5/46A	UER	1906	-	-	-	-	5
Hyde Park Corner	5/46A	UER	1906	-	-	-	-	6
Leytonstone	5/38A	LT	1947	-	-	-	Office	-
Loughton	5/38A	LT	1948	-	-	-	-	7
Marble Arch	5/37C	CLR	1900	-	-	-	-	-
Morden	5/40A	UER+	1926	-	-	-	Office	-
Mornington Crescent	5/39B	UER	1907	-	-	-	-	8
Neasden North	5/42B	LT	1939	-	-	-	-	-
Neasden South	5/42B	LT	1939	-	-	-	-	-
Newbury Park	5/38A	LT	1947	-	-	-	-	-
North Acton	5/37B	LT	1947	-	-	-	Bricked up	-
Northfields	5/43B	UER	1932	-	-	-	Office	-
Parsons Green	5/44A	UER	1905-	-	-	-	-	9
Queens Park	5/41B	UER+	1913	-	-	-	-	-
Ruislip Gardens	5/37A	LT N/S	1948	-	-	-	-	-
St Johns Wood	5/43A	Met N/S	nk	-	-	-	-	-
Stanmore	5/42A	LT	1938	-	-	-	-	-
Turnham Green	5/44A	UER	1932	-	-	-	-	-
Uxbridge	5/42A	LT	1938	-	-	-	Office	-
Wembley Park	5/42B	Met 4	1932	-	-	-	-	-
West Ruislip	5/37A	LT	1948	-	-	-	Office	-
Whitechapel E.L.	5/45C	Met N/S	1913	-	-	-	Office	-
White City	5/37B	LT	1948	Westinghouse N pf	1948	47	-	-
Willesden Green	5/42B	LT	1938	-	-	-	Office	-
Woodford	5/38A	LT	1947	-	-	-	P.Way	-
Wood Lane	5/37B	UER	1920	-	-	-	-	-

Notes

1 East end of Westbound platform.

2 Believed never brought into use.

3 Structure much altered.

4 Epping box being renovated by local preservation groups. Frame ex Hainault will be installed when renovation complete.

5 Electric Switchgear Room. South end of Aldwych platform.

6 West end of Eastbound platform.

7 59-lever Westinghouse N pf frame of 1948 has been transferred to the LT Museum, Covent Garden.

8 North end of Northbound platform. Windows bricked up.

9 New top on old base 1905. Now Carriage Cleaners' Room.

NB (1) Several others of the above may still have all or parts of the power frames in situ.

(2) Disused 'boxes' that are merely underground rooms with no visible identifying structure are not included here.

SECTION 7(3): OTHER PRESERVED AND DISUSED BOXES; OTHER SYSTEMS IN GREAT BRITAIN

Box Name	Quail Map	Box:- Type	Date	Frame:- Design	Date	No. of Levers	Present State	Notes
Douglas M	-	IOMR	1890	Dutton 1889 Pat.	1890	36	Preserved within station	-
Southend Pier North M	-	Local	1929	Westinghouse gf	1929	7	Southend Pier Museum	-

SECTION 7 (4&5): OTHER PRESERVED AND DISUSED BOXES: IRELAND

Box Name	Quail Map	Box:- Type	Date	Frame:- Design	Date	No. of Levers	Present State	Notes
Abbeydorney	-	GS&W Gabled	1912	RSCo Tappet 4"	1912	14	Derelict	-
Adavoyle	6/17B	**	nk	-	-	-	Derelict	-
Athenry	6/10C	GS&W Hip	1927	-	-	-	Abol. 2003	-
Balla	6/11C	RSCo[MGW]	1887	-	-	-	Derelict	1
Ballinasloe	6/10B	RSCo [MGW]+	1891	RSCo Tappet	1891	27	Abol. 2003	-
Ballingrane Junction	6/8E	GS&W Hip+	1923-	GS&W Tappet	c1923	28	No use	2
Ballinlough	6/11A	RSCo[MGW]	1903	-	-	-	Derelict	-
Ballybay	-	GNRI 3a	1892	-	-	-	Garage	-
Ballybrack	6/9B	GS&W Hip	c1924-	-	-	-	Derelict	3
Ballyduff	-	GS&W Gabled	nk	-	-	-	Holiday home	-
Ballyglunin	6/12E	GS&W Hip	1924-	RSCo Tappet	nk	14	No use	4
Ballyhooley	-	GS&W Gabled	1913	-	-	-	Shed, good	-
Ballykelly	6/20B	NCC ARP	1943	gf 4 7/8"	1943	6	Derelict	-
Ballymena	6/19D	NCC	c1912	-	-	-	Abol. 1994	-
Ballymote	6/14D	RSCo[MGW]	1912	-	-	-	P.Way mess	-
Ballynoe	-	RSCo[BCD]	1892	-	-	-	Derelict	-
Ballysodare	6/14D	GS&W Hip	1930	GS&W Tappet	1930	30	No use	5
Ballyward	-	GNRI 3a	1906	-	-	-	Very good	-
Ballywillan	-	MGW Gabled	1923	-	-	-	Very good	-
Baltinglass	-	RSCo[GS&W]	1886	-	-	-	Derelict	-
Belcoo	-	S&F 5 [SLNCR]	1879	-	-	-	Restored	-
Belmont	-	GS&W Hip	c1924-	-	-	-	Shed	6
Beragh	-	GNRI N/S	c1904	-	-	-	Good	-
Bruree	-	N/S	nk	-	-	-	Derelict	-
Bundoran Junction West	-	RSCo[GNRI]	nk	-	-	-	Poor	-
Cappoquin	-	RSCo[WD&L]	c1893	-	-	-	Shed	-
Carrickfergus	6/18D	NCC N/S	nk	nk	nk	nk	Boarded up	-
Carrickfergus Hbr Jct M	-	nk	nk	-	-	-	Greenhouse	7
Carrick-on-Shannon	6/14C	MGW Gabled	1924-	RSCo Tappet	1893	22	Good	8
Carrowduff	6/10A	RSCo[MGW] 2h	c1928	-	-	-	Shed	9
Castlebar	6/11C	RSCo[MGW]	1904	RSCo Tappet	1904	24	Good	10
Castletown	6/13E	MGW Gabled	1923–	-	-	-	Good	11
Castletownroche	-	GS&W Hip	c1923	-	-	-	Shed/Store	-
Cherryville Junction	6/3A	GS&W N/S	nk	-	-	-	Good, P.Way	-
Claremorris North M	-	RSCo[MGW]	1895	-	-	-	-	12
Claremorris South M	-	RSCo[MGW]	1894	-	-	-	-	12
Cloughjordan	6/6B	GS&W Hip	1924	RSCo Tappet 4½"	1924	13	Good	-
Colbinstown	-	GS&W Hip	c1923-	-	-	-	Good	13
Cookstown	-	B&NC	nk	-	-	-	Office	-
Cork 'A'	6/4D	GS&W N/S	u1893	-	-	-	Good	14
Culloville	-	GNRI 3b	1922	-	-	-	Derelict	-
Donabate	6/16C	GNRI 3a	1895	McK&H nk 4"	1895	14	Abol. 1983	-
Dromkeen	6/6E	RSCo[W&L]	1892	GS&W Tappet	nk	3R	-	-
Drumsna	6/14B	MGW Gabled	1924	-	-	-	Holiday cottage	-
Dundalk Central M	6/17B	GNRI N/S	c1888	RSCo Tappet	nk	52	Good	15
Dun Laoghaire Pier	-	CIE Flat Roof	1962	-	-	-	Tourist Office	-
Dunlavin	-	GS&W Hip	c1924-	-	-	-	Shed	16
Dunleer M	6/17A	GNRI 3a	1892	Dutton D.T. 4½"	1892	14	-	17
Durrow & Stradbally	6/7E	GWCo	1878	-	-	-	Derelict	-
Fermoy	-	GS&W Hip	1921	-	-	-	Derelict	-
Fiddown	6/7C	GS&W Hip	1924	-	-	-	Good	-
Foynes	-	RSCo[W&L]	nk	-	-	-	-	18
Galway	6/10D	RSCo [MGW] +	c1892	RSCo Tappet	c1892	42	Abol. 2003	-
Glenbeigh	-	GS&W Hip	1924	-	-	-	Good (Hotel)	-
Glenfarne	-	S&F 5 [SLNCR]	1880	-	-	-	Good	-
Gormanston M	6/16B	GNRI 3a	1892	RSCo-GNI 4"	1918	24	-	19
Gort	6/12C	RSCo [W&L]	nk	RSCo Tappet	nk	14	Abol. 2003	-
Gortatlea	6/9D	GS&W Hip	1924	-	-	-	Derelict	-
Headford Junction	6/9A	GS&W Hip	1924-	-	-	-	Derelict	20

SECTION 7 (4&5): OTHER PRESERVED AND DISUSED BOXES: IRELAND

Box Name	Quail Map	Box:- Type	Date	Frame:- Design	Date	No. of Levers	Present State	Notes
Hill of Down	6/13C	RSCo[MGW]+	1888	McK&H 1886 Pat, R.T	nk	20	-	21
Horse & Jockey	-	GS&W Hip	c1923	-	-	-	Derelict	-
Inchicore	6/2A	GS&W N/S	nk	GS&W Tappet	nk	26	Abol. 2002	-
Irvinestown	-	GNRI 3a	nk	-	-	-	-	-
Kells	-	GS&W Hip	1924-	-	-	-	Poor	20
Killeagh	-	RSCo/GS&W	nk	RSCo Tappet	nk	15	Derelict	-
Killough	-	RSCo[BCD]	1892	-	-	-	Shed, good	-
Killylea	-	GNRI 3a	1892	-	-	-	Derelict	-
Kilmacthomas	6/7D	GS&W Hip	c1928	GS&W Tappet	c1928	20	Derelict	-
Kilmessan	-	MGW Gabled	1924	-	-	-	Very good	-
Kiltimagh	-	GS&W Hip	c1924-	RSCo Tappet	1895	15	Restored	22
Kingsbog Junction M (see Downpatrick, Downpatrick Railway Museum)								
Lisburn	6/17E	GNRI 3b	1919	-	-	-	Railway Office	-
Lombardstown	-	RSCo/GS&W	nk	-	-	-	Derelict	-
Mageney	6/5C	GS&W Hip	1920s	-	-	-	-	-
Malahide	6/16A	GNRI 3a	1891	-	-	-	Abol. 1994	-
Maynooth	6/13b	MGW Gabled +	1924	RSCo Tappet	1924	30	Good	23
Midleton	-	RSCo/GS&W	1895	nk	nk	18	Derelict	-
Milltown	6/12F	GS&W Hip	1924	-	-	-	Derelict	-
Mogeely	6/5A	Hut	1936	McK&H 1886 Pat gf	nk	nk	Boarded up	-
Moira M	6/17E	GNRI 3a	c1891	RSCo-GNI	1918	24	Preserved	24
Moorfields	-	GWCo[B&L]	1878	-	-	-	Shed, poor	25
Mosney	6/16C	GNRI 4	1948	RSCo-GNI	1948	30	Abol. 1994	26
Newbliss	-	GNRI 3a	1892	-	-	-	Shed, poor	-
Newtowncunningham M	-	L&LS	nk	-	-	-	-	27
Oola	-	GS&W Hip	*1920s	-	-	-	Derelict	-
Palace East	6/6E	DSE Gabled	1924	-	-	-	Shed, poor	-
Patrickswell	-	GS&W Hip	1925	GS&W Tappet	1925	24	Boarded up	-
Poyntzpass	6/17C	GNRI 3b	1921-	RSCo-GNI	1918	24	Good	28
Rathduff	6/8E	GS&W Hip+	c1923	RSCo Tappet	nk	14	Good	29
Rathluirc 'B'	6/4B	RSCo Hut	1890	RSCo Tappet	1890	8	-	-
Rathvilly	-	G&SW Hip	c1923	-	-	-	Good	30
Roscrea 'B'	6/6A	Hut	nk	gf 4 7/8"	nk	7	OOU 1990s	-
Rosslare Harbour Pier GF	6/8C	CIE Hut	nk	-	-	-	-	31
Rush & Lusk	6/16B	GNRI 3a	1892	McK&H 1886 Pat 4"	1892	11	Abol. 1994	-
Saintfield	-	BCD	1892	-	-	-	Good	-
73rd Mile	6/13E	RSCo (2h)	1929	-	-	-	Derelict	32
Skerries	6/16B	GNRI 3a	1891	McK&H 1886 Pat 4"	1891	14	Abol. 1994	-
Skibbereen	-	uRSCo[CB&SC]	nk	-	-	-	Inhabited	-
Suir Bridge	6/7D	Bridge box	1906	uS&F	1906	6	Abol. 1995	-
Sutton	6/16a	GNRI 3a	1892	-	-	-	Abol. 1982	-
Swinford	-	RSCo[W&L]	1895	RSCo Tappet	1895	12	Derelict	-
Tuam	6/12E	RSCo[W&L]+	1893	RSCo Tappet	1893	25	Poor	33
Tubbercurry	-	RSCo[W&L]	1895	RSCo Tappet	1895	18	Derelict	-
Tullamore	6/9E	RSCo/GS&W	nk	-	-	-	Good	-
Tullymurry	-	BCD	c1896	-	-	-	Derelict	-
Tynan	-	GNRI 3a	1892	-	-	-	Poor	-
Whitehead	6/18D	NCC	nk	-	-	-	Good	-
Wicklow Junction	6/15C	nk	nk	-	-	-	-	34
Woodlawn	6/10B	RSCo [MGW] +	c1885	RSCo Tappet	c1885	21	Abol. 2003	35
Youghal	6/5A	RSCo/GS&W	nk	nk	nk	12	Boarded up	-

Notes

1 Derelict, boarded up (abol. 6/11/1988). Also has 3-lever WB&SSCo slide power frame for Manulla Junction.

2 New top on RSCo base, c1923. Rewindowed 1970s. Now boarded up.

3 New top on old base, nk design, c1924.

4 New top on RSCo base, 1924. Abolished 25/5/1980. Reasonable condition.

5 Abolished c1977. Also has 3-lever WB&SSCo slide power frame for Collooney Junction. Boarded up.

6 New top on old base, c1924. Used as a shed, poor condition, tinned up.

7 In private garden of house in Greenisland.

8 New top on old (1893) base, 1924. Rewindowed 1980s. Abolished 1/5/1988.

9 Second hand RSCo top on concrete blocks base c1928. Believed to be top of 85th Mile Box. Abolished 1963

10 Abolished 11/1988.

11 Box abolished as BP 1/2/1988, continued to function as gate box until 2003.

12 Workshops building at Claremorris, clearly made up from tops of two RSCo boxes, believed to be/may be these boxes.

13 New top on old (1886?) base. Was used as a telephone exchange after the line was closed but now unused.

14 Platform box, in wall. May be effectively RSCo/GS&W design. RSCo markings on some box component parts.

15 Abolished 4/1996, top removed, re-erected on plinth on platform at Dundalk station 3/1997.

16 New top on 1886 RSCo[GS&W] base.

17 Abolished 18/5/1997. Box moved to Drumree 7/1998.

18 Abolished 1978. Frame removed. Condition deteriorated, but box refurbished 1999, and ETS instrument moved in from previous location in office. Line closed to traffic, and subsequently made an Engineer's Siding from 12/2001, so box out of use again.

19 Abolished 4/2/1990. Box moved to Dromod, Cavan & Leitrim Railway, 8/1999.

20 New top on old base 1924.

21 New flat roof c1970s. Abolished 15/9/1989.

22 Rebuild of 1895 RSCo box.

23 Abolished as BP 12/2000. Rewindowed 1990s.

24 Re-erected on new site close to old. No access, but can be seen from station platforms.

25 Ballymena & Larne Railway. Gable-to-tracks. Carries plate 'Courtney Stephens & Bailey Glos Wagon Co's Agents'.

26 Taken over by holiday camp owner and preserved, with frame and fittings. Boarded up owing to theft.

27 Dismantled, now located at Co. Donegal Railway Museum, Donegal town.

28 Abolished as BP 17/11/1996. Box built 1892 (as Type 3a), burnt 1921 and top rebuilt as Type 3b.

29 Rewindowed.

30 Extended at rear post-closure.

31 Abolished 22/7/1991 when pier re-arranged as sidings and new open gf opened. Frame removed, now shunters' cabin.

32 Box 2h ex Monksland (1891). Abolished 6/1962.

33 New roof. Last staffed 25/5/1991, closed without specific abolition date.

34 Very heavily altered. Now a holiday home.

35 New top on 1890 RSCo base. Abolished as BP 2/9/1985, but used as gate box until 2003.

APPENDIX:- 'REPLICA BOXES'

- These are wholly new structures which might be mistaken for original signal boxes.

- None are functional (similar structures which are, or will shortly become so on heritage railways are included in Section 6).

- They are not strictly eligible for inclusion in this Directory but are included because:

        they may be of interest to the signalling enthusiast; and

        to avoid the possibility of their being taken as original signal boxes by the uninitiated.

- This is certainly not a complete listing of such structures but only some of the more publicly visible ones.

Arrochar & Tarbet	NB 6a	Replica built midway on island platform of the station.
Beamish	NE	New box in imitation of Consett East with frame from Carr House East, Stevens (McK&H28) 26 levers.
Bideford	LSW1	New box built 1991 as replica of original demolished 1970. Frame - part ex Netley.
Braughing	GE7	Replacement is BTF box for original wooden box destroyed in 1987 storms.
Crathes	GNS1	Replica top (1995) on original base, no frame. Used as a museum.
"Dearham Bridge"	-	Frame - Stevens Knee, made up from many parts. Located at Crosby near Maryport.
(Derby Industrial Museum)	"Mid"	(Some real parts). Frame - 8 levers ex Gorsey Bank.
Ludborough	GN1	New box. Frame - 18-levers McK&H 1873 Pat. ex Hainton Street. Built by GN & ELR.
"Mwyndy Junction"	-	c1983. Private garden, Hereford. Frame - 30 levers GWR VT 3 ex Pandy.
Pontsticill Junction	-	New top on original box base. Used as a holiday flat.
"Severn Beach"	"GW"	GW VT 3 frame ex Llanstephan Crossing (some parts ex elsewhere). At Moors Valley Railway.
"Stoneycombe Sidings"	"GW"	Private garden at Stone. No frame.

Thornhill (2000) – The 1943-built LMS Type 13 box was to an ARP design. Although Thornhill on the Nith Valley route in Scotland would not have been a major target for enemy air raids, like many boxes built at this time it incorporated a reinforced concrete roof.